D1432772

Mathematics for Modern Management

Mathematics for
Modern Management

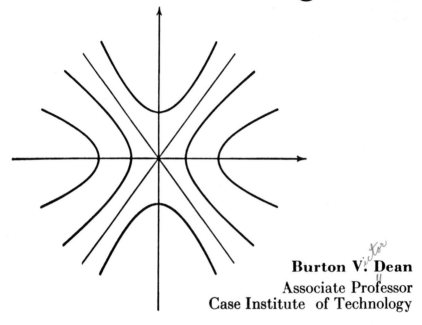

Burton V. Dean
Associate Professor
Case Institute of Technology

Maurice W. Sasieni
Assistant Professor
Case Institute of Technology

Shiv K. Gupta
Assistant Professor
Case Institute of Technology

JOHN WILEY AND SONS, INC.   NEW YORK • LONDON • SYDNEY

Library of Congress Catalog Card Number: 63–8055
Printed in the United States of America

Preface

Recent, widely circulated reports by the Ford and Carnegie foundations and the Mathematical Association of America agree that distinctive and more challenging mathematics should be an essential part of the modern college curriculum for management students. Unfortunately, most of the available texts have been written for students of the physical or engineering sciences and for this reason draw their illustrations and applications from classical mechanics. This book is a mathematics text specifically written for business and economics students; all its examples and exercises cover topics which are familiar to the student of management from other parts of his curriculum.

The usual content of mathematics courses available to undergraduates in the physical and biological sciences, engineering and liberal arts programs must be revised to meet the needs of the management student. (1) The finite mathematics of discrete functions, useful in such areas as probability, linear programming, and difference equations, must receive increased attention, and (2) emphasis ought to be placed on determining solutions to management problems and the quantitative methods required to accomplish this objective. Moreover, an appropriate mathematical education for the undergraduate management student would increase his effectiveness in a graduate management program.

This textbook is an outgrowth of a graduate course, Mathematics for Management Systems, given by the authors in the Department of Management at Case Institute of Technology. The course is taken by first-year graduate students who have not had undergraduate courses in the calculus or who require additional education beyond the courses they have had. Similar material has been presented in short courses to managers, technical staff, and college teachers of mathematics and engineering who desired to increase their ability to apply quantitative methods to the optimization of systems. Many of the exercises and examples have been used in courses for undergraduates in management science.

Each new subject is introduced by means of examples, and numerous exercises are included at the end of each section as well as at the end of each chapter. There are two types of exercises: the first develops the reader's ability to apply mathematical concepts to the solution of management problems and the second develops the reader's ability to solve mathematical problems.

While many teachers in business schools will agree that their students should study mathematics, it is hard to find agreement on the specific topics to be taught. Rather than limit the book to the subject matter that we would cover in a one (or two) semester program, we have preferred to include all the mathematics we consider relevant, leaving it to individual instructors to make their own selection. The result is that any complete coverage of the entire book would take rather more than two semesters. The book has been written in such a way that certain chapters may be omitted, whereas others may be read out of sequence without loss of continuity. Needed minor repetitions are given whereever similar problems are treated from different points of view.

It is assumed that the reader will have completed the equivalent of college algebra and trigonometry. In undergraduate curricula this book is intended for use in mathematics and business departments at the freshman and sophomore levels, where the essential elements may be included in a one-year program. However, it will also be useful for a single semester, and in this case we suggest the following chapters and sections.

A. 1, 2, 3, 5.7, 6, 7, 9, 10.1, 10.2, 10.3, 10.5 (those interested in differential and integral calculus)
B. 1, 2, 3, 12.1 through 12.9, 13, 14, 15, 16, 17 (those interested in linear programming, financial and actuarial mathematics)

For a two semester sequence we suggest
1, 2, 3, 4, 5, 6, 7, 9, 10, 12, 13, 14, 15 together with 8, 11, and the appendix for those interested in calculus *or* 16 and 17 for those interested in financial and actuarial mathematics.

In a graduate school, where progress is normally a little faster, either of the two semester sequences above could be covered in a single semester; each should provide enough understanding for the reader to use advanced mathematical texts on management or to read articles in such journals as *Operations Research* and *Management Science*.

For executives who wish to keep abreast of recent advances this book provides a convenient reference. Such advances require a competence in the newer quantitative methods and techniques. Books and articles written by management scientists have presupposed a knowledge of these concepts on the part of the reader. However, often the manager finds it difficult to understand and apply these works because of a lack of knowledge of the underlying mathematics. It is hoped that the index to this book is sufficiently comprehensive to permit it to serve as a "dictionary" of the mathematical terms used in management science.

We would like to acknowledge the helpful guidance and comments of Professor Russell L. Ackoff, Director, Operations Research Group, Case Institute of Technology, who suggested that a course involving these concepts be taught. We would like to thank the students and faculty at Case and, in particular, Professor Vernon C. Mickelson, Head of the Department of Management, for the opportunity to develop, use, and modify this text. In Chapter 14 on Linear Programming use has been made of material previously published in *Operations Research—Methods and Problems*, John Wiley and Sons, 1959. In Chapter 16 we are indebted to the Chemical Rubber Publishing Company for permission to abstract Tables 16.1 and 16.2 from the *Interest Tables* published in their *Standard Mathematical Tables*, 11th ed. Thanks are due Mrs. Grace White and her excellent departmental secretarial staff for painstaking care in preparing and revising the manuscript.

Burton V. Dean
Maurice W. Sasieni
Shiv K. Gupta

Cleveland, Ohio
November, 1962

Contents

1

Introduction

■ 1.1 The Rise of the Managerial Class

In reviewing the development of human society, the anthropologist first recognizes our primitive forbearers as creatures who differed from other animals by their ability to make and use tools. Early men were able to use heavy stones or pointed bones in their competition with the rest of the animal world. Later, metals and pieces of wood were specially fashioned to adapt them for specific purposes, and eventually a society developed in which man no longer spent his time hunting, gathering wild fruits, and defending himself. Instead he domesticated animals and reared flocks; he ploughed land and grew crops; and he found he had spare time over and above that necessary to produce and gather the food required for mere survival. At a much later stage men began to specialize; some performed physical work of various types, while others organized and directed their labors. It was found that in this way the total production of a community was greater than if each man endeavored to produce all of his own requirements, and, provided a system of exchange was available, everybody benefited.

As more and more elaborate tools were invented an appreciable time elapsed between the manufacture of tools and their eventual use in the production of what is now known as consumer products. This meant that part of a community's income (production) had to be set aside and invested so as to increase productive capacity in the years to come. Until about the year 1800 most invested income belonged to individuals who then owned the tools produced by their investment. Around this time the tools of production became so costly that few individuals could afford the investments necessary. Furthermore, the risk of investing all one's capital in one enterprise was too great.   Greater safety could be achieved by investing smaller amounts in several enterprises, and so groups of men pooled their resources to produce "tools" of a size and complexity unknown to previous generations.   These arrangements were much facilitated by the various company acts passed in the early nineteenth century and continuing until the present day.   For our purposes, these acts did two things.

1. They gave a corporation—set up to carry on a business—a *corporate existence*, independent of the individuals who invested in it.   That is, suitably formed corporations were treated in law almost as if they were individuals.   They could buy, sell, and enter into other contracts as corporations.

2. The liability of individuals investing in such corporations was *limited*.   That is, individual shareholders could no longer be held responsible for the debts of the corporation.

The result was that as the tools of production grew more and more elaborate and expensive, they were directly owned by the corporation, and only indirectly by individuals through the medium of owning *shares* in the corporation.   Now another problem arose.   When an individual built a factory, a ship, or a trading organization, he managed it and ran it as he saw fit.   With the development of corporations, no longer were there owners in the old sense, and a class of *managers* evolved.   Managers frequently own little or no stock in the corporations they direct.   Instead they are motivated by salary and bonus incentives to further the interests of the corporation.   It is not our purpose to discuss what these interests are or should be—it is all very well for a corporation to be treated in law as an individual—but only human individuals can have aims and interests.

For our purposes we note the existence of the nonowning manager and the complex range of problems with which he is faced.   It is clear, however, that the manager not only needs the aid of all available skills and experience but he also requires justification for his decisions so that, if necessary, they can be explained to others.   Of course, a manager who makes successful decisions can usually justify them by the results, but, fortunately, the methods most likely to result in success are usually the methods most readily explained to others.   To understand these methods we must examine the decision-making process.

■ 1.2 Decision Processes

Basically, a decision becomes necessary only when we have a choice. When only one course of action is available, we may be concerned (even to the point of neurosis) with the expected outcome, but we are not required to make a decision. Furthermore, if we are indifferent to the outcomes of the various courses of action, we have no problem because all courses are equally good or equally bad. The real problem occurs when we have a choice and preferences among the various outcomes. Thus we picture the decision-making process as having the following ingredients:

1. An individual, or group of individuals, has a set of objectives or preferences.

2. He is faced with alternative courses of action, not all of which are equally good in the light of (1).

3. He wishes to choose the course of action that is, in some sense, "best."

It is possible that if several individuals are involved, their preferences may conflict; in such cases part of the definition of "best" may require reconciliation of the conflicts. Once the objectives have been reconciled, we are then faced with two tasks:

1. We must forecast the outcome of each possible course of action.

2. We must pick the best of the outcomes.

At first sight, provided we know the outcomes and can measure them relative to our preferences, the second task may appear simple. Unfortunately this is not so, for even if the number of outcomes is finite, it may be far too large to consider all possible cases individually. For example, suppose we have n tasks, each of which is to be processed on some or all of m machines, and suppose we can measure the time required for any given sequence of operations. In principle we can examine all possible sequences and select the one with shortest time: but there are $(n!)^m$ possible sequences.* If $m = 5$ and $n = 5$, there are approximately 25 billion sequences to be investigated, and even the largest computor, would find the task of enumerating all cases impossibly long.

We thus see one role for the mathematician in decision making. He must be able to find efficient methods for selecting the best decision when all outcomes are known and the number is too large for direct enumera-

---

* $n!$ (read "n-factorial") is defined as $n(n-1)(n-2) \ldots 3 \cdot 2 \cdot 1$.

tion. The second role for the mathematician lies in forecasting the outcome of individual courses of action. There are two possible methods open to the decision maker. In the first place, if the number of outcomes is not too large, he can experiment and try each course of action in turn. The use of pilot plants for this purpose is both well known and effective. Unfortunately experiments take time and money. Moreover, it often happens that performing an experiment actually changes the system under study. For example, suppose we wish to set a budget for television advertising and we believe the present budget is too high. If we drastically reduce our budget for a year, we find our sales suffer a serious decrease. The decrease may be so large that it may take years and vast expenditures to regain our market position. In such cases, experiments, at least in a naive fashion, are clearly undesirable. The second method of forecasting outcomes is to form an hypothesis as to how the system operates and to reason what the consequences of the hypothesis must be. If the hypothesis is well founded on experience and if the consequences are in accord with subsequent observations, we can have a high degree of confidence in its ability to predict. Unless our hypothesis and the situation it describes are extremely simple, the only efficient method of investigating alternative hypotheses and the consequences of decisions is with the aid of mathematics.

To summarize, we see a double role for mathematics in management science. It can be used to predict the outcomes of the various courses of action and to select the best course of action when the number is too large for enumeration. Mathematics has a number of ancillary roles. Part of the decision process may be concerned with the collection and analysis of data, either utilizing census-type survey or experimentation. In either case mathematics can be profitably used to ensure that the data collected are both relevant and meaningful for the decision process.

We are not suggesting that managers of the future will be mathematicians; neither are we implying that all decision making can be reduced to mathematics. We are not even saying that mathematics is the only scientific tool to be used in making decisions. We do believe that in the years to come managers will rely increasingly on staff mathematicians for advice, and to this extent managers will need to understand enough mathematics to appreciate the advice offered. It is the aim of this book to give the business or management science student an understanding of those areas of mathematics that seem pertinent at this time.

■ 1.3   Translating the Problem into Mathematics

One of the most difficult tasks, perhaps the one that distinguishes the operations research worker from the mathematician, is the translation of a real problem situation, comprising men, machines, raw materials, finished goods, and money, into a set of mathematical symbols and relationships that reproduces their behavior. The symbols, as well as the relationships between them, must be drawn up in such a way as to reproduce the behavior of the real world with acceptable accuracy. The two systems cannot be identical, for no abstraction is identical with reality. Part of the skill lies in choosing the relevant parts of the system for representation and then in choosing a set of relationships between them, which, while simple, will result in acceptable predictions. To this end, note that the relevant variables fall into two groups:

1. *Control variables.* These are the elements of the system that can be changed by our decisions. The amount and type of goods produced or the size of an advertising budget are examples.

2. *Noncontrol variables.* All other variables fall into this group. It comprises those variables that cannot be directly influenced by our decisions. Some of them may be controlled by competitors (e.g., rival advertising budgets) or by nature (e.g., rate of population growth), while still others may depend on our customers, suppliers, or the government. Some variables that cannot be controlled in the short run may be controllable over long-time periods.

Frequently it will happen that we have only limited control, even on the variables that we can choose. We say that there are *constraints* that prevent a free choice. For example, total expenditure may be limited by available funds. Thus we are only free to set departmental budgets subject to the stated total over-all budget.

We now turn to the classification of problems and methods of solution. Nearly all problems can be reduced to finding the maximum or minimum of some function. The simplest cases are those in which the outcomes are *deterministic.* That is, we can compute precisely what will happen if we choose any specified values for the control variables. This may be contrasted with *probabilistic* or *stochastic* situations, where we do not know all the values of the noncontrol variables in advance, and we must allow for the probability that they take various values. An example is a production planning problem where profits depend on future sales, which cannot be predicted other than in a probabilistic sense.

■ 1.4   The Structure of the Book

This book is divided into five parts. Part One is concerned with fundamental concepts and Part Two with deterministic problems. The simplest management problems are those that have a single control variable where there are no constraints and where the outcome of any decision can be computed as a function of the control variable. The solution of such problems requires the use of the differential calculus. Before we can discuss the calculus we require a great deal of background study. In Part One we discuss introductory material, including graphs, the concept of a function, which in turn needs an appreciation of the theory of sets, and the theory of limits and series (Chapters 2 to 5). The theory of infinite series is useful because it has a direct application to certain problems in finance and population growth and is useful in computing numerical values of functions.

In Part Two we discuss the problem of optimization of a function; a single control variable is discussed in Chapter 6. Once we understand problems with a single unconstrained variable, it is easy enough to include constraints and then to extend our methods to problems with several variables and constraints (Chapter 7). Applications of the concepts and methods developed in Chapters 2 to 8 are made to deterministic models (Chapter 9).

In Part Three (Stochastic Models) we reverse the processes of the differential calculus and study methods of the integral calculus (Chapter 10). Differential equations are studied (Chapter 11) and applied to problems of competition and growth. Applications of integral calculus are made to decision-making problems involving probabilistic situations (Chapter 12).

However, we find ourselves up against problems of size, which are discussed in Part Four. Methods that work well for two or three variables become impossibly time consuming when there are scores or hundreds of variables. We will see that there are many situations in which there are literally hundreds of control variables with scores of constraints. In such cases we cannot reduce the number of variables, but it frequently happens that, because the functions involved are simple enough, we solve them by special techniques. If all the functions involved are *linear* (no powers), there is a branch of mathematics called *linear programming* that will solve such problems. To understand such problems we will first have to study linear systems and *matrices* (Chapter 13) and then linear programming (Chapters 14 and 15).

Part Five deals with the mathematics of finance. We examine some applications of mathematics to problems of finance, compound interest, and actuarial life tables (Chapters 16 and 17).

■ **Bibliography**

We have touched lightly on a number of topics that some readers may wish to pursue further. Accordingly, we suggest the following supplementary reading.

Ackoff, R. L. (Ed.), *Progress in Operations Research*, vol. 1, John Wiley and Sons, 1961. Recent developments of concepts and techniques in operations research.

Ackoff, R. L., *Scientific Method*, John Wiley and Sons, 1962. A complete description of the philosophy and methods of science.

Bass, F. M., et al., *Mathematical Models and Methods in Marketing*, Richard D. Irwin, Homewood, Illinois, 1961. Applications of mathematics to marketing problems.

Calabro, S. R., *Reliability Principles and Practices*, McGraw-Hill Book Company, 1962. Applications of mathematics to equipment and system reliability problems.

Charnes, A. and W. Cooper, *Management Models and Industrial Applications of Linear Programming*, vols. I and II, John Wiley and Sons, 1961. Utilization of linear programming in allocation problems.

Cherry, C., *On Human Communication*, Technology Press and John Wiley and Sons, 1957. Communication systems and organization performance.

Chernoff, H. and L. E. Moses, *Elementary Decision Theories*, John Wiley and Sons, 1959. An elementary description of the application of statistics to the decision process.

Churchman, C. W., R. L. Ackoff, and E. L. Arnoff, *Introduction to Operations Research*, John Wiley and Sons, 1958. A description of the nature and methods of operations research.

Churchman, C. W. and P. Ratoosh, *Measurement: Definitions and Theories*, John Wiley and Sons, 1959. An exposition and summary of the theories of measurement.

Churchman, C. W., *Prediction and Optimal Decisions*, Prentice-Hall, 1961. Application of operations research methods and techniques to value theory.

Eckman, D. P., *Systems: Research and Design*, John Wiley and Sons, 1961. System research and engineering.

Hanssmann, F., *Operations Research in Production and Inventory Control*, John Wiley and Sons, 1962. Application of mathematics to production planning and inventory control problems.

Luce, R. D. and H. Raiffa, *Games and Decisions*, John Wiley and Sons, 1958. Elements of game theory and related decision-making models.

McCloskey, J. F. and F. N. Trefethen, *Operations Research for Management,* vols. I and II, The Johns Hopkins Press, Baltimore, 1954 and 1956. Methodology and utilization of operations research in management problems.

Sasieni, M., A. Yaspan, and L. Freidman, *Operations Research: Methods and Problems,* John Wiley and Sons, 1959. The use of mathematics in the solution of operations research problems.

Part One

Fundamental Concepts

2

Sets and Relations

■ **2.1 Introduction**

A basic concept in the study of management systems is that of a set of objects or elements. For example, consider a library as a collection of elements, the published and unpublished materials represented in Figure 2.1. The library may be divided into subsets of elements, each subset consisting of one of the sets, such as journals, catalogues, books, and theses. The subset of books may be further classified into subsets according to management, mathematics, statistics, economics, etc. The subset of mathematics books may be classified according to area of specialization: algebra, geometry, calculus, differential equations, linear programming, etc. The card catalogue of the library lists all library materials, and the Dewey decimal system is a method for enumerating and identifying the various subsets.

As another example, a company consists of sets of resources, such as personnel, machines, product stocks, and cash reserves. The relationships between these sets and between the subsets of each set is important and is used to equate assets of one kind with another. The subset of highly skilled production workers, within the set of all production workers, is a critical subset that determines the productivity of other personnel. Certain subsets of company products are highly profitable or subject to deterioration and must be stocked in greater quantities than others.

This chapter presents the basic concepts of sets and subsets and develops the laws of set operations. Graphical methods of relating sets are introduced to provide an understanding of the basic laws.

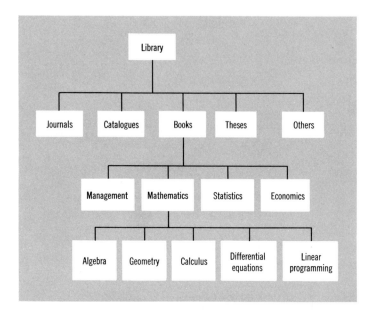

Figure 2.1   Library materials.

■ **2.2   Definition of a Set**

A collection of objects is defined as a *set*. No attempt is made to define an object, as, for example, a point. A collection of items, such as the equipment in a firm or the personnel in an organization, is an example of a *finite set*. An *infinite set*, on the other hand, contains an uncountable number of objects, for example, the set of integers or the set of real numbers. A set may be designated as S or as the collection of its items or elements, $\{x_1, x_2, \ldots, x_n\}$. An element x belonging to a set S is designated as $x \in S$.

A *subset* S of another set T is a set such that every element in S is also an element of T and is designated as $S \subseteq T$. If two sets S and T contain the same elements, then they are considered to be *identical*, $S = T$, and we must have $S \subseteq T$ *and* $T \subseteq S$.

Example 1. In a survey of 1000 people conducted by a soap manufacturer, the number of individuals purchasing different brands of soap A, B, and C was determined. Whenever two brands were purchased, such as A and B, this is denoted by AB. We have eight overlapping subsets.

Brand	Number
A	270
B	360
C	450
AB	70
AC	30
BC	60
ABC	20
None	60

Example 2. Consider the infinite set of positive integers, 1, 2, 3, ..., etc. Particular subsets of this set are the following infinite subsets:

1. the even integers = $\{2, 4, 6, \ldots\}$
2. the odd integers = $\{1, 3, 5, \ldots\}$
3. the primes = $\{1, 2, 3, 5, 7, \ldots\}$
4. the perfect squares = $\{1, 4, 9, 16, \ldots\}$

As an example of a finite subset we might consider the set of positive integers less than or equal to a given integer.

Example 3. Consider the set T consisting of three elements, x, y, z. The subsets of T are the following:

$$\{x\}, \{y\}, \{z\}, \{x, y\}, \{y, z\}, \{x, z\}, \{x, y, z\}.$$

For completeness, the empty set $\emptyset$, consisting of no elements, may also be considered a subset of T. Thus there are eight subsets of T. A *proper* subset of a set T is one that is nonempty and not the entire set T.

Exercises

1. Let S be the set of positive integers. Classify the following subsets according to whether they are finite or infinite. In the case of finite subsets determine the number of elements in each.

  (a) The set of integers that are perfect cubes.
  (b) The set of integers that are perfect cubes and that are less than 1000.
  (c) The set of integers that are less than 1000; less than N.

2. Consider all packages of screws, nails, and tacks that contain a total of three items.

(a) List all possible packages as sets of elements.
(b) List the sets that have more screws than nails.
(c) List the sets that have no nails.
(d) List the sets that have one nail.
(e) Find three proper subsets in (b) that are also proper subsets in (c).

3. Show that for any finite set of n elements there are 2^n subsets. *Hint*: prove by mathematical induction.

4. Show that the number of subsets of size m, of a set of n elements, is

$$\binom{n}{m} = \frac{n!}{m!(n-m)!} ; \qquad 0 \le m \le n, \quad 0! = 1, \quad k! = k(k-1)\ldots 2\cdot 1$$

■ **2.3   Set Operations**

Operations among sets have properties similar to those possessed by numbers.

Example 1.   Refer to Example 1 of the previous section.

How many persons purchase only brand A? The persons who purchase only brand A are given by (1) the number that purchase A, 270 less (2) the number that purchase A and B, and A and C, $70 + 30 = 100$ plus (3) the number that purchase A, B, and C [since we have subtracted such persons twice in (2)], 20. Hence the number purchasing A alone is $270 - 100 + 20 = 190$.

Example 2.   The operations that combine sets may be illustrated by the following example of a company mailing list, where we consider a sample of six persons with the characteristics listed in Table 2.1.

TABLE 2.1   A SAMPLE OF A
COMPANY MAILING LIST

Person	Annual Income, $	Marital Status	Housing
1	5000	Single	Rented
2	6000	Married	Owned
3	7000	Married	Owned
4	6000	Single	Rented
5	5000	Married	Rented
6	6000	Single	Owned

In this example, the set of single persons is composed of $S_1 = \{1, 4, 6\}$; the set of married persons is composed of $S_2 = \{2, 3, 5\}$; and the set of all persons, sometimes called the *universe*, is the combination or *union* of the two sets. Now, the set of persons who rent is composed of $T_1 = \{1, 4, 5\}$ and the set of persons who own their home is composed of $T_2 = \{2, 3, 6\}$. The set of single persons who rent is composed of the common elements of S_1 and T_1 or $\{1, 4\}$ and may be denoted by $S_1 \cap T_1 = \{1, 4\}$ (read as the *intersection* of S_1 and T_1). The set of married persons who own their own homes is composed of common elements of the sets S_2 and T_2 or $\{2, 3\}$ and may be denoted by $S_2 \cap T_2 = \{2, 3\}$. The persons who earn \$5000 per year are $W_1 = \{1, 5\}$; the persons who earn \$6000 per year are $W_2 = \{2, 4, 6\}$; and $W_3 = \{3\}$ is composed of the individual who earns \$7000 per year. It may be computed that the only individual who earns \$6000, is single, and who owns his home is number 6; and, in fact, the three-way classification of income, marital status, and ownership yields a unique one-to-one correspondence with individuals.

We now consider *operations with sets*. We will demonstrate that set operations obey rules analogous to those carried out with numbers in arithmetic. For two sets, S and T, the *union* of S and T, denoted

$$S \cup T$$

is the set of items belonging to either S or T or both. For example, if

$$S = \{x, y\} \qquad \text{and} \qquad T = \{y, z\},$$

then $\qquad\qquad S \cup T = \{x, y, z\}$

For two sets S and T, the *intersection* of S and T, denoted by

$$S \cap T \qquad \text{(or sometimes more briefly by } ST)$$

is the set of items belonging to both S and T. In the above example,

$$S \cap T = \{y\}$$

For any sets S and T, the *complement* of S in T or the *difference* of T and S, denoted by

$$T - S$$

is the set of points in T that are not in S. When T is understood, we often write S' or $\bar{S}$ for $T - S$; i.e., $\bar{S}$ comprises elements not belonging to S. In the above example,

$$T - S = \{z\} \qquad \text{and} \qquad (S \cup T) - (S \cap T) = \{x, z\}$$

If two nonempty sets are nonoverlapping, or have no elements in common, then the intersection is the empty set and they are said to be *disjoint*.

Example 3. A survey of 500 males and 500 females showed that three brands, A, B, and C, were preferred among cigarette smokers, as indicated in Table 2.2.

TABLE 2.2 CIGARETTE SMOKER PREFERENCES

	A	B	C
Males	150	60	210
Females	70	140	120

(a) How many males and females did not prefer any brands?
Let T = set of males; T has 500 elements.
Let S = set of males who prefer one of the three brands; S has $150 + 60 + 210 = 420$ elements.
Then $T - S = S' = $ the set of males who do not prefer any brand. The number of elements in $S' = 500 - 420 = 80$.
Similarly, the number of females who do not prefer one of the three brands $= 500 - (70 + 140 + 120) = 500 - 330 = 170$.
(b) How many people prefer brand A?
Let S = set of males who prefer brand A.
Let T = set of females who prefer brand A.
$S \cup T$ = set of people who prefer brand A.
The number of elements in $S \cup T = 150 + 70 = 220$.
Similarly, the number of people who prefer brands B and C are 200 and 330, respectively.

Some properties of set operations are similar to those of arithmetic addition and multiplication of numbers. They are:

Associative: $S \cup (T \cup R) = (S \cup T) \cup R$
$\qquad\qquad S \cap (T \cap R) = (S \cap T) \cap R$
Commutative: $S \cup T = T \cup S$
$\qquad\qquad S \cap T = T \cap S$
Distributive: $S \cup (T \cap R) = (S \cup T) \cap (S \cup R)$
$\qquad\qquad S \cap (T \cup R) = (S \cap T) \cup (S \cap R)$

On the other hand, note the following differences from ordinary arithmetic:

$$S \cup S = S$$

$$S \cap S = S$$

Because of the associative and commutative laws, operations may be grouped in a single symbol, for example,

$\bigcup_{i=1}^{n} S_i$ = the set of elements belonging to at least one of the sets S_i, $i = 1, 2, \ldots, n$

$\bigcap_{i=1}^{n} S_i$ = the set of elements belonging to each set S_i, $i = 1, 2, \ldots, n$

Example 4. Refer to Example 3 above.

$$S = \text{set of males who prefer } A.$$
$$T = \text{set of males who prefer } B.$$
$$R = \text{set of males who prefer } C.$$

$K = T \cup R$ = set of males who prefer B or C; it has 270 elements.
$S \cup K$ = set of males who prefer A or B or C; it has 420 elements.
$L = S \cup T$ = set of males who prefer A or B; it has 210 elements.
$L \cup R$ = set of males who prefer A or B or C; it has 420 elements.

Now we observe that

$$S \cup K = L \cup R = S \cup (T \cup R) = (S \cup T) \cup R$$

This verifies the *associative* law.

Exercises

1. Refer to Example 1, Section 2.2.

   (a) How many people purchase only brand C?
   (b) How many people purchase only brands A and B?

2. A soft drink manufacturer has interviewed 100 people on their attitudes concerning a potential product. These attitudes are indicated in Table 2.3.

TABLE 2.3 SOFT DRINK ATTITUDES

	Liked L	Indifferent I	Disliked D
Single males	10	5	5
Married males	5	5	15
Single females	20	10	0
Married females	10	5	10

Let S = set of single persons L = set that liked
     M = set of males I = set that was indifferent
     F = set of females D = set that disliked

Find the number of people in each of the following categories:

(a) S, M, and F
(b) L, I, and D
(c) $S \cap L$
(d) $S \cap F \cap D$
(e) $(S \cap M \cap D)'$
(f) $D' = L \cup I$
(g) $S \cap M \cap D'$
(h) $I \cup D$

3. For exercise 2, verify the following distributive laws:

(a) $S \cap (L \cup I) = (S \cap L) \cup (S \cap I)$
(b) $M \cup (F \cap L) = (M \cup F) \cap (M \cup L)$

4. Verify the laws of set operations for subsets of the set of three elements.

5. Consider finite sets S and T. Let $n(S)$, $n(T)$, $n(S \cup T)$, and $n(S \cap T)$ denote the number of elements in the sets: S, T, $S \cup T$, and $S \cap T$, respectively. Show that

$$n(S \cup T) = n(S) + n(T) - n(S \cap T)$$

6. Verify exercise 5 for Example 2, Section 2.3, where S = the set of married persons and T = the set of persons who rent.

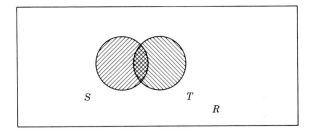

Figure 2.2   Venn diagram of the S, T, and R sets.

■ 2.4 Venn Diagrams

An aid in visualizing set operations and performing calculations with sets is the *Venn* diagram. Consider a large set R, called the universe, and subsets S and T of R, illustrated in the Venn diagram in Figure 2.2. The shaded circles represent the sets S and T, and the rectangle represents the set R. The total shaded area is $S \cup T$, and the cross-hatched area is $S \cap T$. The complement of $(S \cup T)$ in R is the nonshaded area of R, $(S \cup T)' = R - (S \cup T)$.

Other set operations may be considered in the Venn diagram of Figure 2.3, such as $S - T = S \cap (R - T)$.

Exercises

1. Construct the Venn diagram for the subsets in the company mailing list, Example 2, Section 2.3. Let R = the universe of six persons, S = the set of persons with annual income of \$6000, T = the set of married persons, and U = the set of persons who rent.

2. Draw the Venn diagram for the subsets in Example 1, Section 2.2, and find the number of elements in each of the eight subsets.

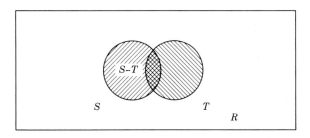

Figure 2.3   Illustration of set difference or complementation.

■ 2.5   Equivalence Relations

An important method of subdividing a given set S into disjoint subsets $\{S_i, i = 1, 2, \ldots, n\}$ is by means of an *equivalence relation*, which is a relation R between elements $x, y \in S$ denoted by $x \, R \, y$ (read x is related to y) with the following three properties:

1. $x \, R \, x$.   (reflexive)
2. If $x \, R \, y$, then $y \, R \, x$.   (symmetric)
3. If $x \, R \, y$ and $y \, R \, z$, then $x \, R \, z$.   (transitive)

Example 1.   The relationship of equality, in arithmetic, is an equivalence relation.

Example 2.   The relationship of "congruent triangles," in geometry, is an equivalence relation.

Example 3.   However, "less than or equal to" does not satisfy (2) above and is not an equivalence relation.

Now, consider a set S on which is defined an equivalence relation, i.e., the elements of S can be related by a rule that has the properties defined above. Note that it is not necessary for every element to have a different element to which it is related, but if elements are related, the reflexive, symmetric, and transitive properties hold. The subsets of S, which contain elements that are equivalent, have the properties that

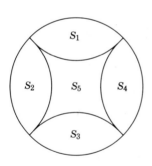

Figure 2.4   Disjunct partitioning of S into sets of equivalent elements.

1. The intersection of any two subsets is empty, i.e., the subsets are disjoint.
2. The union of these subsets is the entire set S. This is best illustrated by the Venn diagram in Figure 2.4.

The elements of each S_i, $i = 1, 2, 3, 4, 5$ are equivalent only to other elements of the same S_i. Now, any partitioning of a given set S into disjunct subsets yields an equivalence relationship that satisfies properties (1) and (2). This proves the result

There is a one-to-one correspondence between equivalence relationships and disjoint partitions of a set of elements.

Exercises

1. What are the totality of equivalence relations on a set of three elements?

2. The organization of a company into independent operating divisions yields an equivalence relationship. Define it.

Exercises for Chapter 2

1. List all subsets of the set of four elements, a, b, c, and d. Find the number of subsets containing exactly one, two, three, and four elements.

2. State which of the following are correct:

   (a) $S \cup (T \cap R) = (S \cup T) \cap R$
   (b) $(S \cup T) - R = S \cup (T - R)$
   (c) $(S \cup T)' = S' \cap T'$
   (d) $S \cup T \cup R = S \cup [T - (S \cap T)] \cup [R - (S \cap R)]$

3. Let S, T, and R be any three events. Find the expressions for the following:

   (a) at least one event occurs.
   (b) at least two events occur.
   (c) exactly one event occurs.
   (d) two events do not occur.

4. In a survey concerning the smoking habits of consumers it was found that

         55% smoke cigarette A.
         50% smoke cigarette B.
         40% smoke cigarette C.
         30% smoke cigarettes A and B.
         20% smoke cigarettes A and C.
         12% smoke cigarettes B and C.
         10% smoke all three cigarettes.

What per cent do not smoke?
What per cent smoke exactly two brands of cigarettes? (Draw the Venn diagram.)

5. A company is considering the performance of five research projects. How many subsets of projects contain exactly two projects; exactly three projects?

6. A market research group conducted a survey of 1000 consumers and reported that 720 consumers liked product A and 450 consumers liked product B. What is the least number that must have liked both products?

7. For three sets, R, S, and T, show that

$$n(R \cup S \cup T) = n(R) + n(S) + n(T) - n(R \cap S) - n(R \cap T)$$
$$- n(S \cap T) + n(R \cap S \cap T)$$

Hint: Prove by drawing the Venn diagram and showing that a point in the union of all regions, R, S, and T, is counted exactly once on the right side of the equation.

8. Verify the result of exercise 7 for the subsets, A, B, and C in Example 1, Section 2.2.

9. A company study of the product preferences of 10,000 consumers reported that each of the products A, B, and C was liked by 5010, 3470, and 4820, respectively. The study reported that all products were liked by 500 people; products A and B were liked by 1000 people; products A and C were liked by 840; and products B and C were liked by 1410. Show that the reported study results are in error. On checking the study results it was found that an error was made in recording the number of consumers liking products B and C; what is the greatest value of this number?

10. Develop a general formula for the equation of exercise 7, for an arbitrary number of sets.

11. Prove the associative, commutative, and distributive laws for set operations.

12. Show that

$$\binom{n}{0} + \binom{n}{1} + \binom{n}{2} + \cdots + \binom{n}{n} = 2^n$$

by using the fact that a set with n elements has 2^n subsets.

13. Which of the following are equivalence relationships?

(a) The relationship of being a brother, that is, $A \, R \, A$ and $A \, R \, B$ if A is a brother of B, where we are considering the entire population of a community.

(b) The relationship of being a brother when we only consider a population of men.

(c) The family relationship R defined by $A \, R \, A$ and $A \, R \, B$ if A is the father, mother, son, daughter, brother, or sister of B.

(d) We assume a skilled workman in England earns ten shillings per hour and his opposite number in the United States earns \$2.50 per hour and define a true price relationship R as follows:

(i) If A and B are purchased in the same country, then $A \, R \, B$ when their prices are the same.

(ii) If A and B are purchased in different countries, then $A \, R \, B$ when the price of one in dollars is one fourth times the price of the other in shillings.

14. If $\ldots x_r, x_{r-1}, \ldots x_2, x_1, x_0$ are the digits of an ordinary number, we ordinarily interpret the number as $N = \cdots 10^r x_r + 10^{r-1} x_{r-1} + \cdots + 10^2 x_2 + 10 x_1 + x_0$ (where all x_i are less than 10). The number 10 is called the *radix*. Sometimes it is more convenient to express N as $\ldots y_s, y_{s-1}, \ldots, y_2, y_1, y_0$ interpreted as $N(\alpha) = \cdots \alpha^s y_s + \alpha^{s-1} y_{s-1} + \cdots + \alpha^2 y_2 + \alpha y_1 + y_0$, where α is an integer and all y_i are positive integers less than α. Show that any two such representations are equivalent.

15. A company has three warehouses A_1, A_2, and A_3. For any customer it is possible to determine the costs c_1, c_2, c_3 of delivering from each warehouse. Delivery is normally made from the warehouse where the delivery costs are least. The company divides its market into regions S, T, and U by the following definitions: in area S, $c_1 < c_2$; in area T, $c_1 < c_3$ and in area U, $c_2 < c_3$. Let D_1, D_2, D_3 be the regions in which deliveries are made from A_1, A_2, and A_3, respectively. Express D_1, D_2, and D_3 in terms of the unions and intersections of S, $\bar{S}$, T, $\bar{T}$, U, $\bar{U}$. Since any customer must belong to one and only one of D_1,

D_2, and D_3, what relationships must hold between S, T, U, and their complements?'

16. In exercise 15 let A_1, A_2, A_3 lie at the vertices of a triangle. Assume that the cost of delivery is proportional to the distance from the warehouse. Draw in the regions S, T, U and also D_1, D_2, D_3.

17. In a market survey people are to be classified according to whether they smoke cigarettes, pipes, cigars, or do not smoke at all. Let A, B, C be the classes who smoke cigarettes, pipes, and cigars, respectively. Describe the persons who belong to the following classes:

(a) $A \cup B \cup C$ (e) AC (h) $\bar{A}\bar{B}\bar{C}$
(b) $\bar{A} \cup \bar{B} \cup \bar{C}$ (f) BC (i) $AB\bar{C}$
(c) AB (g) $A(\bar{B} \cup \bar{C})$ (j) $A \cup B\bar{C}$
(d) ABC

18. In a classification of smoking habits in exercise 17, the following are mutually exclusive and exhaustive classes because every individual must belong to one of them and nobody can belong to more than one.

$$\alpha_1 = ABC \qquad \alpha_5 = \bar{A}\bar{B}C$$
$$\alpha_2 = \bar{A}BC \qquad \alpha_6 = \bar{A}B\bar{C}$$
$$\alpha_3 = A\bar{B}C \qquad \alpha_7 = A\bar{B}\bar{C}$$
$$\alpha_4 = AB\bar{C} \qquad \alpha_8 = \bar{A}\bar{B}\bar{C}$$

(a) Describe, in words, the characteristics of each of these classes.
(b) Verify that the intersection of any two of these classes is null.
(c) Verify that the union of all eight classes comprises the universe.
(d) Express each of the classes in exercise 17 in terms of the classes α_1, α_2, ..., α_8.

(Since α_1, ..., α_8 are mutually exclusive and exhaustive, all classes of the universe can be expressed in terms of the union of a nonintersecting subset of them. It follows that the number of individuals in *any* class can be found by adding over the appropriate subset of α's.)

19. We can form a hierarchy of classes as follows:

(a) A, B, C, $\bar{A}$, $\bar{B}$, $\bar{C}$
(b) AB, AC, BC, $\bar{A}B$, $A\bar{B}$, $\bar{A}C$, $A\bar{C}$, $B\bar{C}$, $\bar{B}C$, $\bar{A}\bar{B}$, $\bar{A}\bar{C}$, $\bar{B}\bar{C}$
(c) ABC, $\bar{A}BC$, $A\bar{B}C$, $AB\bar{C}$, $\bar{A}\bar{B}C$, $\bar{A}B\bar{C}$, $A\bar{B}\bar{C}$, $\bar{A}\bar{B}\bar{C}$ (the ultimate classes).

We have seen (exercise 18) that the number in any class may be found by adding over appropriate members of (c). It is not necessary to know the numbers in (c) to obtain the numbers for all classes. For example, we might be given $n(ABC)$, $n(\bar{A}BC)$, $n(AB\bar{C})$. $n(\bar{A}BC)$, $n(\bar{A}B\bar{C})$, $n(A\bar{B}\bar{C})$, and $n(\bar{B}\bar{C})$. How would you find $n(\bar{A}\bar{B}\bar{C})$?

20. Which of the following permits us to infer the number in the ultimate classes and hence the number in any class? Where there is insufficient information, what else is required?

(a) $n(A)$, $n(B)$, $n(C)$, $n(\bar{A})$, $n(\bar{B})$, $n(\bar{C})$
(b) $n(A)$, $n(A\bar{B}C)$, $n(AB\bar{C})$, $n(A\bar{B}\bar{C})$, $n(\bar{A})$, $n(\bar{A}BC)$, $n(\bar{A}B\bar{C})$, $n(\bar{A}\bar{C})$
(c) $n(AB)$, $n(AB\bar{C})$, $n(A\bar{C})$, $n(B\bar{C})$, $n(\bar{A}\bar{B}C)$, $n(\bar{B}\bar{C})$, $n(\bar{A}C)$, $n(\bar{A}\bar{B})$.

21. A field investigator reports that 80% of those interviewed were married, 44% were married men, 12% were married women with no children, and 30% were married women with children. Can this be correct?

22. A survey reports that 80% of the population is married and 55% is male. What is the least possible percentage of married men? Of married women? ("Married" includes "widowed" and "divorced.")

23. As a result of interviewing several large groups of housewives, a detergent manufacturer obtained the following data:

Did you use our brand?	% answering "Yes"
1. last month (June)	59
2. in May	63
3. in April	61
4. in May and June	35
5. in April and May	33
6. in April and June	31
7. in April, May and June	22

Show that some of the housewives have faulty memories.

3

Functional Representation

Before managerial decisions can be made on a scientific basis it is necessary to determine the quantitative or functional relationship between important factors and to relate their significant aspects. For example, an analysis of advertising effort and resulting sales might indicate that the result of increasing advertising effort is to increase sales. In order to determine the optimum amount of advertising effort it is necessary to relate the amount spent on advertising effort to the sales volume. In this chapter we consider various types of relationships and the ways of representing them for the purpose of analysis.

The concept of a functional relationship between two or more quantities is a basic notion in all of science. As an example, consider the relationship between husbands and wives in a society. In a monogamous society there is a one-to-one relationship between the set of husbands and the set of wives, namely, to each element of the husband set there corresponds one and only one element of the wife set. In a polygamous society there is a one-to-many relationship between the two sets, namely, to each element of the husband set there are one or more elements of the wife set. In a polyandrous society there is a many-to-one relationship between the two sets, where one or more elements of the husband set may correspond to one element of the wife set. These relationships are illustrated in Figure 3.1.

Another example of a correspondence that may be considered is the possible assignment of personnel to jobs, where each person i may perform a number of jobs $j_1, j_2, \ldots, j_i$. This possible one-to-many assignment is illustrated in Table 3.1, where a zero corresponds to an impossible

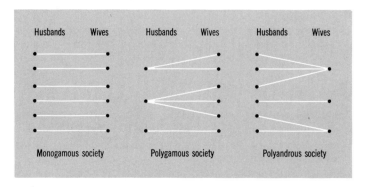

Figure 3.1 Correspondence between husbands and wives in three societies.

assignment, for example, person 1 cannot perform job 1, and 1 corresponds to a possible assignment. Of course, the performance levels of the persons in each job may be different. The optimal assignment of n persons to n jobs is discussed in Chapter 15.

A further example of a discrete relationship is that between a man's age at last birthday and income at that age, as given in Table 3.2.

Income is a function of age and is only defined when age is one of the integers 0, 1, 2, ... The last entry in the table would be the man's age at death and would presumably be less than, say, 150. Income is not defined for negative or nonintegral values of the age. In fact, we would not even be interested in such a definition, for it would have no counterpart in the real world. Although mathematicians like to think of a function as being a set of rules for computing income from age, an electronic digital computer often "thinks" of a function as a table; the entries for age being so close that intermediate values are of little interest.

**TABLE 3.1 ILLUSTRATIVE POTENTIAL
JOB ASSIGNMENT, 4 MEN AND 4 JOBS**

	Job			
Person	1	2	3	4
1	0	1	0	1
2	1	0	1	1
3	0	0	1	1
4	1	1	1	0

0: Performance impossible
1: Performance possible

TABLE 3.2 RELATIONSHIP BETWEEN AGE AND INCOME

Age	0	1	2	...	16	17	18	19	20	21	22	...	64	65	66
Income	0	0	0	...	0	175	435	870	910	4750	5250	...	21,000	14,000	14,000

As another example, consider the "seasonal" relationship between month of the year and household refrigerator sales represented by Table 3.3. In this case the sales function is clearly month-dependent, for warm weather sales are significantly greater than cold weather sales.

TABLE 3.3 MONTHLY REFRIGERATOR SALES

Month	Jan.	Feb.	Mar.	Apr.	May	June	July	Aug.	Sept.	Oct.	Nov.	Dec.
Sales quantity	800	1000	1200	1500	2000	2800	3200	3600	2400	1800	1200	1000

■ **3.2 Functional Rules**

A *function* is a rule that assigns to elements of a set S the elements of another set T. The set S is called the *domain* of the function, and the set T is called the *range* of the function. As an example, consider the pictorial correspondence represented in Figure 3.2. Note that the function assigns the five elements of the set S to a total of three elements of the set T. A correspondence may be further described as a transformation on elements of two sets that relate elements of the first set to elements of the second set.

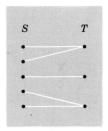

Figure 3.2 Pictorial representation of a function.

■ **3.3 Tabular Representation**

Different methods of representing functions exist. A *tabular* representation is one where both the domain and range are specified in a table of values. We have already seen examples of this with the individual and his income (Table 3.2) and monthly sales (Table 3.3). The tabular representation is useful in statistical and numerical analysis.

■ 3.4   Graphical Representation

Let us consider another possible method of stating a relationship. Suppose that a firm has determined that the annual cost of ordering is related to the number of purchase orders placed each year, as given in Table 3.4.

TABLE 3.4   COSTS OF PURCHASING FOR 4 YEARS

	Year			
	1	2	3	4
Number of purchase orders N	1200	1600	2200	2400
Annual cost of purchasing C	$9600	$12,800	$17,600	$19,200

Now let us graph this relationship, as in Figure 3.3. We plot the tabular values as a point on the graph, where the coordinates of each

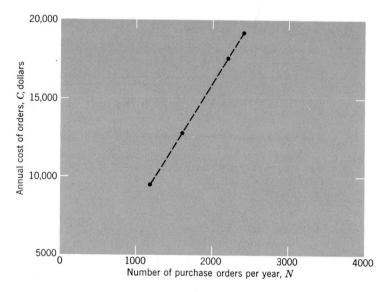

Figure 3.3   Relationship between number of purchase orders and ordering costs.

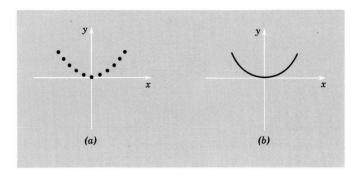

Figure 3.4   Graphical representation of y and x.   (a) Values of y and x. (b) Curve of y and x.

point are given by a pair of tabular values (the number of purchase orders, the annual cost of purchasing).

Suppose that we have tables showing the corresponding values of the two variables y and x and that we have plotted the points on a graph (Figure 3.4a).   If values of y can also be computed for intermediate values of x, we could add further points, but if we feel the relationship is "smooth," we can sketch a curve joining the points, as in Figure 3.4b. The relationship is now represented by the *curve* or *graph*, and the rule for computing y may be replaced by: "Read y from the graph corresponding to any given x."

It is necessary to exercise care in sketching smooth curves from empirical data. Suppose x represents a year and y represents the population of a city where values of x and y are known from decennial census figures. It is by no means obvious that the values at intermediate years lie on a smooth curve. For example, a large influx of war workers in 1942 and 1943 may cause the population to be very different from that suggested by a smooth curve through the figures for 1920, 1930, 1950, and 1960.

Example 1.   A firm has found that sales volume depends on the sales price, as shown in Table 3.5.

TABLE 3.5   SALES PRICE AND VOLUME

Sales price p	$1	$3	$5	$7
Sales volume s	6000	3000	2000	1500

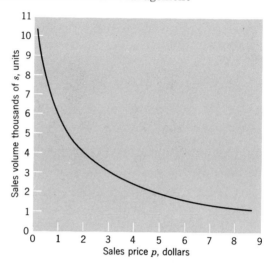

Figure 3.5   Sales price and volume.

What is the graphical representation of the relationship between sales price and sales volume?

The tabular pairs are plotted in Figure 3.5.

Example 2.   A firm has determined that sales volume and profits depend on the sales price, as shown in Table 3.6.

The data in Table 3.6 are presented graphically in Figure 3.6.

TABLE 3.6 EFFECT OF SELLING PRICE ON REVENUES AND PROFITS

Selling price p, dollars	1	2	3	4	5	6	7
Sales volume s, thousands of units	8	7	6	5	4	3	2
Sales revenue S, thousands of dollars	8	14	18	20	20	18	14
Costs C, thousands of dollars	8	7	6	5	4	3	2
Profits P, thousands of dollars	0	7	12	15	16	15	12

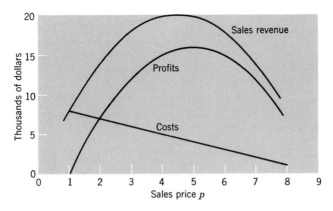

Figure 3.6   Effect of sales price on costs, revenues, and profits.

Exercises

1. The labor cost of producing a certain item is $2.70 per 100 items. Raw materials cost $.07 per item, and each time a new run is started there is a setup cost of $8.75. Let x be the number of items in a run and y the cost of labor and materials. Draw the graph of y and x for the range of x from 10 to 500. What is the value of y when $x = 200$?

2. In exercise 1, suppose that after the first 700 items are produced it is necessary to work overtime at a 50% increase in labor cost. What are the costs of producing 800, 900, 1000 units? What is the relationship between y and x when x exceeds 700? Draw the graph of y and x for the range of x from 10 to 1000.

3. A firm has a storage cost of 12% of the average value of the inventory on hand. What are the storage costs for items of value $10, where the annual usage is 1000 units; 2000 units? Draw the graph of storage cost and inventory level. (Assume that a year's supply is taken into stock on January 1. What is the effect of producing $1/n$ year's supply n times per year?)

■ 3.5   Symbolic Representation of a Function

Example 1.   Let us consider the situation discussed at the beginning of Section 3.4. We observe that in the first year 1200 orders are placed at a total cost of $9600 or an average cost of $8 per order. Similarly, in each of the following years we see that the average cost per order is

\$8. Hence the total cost of placing N orders is eight times N, that is, the cost C is given by

$$C = 8N$$

We have verified that for each of the four years this relation holds. We call this representation, the *symbolic representation*. In general, a function of the form $y = ax + b$, where a and b are constants, is called a *linear* function. In this example, ordering costs are a linear function of the number of orders placed.

Example 2. Referring to Example 2 in Section 3.4, we see that the relationship between sales s, in thousands of units, and price p, in dollars, is

$$s = 9 - p$$

The total sales revenue is

$$S = sp = (9 - p)p = 9p - p^2$$

The cost of sales is given by

$$C = 1s = 9 - p$$

The net profit is given by

$$P = S - C = (9p - p^2) - (9 - p)$$

and therefore $P = -p^2 + 10p - 9$

A function of this form or, in general, $y = ax^2 + bx + c$, where a, b, and c are constants ($a \neq 0$), is called a *quadratic* function. If $a = 0$, the function is linear in x. We see that the profit function is a quadratic function of the sale price.

Example 3. Consider Example 1 of Section 3.4. Let us calculate the total sales revenue, sp, and, also, $s + sp$, as in Table 3.7.

TABLE 3.7 SELLING PRICE AND SALES REVENUE

Price p (dollars)	Sales Volume s (units)	Sales Revenue sp (dollars)	$s + sp$
1	6000	6000	12,000
3	3000	9000	12,000
5	2000	10,000	12,000
7	1500	10,500	12,000

We note that all values in the fourth column are equal to a constant 12,000. We have

$$s + sp = 12,000$$

$$s(1 + p) = 12,000$$

$$s = \frac{12,000}{1 + p}$$

A function of the general form

$$y = \frac{a}{b + x}$$

where a and b are constants, is called a *hyperbolic* function. Sales volume is a hyperbolic function of the sales price.

Exercises

1. A company has determined that the cost of ordering, y, is $5 plus $1 for each item, x, on the order list. Graph the ordering cost function. What is the cost of ordering five items?

2. A company has determined that the cost of storage of a product with a short shelf life is equal to $C_1 = x^2$, x in days, whereas the storage cost of a product with a long shelf life is equal to $C_2 = 2x$,x in days. Graph each storage cost function and determine the storage time where both costs are equal.

3. The sales volume is given for five different unit sales prices in the following table:

Price p	$15	$20	$25	$30	$35
Sales volume s	7000	6000	5000	4000	3000

(a) Find the sales revenue sp and show that the revenue is maximum at $p = 25.
(b) Find the graphical representation between s and p and sp and p.
(c) Show that the symbolic representation is given by

$$s = 10,000 - 200p$$

and therefore $sp = (10,000 - 200p)p = 10,000p - 200p^2$

4. A pump manufacturer acquires a machine tool at a cost of $24,000 and with annual operating costs as follows:

Age t, years	1	2	3	4	5	6	7
Costs c, thousands of dollars	3	5	7	9	11	13	15

(a) Show that the total cost and average annual costs of acquisition and operation, if the tool is replaced at age T, are as given below.

Year, T	1	2	3	4	5	6	7
Total cost C, thousands of dollars	27	32	39	48	59	72	87
Average annual cost, thousands of dollars	27	16	13	12	11.8	12	14.4

(b) Determine the graphical relationship between operating cost and age, and show that the symbolic form is

$$c = 1000 + 2000t$$

(c) Graph the average annual cost for all value of T
(d) Verify that the average annual cost is given by

$$2000 + 1000T + \frac{24,000}{T}$$

■ 3.6 Inequalities

Example 1. The amount of productive capacity in a manufacturing plant is limited by the number of manufacturing personnel and machines. If a machine is operated two shifts a day, 5 days a week, the productive capacity C is less than or equal to $5 \times 2 \times 8 = 80$ machine hours. We write this fact as

$$C \leq 80 \text{ (Read “}C\text{ is less than or equal to 80.”)}$$

Example 2. In order for a firm to make a profit it is necessary that the sales revenue R be greater than the costs C:

$$R > C \text{ (Read “}R\text{ is greater than }C\text{.”)}$$

We have the following four relationships and symbols:

Relationship	Symbol
x is less than y	$x < y$
x is less than or equal to y	$x \leq y$
x is greater than y	$x > y$
x is greater than or equal to y	$x \geq y$

The following laws are valid for inequalities:

1. Equal amounts may be added to or subtracted from both sides of an inequality without changing the sign of the inequality.
2. Both sides of an inequality may be multiplied or divided by the same *positive* quantity without changing the sign of the inequality.
3. Both sides of an inequality may be multiplied or divided by a *negative* quantity provided we reverse the inequality.

Example 3.   A firm has limited warehouse space such that the number of items stored N is nonnegative and may not exceed 1000. Write this as a single inequality.

We have $N \geq 0$ and $N \leq 1000$. N may be in the interval expressed by the inequality,

$$0 \leq N \leq 1000$$

Exercises

1. Determine which of the following inequalities are valid:

(a) $0 > 5$ (b) $-2 < -1$
(c) $x > 2x$ (d) $-(-5) < 0$

2. Find the values of x that satisfy the following inequalities:

(a) $x^2 < x$ (b) $x^2 > 2x - 1$
(c) $x + 2 \geq y$ (d) $0 < x < y < 1$

3. By means of examples verify the laws for inequalities.
4. A company desires to spend not more than $100,000 on its research program. It can allocate its research budget to the following five projects:

Project	Requirement
1	$30,000
2	$40,000
3	$10,000
4	$60,000
5	$100,000

(a) Enumerate all 32 subsets of projects.
(b) Calculate the total amount required for each subset.
(c) What subsets could be performed with the limited budget?

5. A firm manufacturing two products has a limited warehouse capacity of 10,000 sq ft. Suppose that each item of product 1 requires 10 sq ft and each item of product 2 requires 20 sq ft. Let x be the num-

ber of items of product 1 and y be the number of items of product 2. Find the three inequalities expressing the space and nonnegativity limitations.

6. We define $|x|$ (Read "the modulus of x" or, more briefly, "mod x.") by the equations:

$$\text{if } x \geq 0, \text{ then } |x| = x$$

$$\text{if } x < 0, \text{ then } |x| = -x$$

Show that $|x|$ is equal to the positive square root of x^2. By considering all possible cases show that $|x| + |y| \geq |x + y|$, and hence

$$\left| \sum_{i=1}^{n} x_i \right| \leq \sum_{i=1}^{n} |x_i|$$

7. Show that if $a \leq b$ and $c \leq d$, then $a + c \leq b + d$. Find examples to show that we may have $a - c \leq b - d$ or $a - c \geq b - d$.

■ **3.7   Functional Notation**

The functions that have been discussed so far have considered quantities x and y as being *variable*. However, numerical coefficients and exponents have been used in the functional forms. Whenever these numerical quantities are fixed, specified, and known, they are referred to as *constants*. On the other hand, *parameters* are quantities that remain constant in the short run but that may vary over time. Thus on any particular occasion they will have to be estimated. For example, in the sales price and revenue formula of Example 3, Section 3.5, s is given by $s = a/(b + p)$, where a and b are constants at a particular point of time: ($a = 12{,}000$, $b = 1$). But if we are considering several items, a and b are better described as parameters.

In some cases the output variable may be a function of more than one variable, for example, sales may depend on advertising effort and unit selling price. In general we will use the symbol $y = f(x_1, x_2, \ldots, x_n)$ to stand for "y is a function of the n variables, $x_1, x_2, \ldots, x_n$." If we have m output variables, such as costs, sales, and profits ($m = 3$), we will write the array:

$$y_1 = f_1(x_1, x_2, \ldots, x_n)$$

$$y_2 = f_2(x_1, x_2, \ldots, x_n)$$

$$\cdots \cdots \cdots \cdots \cdots$$

$$y_m = f_m(x_1, x_2, \ldots, x_n)$$

Example. A company manufactures three products in quantities x_1, x_2, and x_3. What are the profit functions for each product and the total profit function if the unit costs and selling prices are as follows:

Product	Unit Cost	Unit Price
1	$1	$2
2	$2	$4
3	$3	$5

The cost and revenue functions are C and R, where

$$C_1 = x_1 \qquad R_1 = 2x_1$$

$$C_2 = 2x_2 \qquad R_2 = 4x_2$$

$$C_3 = 3x_3 \qquad R_3 = 5x_3$$

The profit functions are

$$P_1 = x_1, \quad P_2 = 2x_2, \quad P_3 = 2x_3$$

and the total profit function is

$$P = x_1 + 2x_2 + 2x_3$$

Exercises for Chapter 3

1. Verify the functional forms for the following machine operating costs c and machine age t.

(a)

t, years	1	2	3	4	5	
						$c = t + 2$
c, thousands of dollars	3	4	5	6	7	

(b)

t, years	1	2	3	4	5	
						$c = t^2 + 3$
c, thousands of dollars	4	7	12	19	28	

2. A firm has found that sales are related to advertising effort, as given in the following data. Find the symbolic form relating s and a.

Advertising effort a, thousands of dollars	10	12	14	16
Sales s, thousands of dollars	100	120	140	160

3. A manufacturer orders 12,000 tons of steel each year. It costs $120 per order.

(a) Prepare a table showing the total cost of ordering if orders are planned in equal quantities of 1000 tons, 2000 tons, ..., 12,000 tons.

(b) Prepare a table showing the total cost of storage versus the order size if the annual cost of storage is $10 per ton (average inventory is one-half the order size).

(c) Show that the total annual cost of ordering is given by $120(12,000/x)$, where x is the amount ordered each time.

(d) Show that the total annual cost of storage is $10(x/2)$.

(e) Using (c) and (d), verify that the total annual cost of ordering and storage is given by

$$C = 5x + \frac{1,440,000}{x}$$

4. A firm has determined that the costs of ordering are given by a fixed cost, independent of the number of orders placed, and a variable cost proportional to the number of orders placed. Find the cost function for the following data:

Number of purchase orders N	1000	2000	3000	4000
Annual cost of purchasing C	$30,000	$40,000	$50,000	$60,000

5. A department store has found that the sales volume of women's dresses is inversely related to its sales price as follows:

Sales price p	$10	$20	$30	$40
Sales volume s	5000	3333	2500	2000

(a) Show that the relationship between sales price and sales volume is $s = 100,000/(10 + p)$.

(b) Find the functional form for profits if the unit cost is $15.

6. The acquisition cost of an item is $54,000, and the cumulative operating costs for the item are given below.

Age t at replacement, years	1	2	3	4	5
Cumulative operating cost, thousands of dollars	1	8	27	64	125
Total cost, thousands of dollars	55	62	81	118	179
Average cost, thousands of dollars/year	55	31	27	29.5	35.8

(a) Show that the cumulative operating cost is given by $C = t^3$.

(b) Show that the average annual cost, including acquisition, is $54/t + t^2$.

7. A manufacturer employs x machine operators at an hourly wage rate of $3 and y supervisors at an hourly wage rate of $4.

(a) Show that functional relationship between z, the total hourly wage rate, and x and y is $z = 3x + 4y$.

(b) What is the value of z for $x = 800$ and $y = 100$?

(c) Show that the values of x and y that do not yield a total hourly wage rate of more than $2800 are given by $x \geq 0$, $y \geq 0$, and $3x + 4y \leq 2800$.

(d) Prepare a table of values for x, y, and z, assuming that there is a constant ratio of eight operators to each supervisor, for $y = 50, 100, 150, 200, 250, 300$.

8. A company's research budget is limited to $50,000. The company is considering allocating this budget to four research projects with the following requirements for each:

Project	Requirement
1	$10,000
2	$30,000
3	$40,000
4	$20,000

Evaluate the total costs of the 16 possible sets of projects, and select the subsets that do not exceed in costs the total planned budget.

9. The reader should be familiar with the graphs of the following functions, which occur frequently (a, b, c, d, e are constants).

(a) $y = ax + b$

(b) $y = ax^2 + bx + c$

(c) $y = ax^3 + bx^2 + cx + d$

(d) $y = ax^4 + bx^3 + cx^2 + dx + e$

(e) $y = \dfrac{a}{bx + c}$

(f) $y = \dfrac{a + dx}{bx + c}$

(g) $y = \dfrac{1}{(ax + b)(cx + d)}$

Choose representative values for the constants and sketch the graphs. In cases (a) − (d) consider separately $a > 0$ and $a < 0$. In cases (e) and (f) consider what happens when x takes values near $-c/b$, and in case (g) consider values near $-b/a$ and $-d/c$.

4

Series, Limits, and Continuity

■ **4.1 Introduction**

In many business problems, the sum of a series of terms must be evaluated. Where equipment is operated over extended time periods, the present value of all future costs is used as a criterion for making replacement decisions; to evaluate alternative inventory policies the discounted sum of future inventory and ordering costs is used as a basic measure. To calculate depreciation charges in future periods and to compare investment policies which result in different earnings and cost streams we discount returns to the present time. In all three examples the present value is found by summing a series of terms. In the simplest cases there are only a finite number of terms and numerical summation is relatively simple. However, it is often convenient to obtain a simple algebraic expression for the sum and use it in preference to repeated addition. The first part of this chapter discusses summation of finite series.

It often happens that the series to be summed goes on indefinitely and in such cases we have to give a meaning to the sum of an infinite sequence of terms; we will see that infinite sums do not always exist, so that it is also necessary to establish criteria to determine which series can be summed. The notion of the sum of an infinite series depends on the concepts of limits and continuity, so that from finite series we turn to these concepts before extending the first part of the chapter to infinite series.

Many price and cost functions have properties that restrict the domain of application. For example, as the production quantities increase and approach plant capacity, the manufacturing cost function may undergo changes in form or in parameter values. In fact, a linear cost function, useful for small production quantities, may become quadratic as the amount manufactured approaches the limit of plant capacity. In order to develop models of such situations, the theory of limits will be described in this chapter. This theory can also be used to formulate a precise meaning of a *rate of change* as is done in Chapter 6.

Price and cost functions are usually smooth or continuous over an interval. However, at break points discontinuities may exist because of economies in volume production or plant or warehouse limitations. These concepts are introduced in this chapter. In later chapters, where optimization procedures are discussed, it is demonstrated that points of discontinuity have to be studied in detail. In some cases the decision is to purchase or produce a given quantity because of the discontinuity that exists at the particular point.

■ 4.2 Arithmetic Series

The method for summing a finite arithmetic series is illustrated in the following examples.

Example 1. A firm incurs a net loss of $10,000 on the first item that it manufactures and a net profit of $5 on each succeeding item produced. The total net profit on the first item is $-$$10,000$; the total net profit on the first two items is $-$$10,000 + $5 = $9,995$; the total net profit on the first three items is $-$$10,000 + 2($5)$; and the total net profit on the first n items, $\$P(n)$, is given by

$$P(n) = -10,000 + (n - 1)5$$

If we arrange the terms in sequence form, we see that

$$-10,000, \ -10,000 + 5, \ -10,000 + 10, \ \ldots, \ -10,000 + (n - 1)5$$

is a sequence where the first term is $-10,000$ and the difference between successive terms is 5. We write this as an *arithmetic sequence*.

$$a, a + d, a + 2d, \ldots, a + (n - 1)d$$

where $a = -10,000$ and $d = 5$.

Example 2. A firm increases its research and development program by $10,000 annually, following the first year of its operation at a level of $50,000. Find the amount spent after 8 years of operation.

We see that the amount spent during the nth year is given by $50,000 + $10,000 (n - 1)$. We arrange the amount spent each year in two ways, as shown in Table 4.1.

TABLE 4.1 RESEARCH AND DEVELOPMENT EXPENDITURES FOR n YEARS

1st year: \$50,000	nth year: \$50,000 + \$10,000$(n-1)$
2nd year: \$60,000	$(n-1)$st year: \$50,000
	+ \$10,000$(n-2)$
. . . .	. . . .
$(n-1)$st year: \$50,000	2nd year: \$50,000 + \$10,000
+ \$10,000$(n-2)$	
nth year: \$50,000 + \$10,000$(n-1)$	1st year: \$50,000

Now, adding across each row of the array, we see that twice the total spent in n years is given by \$$2S_n$, where

$$2S_n = n[50,000 + 50,000 + 10,000(n-1)]$$

or
$$S_n = \frac{n}{2}[100,000 + 10,000(n-1)]$$

For $n = 8$ years, we have

$$S_8 = 680,000$$

In summary, to find the sum of any arithmetic progression of n terms,

$$a, a+d, a+2d, \ldots, a+(n-1)d$$

we write the sum in two ways. We have

$$S_n = a + (a+d) + (a+2d) + \cdots + a + (n-1)d$$
$$S_n = (a + \overline{n-1}d) + (a + \overline{n-2}d) + \cdots + (a+d) + a$$

By adding, term by term, $2S_n = n[2a + (n-1)d]$

and so
$$S_n = \frac{n}{2}[2a + (n-1)d]$$

Alternatively, if we write $l = a + \overline{n-1}d$ for the last term,

$$S_n = \frac{n}{2}(a+l)$$

Exercises

1. Find the nth term and the sum of the first n terms of the following arithmetic series:

    (a) $a = 10$, $d = 2$, $n = 10$
    (b) $a = -5$, $d = 20$, $n = 15$
    (c) $a = 0$, $d = \frac{1}{4}$, $n = 100$
    (d) $a = 100$, $d = -4$, $n = 20$
    (e) $a = 0.4$, $d = 0.05$, $n = 12$

2. A company having annual sales of \$10 million and costs of \$9 million increases sales and costs at the rate of \$500,000 and \$600,000 per year, respectively.

    (a) Find the total sales and costs at the end of 10 years.
    (b) Find the year at which total sales equals total costs.

3. An amount P is invested at *simple* interest at an annual rate of $100\ i\%$.

    (a) Show that the total amount earned after n years is given by $n\ iP$.
    (b) Show that the number of years for the original amount to double is given by $1/i$.

4. A company is considering a salary plan that would pay new employees \$5000 per year, with an increase of \$200 per year.

    (a) Find the total earned salary through 20 years; in the 20th year.
    (b) Find the length of time for the annual salary to double.

■ **4.3 Geometric Series**

Example 1. Suppose a firm invests \$100,000 each year in a research program where the annual rate of return is 20% per year. What is the total value of the investments after 10 years?

    The final value after 10 years of the amount invested at the beginning of the first year is given by \$100,000 $(1.2)^{10}$, of the amount invested at the beginning of the second year is \$100,000 $(1.2)^{9}$, and of \$100,000 invested at the beginning of the 10th year is \$100,000 (1.2). Thus the total value after 10 years is

$$\$100,000\ (1.2 + 1.2^2 + \cdots + 1.2^9 + 1.2^{10})$$

Let $a = 120,000$, $r = 1.2$, and $n = 10$. We wish to find the sum of a series S_n, where

$$S_n = a + ar + ar^2 + \cdots + ar^{n-1}$$

If we multiply both sides by r, we have

$$rS_n = ar + ar^2 + ar^3 + \cdots + ar^{n-1} + ar^n$$

Subtracting the second series from the first, term by term,

$$S_n - rS_n = a - ar^n$$

$$S_n = \frac{a(1 - r^n)}{1 - r}$$

For $a = 120,000$, $r = 1.2$, $n = 10$, we have

$$S_{10} = \frac{120,000(1 - 1.2^{10})}{1 - 1.2}$$

$$= \frac{120,000(1.2^{10} - 1)}{1.2 - 1}$$

$$= \frac{120,000(5.192)}{.2}$$

$$= 3,115,200$$

and the value of the firm's investments is a total of $3,115,200 after 10 years.

Example 2. A firm has contracted to purchase an item on a fixed payment plan of $10,000 per year for 10 years. Payments are to be made at the beginning of each year. The firm earns profits at the rate of 10% per year. What is the present value of the cash flow of payments for an interest rate of 10% per annum?

The present value of the payment this year is $10,000; the present value of next year's payment is $10,000/1.1; the present value of the following year's payment is $10,000/(1.1)^2$; the present value of the last payment is $10,000/(1.1)^9$. The present value of the total cash flow is

$$\$10,000 \left[1 + \frac{1}{1.1} + \frac{1}{(1.1)^2} + \cdots + \frac{1}{(1.1)^9} \right]$$

Now, let $a = 10,000$, $r = 1/1.1$, $n = 10$, and let A_{10} be the present value of the cash flow. Then .

$$A_{10} = \frac{a(1 - r^{10})}{1 - r}$$

$$= \frac{10{,}000[1 - (1/1.1)^{10}]}{1 - (1/1.1)}$$

$$= \frac{10{,}000(0.6146)}{0.0909}$$

$$= 67{,}610$$

Suppose that A_n represents the present value of the annual payments for n years when $a = 10{,}000$ and $r = 1/1.1$. We have $A_{10} = 67{,}610$, $A_{20} = 103{,}650$, $A_{40} = 107{,}570$, and $A_{60} = 109{,}640$, and

$$A_n = \frac{a(1 - r^n)}{1 - r} = \frac{a}{1 - r} - \frac{a}{1 - r} r^n$$

With increasing values of n, and $0 < r < 1$, the second term on the right-hand side becomes small. For very large values of n the contribution of this term is negligible compared to the first term, and hence

$$A_n \sim \frac{a}{1 - r} \qquad \text{for large } n$$

In the above example we see that the maximum value of A_n would be

$$\frac{a}{1 - r} = \frac{10{,}000}{1 - (1/1.1)} = 110{,}000$$

We see in fact that A_{60} differs from this maximum value by less than 0.35%. We say that $a/(1 - r)$ is the limit of the sequence of terms A_n as n increases and write this as

$$\lim_{n \to \infty} A_n = \frac{a}{1 - r} \qquad \begin{array}{l}\text{[Read "limit of } A_n \text{ as } n \text{ approaches infinity is}\\ a/(1 - r)\text{."]}\end{array}$$

Incidentally, we have proved that an infinite geometric series

$$a + ar + ar^2 + \cdots$$

has the sum

$$S = \frac{a}{1 - r}$$

provided that r is a positive quantity less than unity. It is easy enough to see that the result is also true when $-1 < r \leq 0$.

Exercises

1. Find the sum of the first six terms of the following geometric series

   (a) $a = 1$, $r = 1.1$
   (b) $a = 1$, $r = 0.1$

2. Find the present value of \$500 due 10 years from now when the rate of interest is 12% per year and it is compounded annually, semi-annually, quarterly, monthly.

3. Using the notation in Example 2, Section 4.3, find the value of A_n, $n = 10, 20, 40, 100$ and $r = 1/1.2$.

■ **4.4   Limiting Value of a Variable**

Example 1.   Consider the indefinite sequence of terms

$$1, \tfrac{1}{2}, \tfrac{1}{4}, \tfrac{1}{8}, \ldots, \tfrac{1}{2}^{n-1}, \ldots$$

and the sums of the first n terms, S_n, given by

$$S_n = 2 - \frac{1}{2^{n-1}}$$

We see that for any n, S_{n+1} is greater than S_n, that is, S_n increases as n increases; on the other hand, no matter what n we choose, $S_n < 2$, and in fact we can make S_n as close to 2 as we please by taking n large enough.   We have an increasing sequence of partial sums of the first n terms which approach the value of 2.   Let us note the graph in Figure 4.1.   The area of each rectangle corresponds to a term in the original

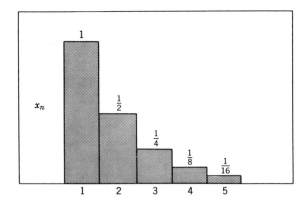

Figure 4.1   The sequence $x_n = 1/2^n$.

sequence. Although the total area increases for increasing values of n, the value is always less than 2.

Definition. Suppose x is a variable quantity. If x may approach more and more closely to a constant value a, in such a way that the absolute value * of the difference $x - a$ becomes and remains less than any pre-assigned number, the constant a is said to be the *limit* of the variable x.

A number of laws on limits of variables are stated below without proof (for sequences that have limits).

1. The limit of the sum of a finite number of variables is equal to the sum of the respective limits.

2. The limit of the product of a finite number of variables is equal to the product of the respective limits.

3. The limit of the product of a constant times a variable is equal to the constant times the limit of the variable.

4. The limit of a quotient of two variables is equal to the quotient of the limits of the variables provided that the limit of the divisor is not zero.

5. If a variable never decreases (increases) and never becomes larger (smaller) than a fixed number, it approaches a limit that is not greater (smaller) than the number.

As an example, the variable in the series $1, \frac{1}{2}, \frac{1}{4}, \frac{1}{8}, \ldots$, is never smaller than 0. By (5) it approaches a limit that is not less than 0. In fact, the limit is zero.

Exercise. Find the nth term in the following sequences and the limit $L = \lim\limits_{n \to \infty} x_n$:

(a) $3, \frac{4}{3}, \frac{5}{5}, \frac{6}{7}, \frac{7}{9}, \ldots$

$$\left(Answer:\ x_n = \frac{n + 2}{2n - 1},\ L = \tfrac{1}{2} \right)$$

(b) $-\frac{1}{2}, 0, \frac{1}{4}, \frac{2}{5}, \frac{3}{6}, \ldots$

$$\left(Answer:\ x_n = \frac{n - 2}{n + 1},\ L = 1 \right)$$

(c) $0, 1\frac{1}{2}, \frac{2}{3}, 1\frac{1}{4}, \frac{4}{5}, \ldots$

$$\left(Answer:\ x_n = 1 + \frac{(-1)^n}{n},\ L = 1 \right)$$

---

* Note that the absolute value (or modulus) of x, written $|x|$ is equal to x if $x \geq 0$ and is equal to $-x$ if $x < 0$. (See exercise 6, Section 3.6.)

■ 4.5 Limits of Functions

In the previous section we introduced the concept of a limit of a sequence. Now we shall extend this idea to functions.

Example 1. Consider the function whose graph is shown in Figure 4.2:

$$y = x + \frac{1}{x^2}$$

This is a combination of the linear and reciprocal of the quadratic functions described in Chapter 3.

The table and graph show that y has a minimum value at $x = 1.26$. As x moves to the right or left of 1.26, the value of y increases indefinitely; the value of the function can be made arbitrarily large by a suitable choice of a small or large value of x. We say that y tends to infinity as x tends to zero or as x tends to infinity, and write this as

$\lim\limits_{x \to 0} y = \infty$ [Read "the limit of y as x tends to zero is infinity."]

$\lim\limits_{x \to \infty} y = \infty$ [Read "the limit of y as x tends to infinity is infinity."]

x	0.2	0.4	0.6	0.8	1.0	1.2	1.4	1.6	1.8	2.0
y	25.20	6.65	3.38	2.36	2.00	1.89	1.91	1.99	2.11	2.25

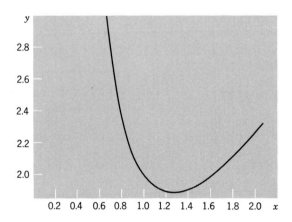

Figure 4.2 $y = x + 1/x^2$.

However, it is possible that y can approach a numerical value as x becomes indefinitely larger, a fact we observed in the infinite geometric series example $(0 < r < 1)$ as well as in the following example.

Example 2. Consider the function whose graph is shown in Figure 4.3:

$$y = 1 + 1/x^2$$

As x increases, the value of y decreases, approaching the value $y = 1$; the value of the function can be made arbitrarily close to 1 by choosing a suitable value for x. As x decreases to zero, the value of y increases indefinitely; the value of the function can be made arbitrarily large by choosing a suitably small value of x. We write this as

$$\lim_{x \to \infty} y = 1$$

$$\lim_{x \to 0} y = \infty$$

Suppose we have a function $f(x)$ and we focus our attention on a fixed value of x, say $x = a$. If we find that as we take values of x very close to a, the value of $f(x)$ is very close to L, we say $f(x)$ has the limit L as x approaches a.

More formally, we have the following definition.

Definition. If $\epsilon > 0$ is chosen arbitrarily small, and it is possible to find $\eta > 0$ such that whenever $|x - a| < \eta$ we have $|f(x) - L| < \epsilon$, we say $f(x)$ tends to L as x tends to a, that is, $f(x)$ can be made as close to L as we please by taking x sufficiently close to a.

x	1	2	3	4	5
y	2	$1\frac{1}{4}$	$1\frac{1}{9}$	$1\frac{1}{16}$	$1\frac{1}{25}$

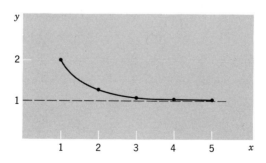

Figure 4.3 $y = 1 + 1/x^2$.

In symbols we write

$$\lim_{x \to a} f(x) = L$$

where L is the value of the limit. Note that this implies that the value of the limit, L, is *independent* of the way that x approaches a.

In the special case where it is desirable to distinguish between *two* values of the limiting function, say between x approaching a so that $(x - a) > 0$ and $(x - a) < 0$, these are designated as

$$\lim_{x \to a^+} f(x) \qquad \text{and} \qquad \lim_{x \to a^-} f(x)$$

respectively.

We now consider *four* cases.

Case 1. $\lim_{x \to a} f(x)$ exists and equals $f(a)$:

   Example: $f(x) = x^2$, $a = 2, L = 4$.

Case 2. $\lim_{x \to a} f(x)$ exists but $f(a)$ is not defined:

   Example: $f(x) = \dfrac{x^2 - 1}{x - 1}$, $a = 1$.

For all values of $x \neq 1$, $f(x) = x + 1$, and as x approaches 1, $f(x)$ approaches 2,

$$\lim_{x \to 1} f(x) = \lim_{x \to 1} (x + 1) = 2$$

But $f(1)$ is not defined because $f(x)$ is a quotient of two quantities where the denominator is zero, and no limit exists [see the fourth law of limits, (4) of Section 4.4].

Case 3. $\lim_{x \to a} f(x)$ does not exist and $f(a)$ is defined:

   Example: $f(x) = \begin{cases} 1 & x < 0 \\ 0 & x = 0 \\ -1 & x > 0 \end{cases}$

and $a = 0$.

   Case 4. $\lim_{x \to a} f(x)$ does not exist and $f(a)$ is not defined:

   Example: $f(x) = \dfrac{1}{x^2}$, $a = 0$

In this example there is no number L such that $f(x)$ becomes close to L as x becomes close to zero. However, $f(x)$ can be made as large as we please by taking sufficiently small x. We may extend our definition of a limit to include such cases as this and say $f(x)$ tends to infinity.

Definition. If for any $M > 0$ it is possible to find $\eta > 0$ such that $f(x) > M$ for all $|x - a| < \eta$, we say $f(x)$ tends to infinity as x tends to a, and we write

$$\lim_{x \to a} f(x) = \infty$$

If $-f(x) \to \infty$, we say $f(x) \to -\infty$.

As a variable x becomes very large, a function $f(x)$ may approach a limit, expressed as

$$\lim_{x \to \infty} f(x) = L$$

Exercises

1. Find

(a) $\displaystyle\lim_{x \to 0} \left(x + \frac{1}{x^4} \right)$

(b) $\displaystyle\lim_{x \to \infty} \left(x + \frac{1}{x} \right)$

(c) $\displaystyle\lim_{x \to 2} (x^2 - x + 1)$

(d) $\displaystyle\lim_{h \to 0} \left[\frac{f(x + h) - f(x)}{h} \right]$

where $f(x) = x^2$.

2. An item costs $10,000. In any year it depreciates by 5% of its value at the beginning of the year. What is the annual depreciation in each of the first 5 years? What is the total depreciation at the end of 20 years? What is the limit of the sum of the annual depreciation costs?

3. The present value of corporate earnings E in a future year n is given by V, where

$$V = \frac{E}{(1 + i)^n}$$

and i is the annual rate of interest.

If annual earnings remain constant, what would be the formula for the present value of the flow of earnings for the next 10 years? For an indefinite period?

If $i = 6\%$, compare the present values for 10 years and for an indefinite period.

■ **4.6 Continuity of a Function**

The concept of a *continuous* or *discontinuous* function is important in many business cost and pricing problems.

Example 1. Total manufacturing cost may be considered as composed of a *fixed* cost that includes overhead costs and the cost of setting up the production run, plus a *variable* cost proportional to the number of items manufactured up to the plant capacity. The manufacturing cost function is represented as

$$C = 0, \quad x = 0$$

$$C = ax + b, \quad 0 < x \le M$$

where C is the total cost, a is the unit cost of manufacturing, b is the fixed cost, x is the number of items produced, and M is the plant's maximum capacity. The graph of this function is illustrated in Figure 4.4, for $a = 1$, $b = 1000$, and $M = 10,000$. In this case a jump occurs at $x = 0$, and the cost function C is said to be *discontinuous* at $x = 0$.

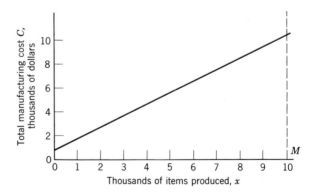

Figure 4.4   Costs of manufacturing.

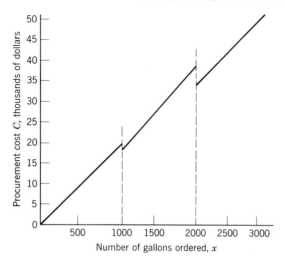

Figure 4.5 Purchasing costs with price breaks.

Example 2. Another example of a discontinuous function exhibiting a number of jumps is a price function. A firm may offer discounts on large order quantities in order to attract large orders and thus to achieve the economies of large production runs. For example, suppose that the total cost of purchasing x gallons is $\$C$ and is proportional to x within each order interval, as given by

$$C = \begin{cases} 20x & 0 \le x \le 1000 \\ 18x & 1000 < x \le 2000 \\ 16x & x > 2000 \end{cases}$$

The total cost is $20 per gallon up to order quantities of 1000, $18 per gallon in the interval between 1000 and 2000 gallons, and $16 per gallon in order quantities over 2000. In fact, the cost function does not have the same limiting value as x approaches 1000 or 2000 from the positive or negative directions. The graph of the cost function is shown in Figure 4.5.

Example 3. Consider the function $y = x^2$ near the point $x = 2$. Write $y = (2 + h)^2$. At $h = 0$, $y = 2^2 = 4$. Now, let h take on the values 1, 0.1, 0.01, 0.001, 0.0001, ... We see that y takes the values 9, 4.41, 4.0401, 4.004001, ..., and approaches arbitrarily close to 4 as the value of h approaches zero. If we allow h to pass through negative values -1, -0.1, -0.01, -0.001, -0.0001, ..., we would have

y approaching arbitrarily close to 4 through values less than 4. We say that y is *continuous* at the point $x = 2$.

We see that $y = f(x)$ exists at the point $x = 2$ and that the limit of the sequence of values of $f(x)$, as x approaches 2, is $f(2)$. In such cases $f(x)$ is said to be continuous at $x = 2$. A formal definition of *continuity* will be given later.

Example 4.   Consider the function $y = 1/h$.   For any nonzero value of h this function is defined.   But at $h = 0$, the functional value does *not* exist.

In the case of the function $y = 1/(x - 2)$ we see that the function is not defined at $x = 2$.   Also, the value of this function is very large as x approaches 2 through values greater than $x = 2$ and is very small as x approaches 2 through values smaller than $x = 2$.   We write

$$\lim_{x \to 2^-} \left(\frac{1}{x - 2} \right) = -\infty \quad \text{and} \quad \lim_{x \to 2^+} \left(\frac{1}{x - 2} \right) = +\infty$$

and $1/(x - 2)$ is not continuous at $x = 2$.

Definition.   We now introduce the concept of continuity in a precise form.   A single valued function $f(x)$ is *continuous* at a point $x = a$, if $f(x)$ is defined for $x = a$, and if

$$\lim_{x \to a} f(x) = f(a)$$

However, if as x approaches a, $f(x)$ becomes and remains greater than any assigned positive constant, then $f(x)$ is said to increase without limit.   This is denoted as

$$\lim_{x \to a} f(x) = \infty \text{ (Read ``}\infty\text{'' as ``infinity.'')}$$

In such cases $f(x)$ is said to be not continuous at $x = a$.   It must be pointed out that infinity is *not* a number and what is really intended is that $f(x)$ increases without a limit.   Similarly, if as x approaches a, $f(x)$ becomes and remains less than any assigned negative number of arbitrarily large negative value, $f(x)$ is said to decrease without limit, or

$$\lim_{x \to a} f(x) = -\infty$$

A function $f(x)$ which is not continuous at $x = a$ is said to be *discontinuous*.   There are four possible cases of discontinuity.

1. $\lim\limits_{x \to a} f(x)$ exists and equals L, but $f(a) \neq L$, or $f(a)$ not defined

2. $\lim\limits_{x \to a^+} f(x) \neq \lim\limits_{x \to a^-} f(x)$

3. $\lim\limits_{x \to a} f(x) = \infty$

4. $\lim\limits_{x \to a} f(x) = -\infty$

Continuity in an Interval

If $f(x)$ satisfies the definition of continuity for every x such that $a < x < b$, we say $f(x)$ is continuous in the *open* interval $a < x < b$. If, in addition, $\lim\limits_{x \to a^+} f(x) = f(a)$ *and* $\lim\limits_{x \to b^-} f(x) = f(b)$, we say $f(x)$ is continuous in the *closed* interval $a \leq x \leq b$. If $f(x)$ is continuous for *all* values of x, we simply say $f(x)$ *is continuous*.

Exercises

1. Show that the following functions are continuous:

(a) $f(x) = 2x + 3$
(b) $f(x) = 3x^2$

2. Show that the sum, difference, or product of two continuous functions is continuous.

3. The total cost $\$C$ of producing x items is given by

$$C = 1000 + 5x, \quad 0 \leq x \leq 500$$

$$C = 2000 + 4x, \quad 500 < x \leq 2000$$

Graph C for different values of x and show that the function is discontinuous at $x = 500$.

4. Suppose that in addition to the cost data of exercise 3 we are given the relationship between the number of items sold x and the sales price per item p

$$x = 3000 - 25p$$

Express p as a function of x. Find the relationship between net profit, P, and sales x. Plot the graph of P versus x for

$$200 \leq x \leq 1500$$

■ 4.7 Convergent and Divergent Series

We have seen, in Section 4.4, that the sum of the first n terms of the sequence $1, \frac{1}{2}, \frac{1}{4}, \ldots, 1/2^{n-1}, \ldots$ is $2 - 1/2^{n-1}$ and that this sum may be made as close to 2 as we please by taking enough terms. It seems reasonable to describe the value 2 as the result of the infinite sum $1 + \frac{1}{2} + \frac{1}{4} + \cdots + 1/2^{n-1} + \cdots$. We now make a more general definition of an infinite sum.

Definition. If $S_n = x_1 + x_2 + \cdots + x_n$ is the sum of the first n terms of the infinite sequence $x_1, x_2, \ldots, x_n, \ldots$, and if the limit S_n exists as n becomes infinite, then this limit is called the sum S of the series, and

$$S = \lim_{n \to \infty} S_n = \sum_{n=0}^{\infty} x_n$$

If the limit of the finite sums does not exist, then the series is said to have no sum.

Example. Since $\lim_{n \to \infty} r^n = 0$ if $|r| < 1$, we see that for the infinite geometric series, where $|r| < 1$, as described in Section 4.3,

$$S = \sum_{r=0}^{\infty} ar^n = \lim_{n \to \infty} S_n = \lim_{n \to \infty} \frac{a(1 - r^n)}{1 - r} = \frac{a}{1 - r}$$

If $|r| > 1$, then S_n has no limit.
If $r = 1$, then S has no limit since the denominator is zero.
If $r = -1$ (see Section 4.9), no limit exists.

An infinite sequence is said to be *convergent* or *divergent* according to whether the infinite series has or has not a sum. If the series has a limit S, then the series is said to converge to S. A series diverges if the limit of S_n fails to exist because S_n becomes infinite or oscillates without approaching a limit, for example,

$$1 - 1 + 1 - 1 + \cdots.$$

Theorem. A necessary condition for a series to converge is that its general term tends to zero. For if

$$\lim_{n \to \infty} S_n = S, \quad \text{then} \quad \lim_{n \to \infty} S_{n+1} = S$$

whence $\lim_{n \to \infty} x_n = \lim_{n \to \infty} (S_{n+1} - S_n) = \lim_{n \to \infty} S_{n+1} - \lim_{n \to \infty} S_n$

$$= S - S = 0$$

However, the nth term approaching zero is not sufficient, as, for example, in the *harmonic* series

$$1, \tfrac{1}{2}, \tfrac{1}{3}, \tfrac{1}{4}, \cdots$$

where the nth term approaches zero but the series is divergent. This is proved as follows. Partition the harmonic series into sums

$$T_1 = 1$$

$$T_2 = \tfrac{1}{2}$$

$$T_3 = \tfrac{1}{3} + \tfrac{1}{4}$$

$$T_4 = \tfrac{1}{5} + \tfrac{1}{6} + \tfrac{1}{7} + \tfrac{1}{8}$$

$$\vdots$$

$$T_m = \frac{1}{2^{m-2} + 1} + \cdots + \frac{1}{2^{m-1}}$$

Then for $m > 1$, T_m contains 2^{m-2} terms, none of which is less than $1/2^{m-1}$ and it follows that $T_m > \tfrac{1}{2}$. Thus $T_1 + T_2 + \cdots + T_m > m/2$, and we can obtain as large a sum as we please by taking a sufficient number of terms of the original series.

■ 4.8   Comparison Test

A useful method of determining whether a specific series converges or diverges is to "compare" it with a known convergent or divergent series. The method of comparison—known as the *comparison test*—is to use the terms of the known series as bounding values for the specific series:

1. A series of constant positive terms is convergent if each of its terms is either equal to or less than the corresponding term of a known convergent series.

2. A series of positive terms is divergent if each of its terms is either equal to or greater than the corresponding terms of the known divergent series.

To prove (1), consider the two series,

(i) $u_1 + u_2 + \cdots + u_n + \cdots$
(ii) $a_1 + a_2 + \cdots + a_n + \cdots$

of positive terms. Suppose that (ii) is convergent and that $u_n \leq a_n$ for $n = 1, 2, 3, \ldots$. Let S_n and T_n be the sums of the first n terms of (i) and (ii). Since $u_n \leq a_n$, $S_n \leq T_n$ for all n. Also, since (ii) is convergent, there is a limit T such that $T_n \leq T$ for all n. Hence

$$S_n \leq T_n \leq T$$

Thus as n increases, S_n is a variable quantity that never decreases, since no terms of (i) are negative, and is always less than the number T. Therefore, by law (5) of Section 4.4, S_n approaches a limit $S \leq T$. Hence the series (i) converges, and in fact has a sum no greater than that of series (ii).

The proof of (2) is similar to that of (1).

It should be obvious that the convergence or divergence of an infinite series is unaffected by any modification we make to a finite number of terms. It follows that the comparison test can be applied even when the inequalities do not hold for some fixed number of terms. This is illustrated in Example 1.

Example 1. Each term (except the first two) of the series

$$\frac{1}{\sqrt{2}} + \frac{1}{\sqrt{4}} + \frac{1}{\sqrt{6}} + \cdots + \frac{1}{\sqrt{2n}} + \cdots$$

is greater than the corresponding term of the divergent harmonic series

$$1 + \frac{1}{2} + \frac{1}{3} + \cdots + \frac{1}{n} + \cdots$$

for, when $n = 3, 4, 5, \ldots,$

$$\frac{1}{\sqrt{2n}} = \frac{1}{\sqrt{2}\sqrt{n}} > \frac{1}{\sqrt{n}\sqrt{n}} = \frac{1}{n}$$

and so the first series diverges.

The reader should generalize this result and show that if $k \leq 1$, the *k-series* $1 + 1/2^k + 1/3^k + 1/4^k + \cdots$ diverges. It can be proved, although not by the methods discussed in this chapter, that if $k > 1$, the series converges. (See Chapter 10, page 262, exercise 17).

Example 2. Test the series

$$1 + \frac{1}{2^2} + \frac{1}{3^3} + \frac{1}{4^4} + \cdots + \frac{1}{n^n} + \cdots$$

If this series is compared with the convergent geometric series,

$$1 + \frac{1}{2} + \frac{1}{2^2} + \frac{1}{2^3} + \cdots + \frac{1}{2^n}$$

we find that each term of the first sum is less than the corresponding term of the geometric series. Hence the original series is convergent.

Exercise. Test the following series for convergence:

(a) $\dfrac{4}{n(n+1)}$

(b) $\dfrac{6n}{(n+2)(n+3)}$

(c) $\dfrac{1}{n+1}$

(d) $\dfrac{1}{n^2+3}$

■ **4.9 Tests for Convergence**

It is not immediately obvious whether a given series converges or not. A large number of tests have been developed to help us make a decision. However, it would take us too far afield to consider more than a few. In this section we will state some of the simpler tests and caution the reader that all infinite series are suspect until proved convergent. The proofs that the tests are valid will be outlined in the exercises at the end of the section. Some of the tests have been described in Sections 4.7 and 4.8, and they are listed here for purpose of reference. It should be clear that convergence is unaffected by the omission of any finite number of terms; thus although all tests are stated in terms of u_0, u_1, u_2, ..., they are still valid if the series satisfies them for the terms u_k, u_{k+1}, u_{k+2}, ...

Limiting Value of the nth Term

A series u_0, u_1, u_2, ... cannot converge unless $\lim_{n\to\infty} u_n = 0$.

Comparison Test

u_0, u_1, u_2, ... is a series of positive terms, and a_0, a_1, a_2, ... is another series of positive terms, known to converge. Then the first series converges if $u_n \leq a_n$ for all n. Conversely, if the second series is known to diverge and $u_n \geq a_n$ for all n, then the first series diverges.

Absolute Convergence

If the series $|u_0|$, $|u_1|$, $|u_2|$, ... converges, then so does u_0, u_1, u_2, ...
Such a series is said to be *absolutely* convergent. Note that the converse
is not necessarily true, i.e., the convergence of u_0, u_1, u_2, ... does not
imply the convergence of $|u_0|$, $|u_1|$, $|u_2|$, ...

Alternating Series

Let u_0, u_1, u_2, ... be a series of positive terms. Then the series $u_0 -
u_1 + u_2 - u_3 + u_4 - u_5$ ... is called an *alternating* series and always
converges provided that (i) $\lim_{n \to \infty} u_n = 0$, and (ii) $u_n \geq u_{n+1}$ for all n.

Ratio Test

The series u_0, u_1, u_2, ... converges if

$$\lim_{n \to \infty} \left| \frac{u_{n+1}}{u_n} \right| < 1$$

It diverges if

$$\lim_{n \to \infty} \left| \frac{u_{n+1}}{u_n} \right| > 1 \qquad \text{(or is infinite)}$$

The test fails if the limit is equal to 1, i.e., in some cases where the limit
is one the series converges, in others it diverges.

Exercises

1. Verify the statement above on absolutely convergent series.
Show that the series can be split into two parts, v_1, v_2, v_3, ... of positive
terms and w_1, w_2, w_3, ... of negative terms. Then if

$$\sum_{n=0}^{\infty} |u_n| = \overline{U}$$

show

$$v_1 + v_2 + v_3 + \cdots \leq \overline{U} \qquad \text{and} \qquad -(w_1 + w_2 + w_3 \ldots) \leq \overline{U}$$

Hence by law (5) of Section 4.4 both subsequences converge, say to V
and $-W$. The series $u_0 + u_1 + u_2 + \cdots$ must therefore converge to
$V - W$.

2. Verify that alternating series converge provided $u_n \to 0$ as $n \to \infty$ and $u_n \geq u_{n+1}$. Define $S_n = u_0 - u_1 + u_2 - \cdots + (-1)^n u_n$. Then show that

    (a) $S_{2n+1} = (u_0 - u_1) + (u_2 - u_3) + \cdots + (u_{2n} - u_{2n+1})$ is an increasing function of n.

    (b) $S_{2n+1} = u_0 - (u_1 - u_2) - (u_3 - u_4) - \cdots (u_{2n-1} - u_{2n}) - u_{2n+1} \leq u_0$.

    (c) Hence $S_1, S_3, S_5, \ldots, S_{2n+1}, \ldots$ tends to a limit S.

    (d) Finally, S_{2n} also tends to S. $(S_{2n} = S_{2n-1} + u_{2n})$.

3. Prove the validity of the ratio test. [Since we are only concerned with $\left| \dfrac{u_{n+1}}{u_n} \right|$ and we know that $u_0 + u_1 + u_2 + \cdots$ converges whenever $|u_0| + |u_1| + |u_2| + \cdots$ converges, we may assume we are dealing with a series of positive terms. The proof proceeds in the steps outlined below.]

Case 1. $L < 1$.

    (i) Since $u_{n+1}/u_n \to L < 1$, there exists r such that $L \leq r < 1$ and for sufficiently large n (say $n \geq k$), $u_{n+1}/u_n < r$.

    (ii) $u_{k+m} \leq u_k r^m$.

    (iii) Now compare the series with a suitable geometric progression.

Case 2. $L > 1$.

    (i) Since $u_{n+1}/u_n \to L > 1$, there exists r such that $L \geq r > 1$ and for sufficiently large n (say $n > k$), $u_{n+1}/u_n > r$.

    (ii) Hence u_n cannot tend to zero and the series cannot converge.

Case 3. $L = 1$. If $u_n = 1/n$, $u_{n+1}/u_n = (n + 1)/n \to 1$, but we have seen that the harmonic series $1 + \frac{1}{2} + \frac{1}{3} + \frac{1}{4} + \cdots$ diverges (Section 4.7).

If $u_n = \dfrac{1}{n(n + 1)}$, $\dfrac{u_{n+1}}{u_{n+2}} = \dfrac{(n + 1)(n + 2)}{n(n + 1)} = \dfrac{n + 2}{n} = 1 + \dfrac{2}{n} \to 1$.

But $u_n = \left(\dfrac{1}{n} - \dfrac{1}{n + 1} \right)$, so that $S_k = u_1 + u_2 + u_3 + \cdots + u_k$

$$= \left(1 - \frac{1}{2}\right) + \left(\frac{1}{2} - \frac{1}{3}\right) + \left(\frac{1}{3} - \frac{1}{4}\right) + \cdots + \left(\frac{1}{k} - \frac{1}{k + 1}\right)$$

$$= 1 - \frac{1}{k + 1}$$

Hence $S_k \rightarrow 1$ as $k \rightarrow \infty$, and the series converges.

4. Test the following alternating series:

(a) $(-1)^n \dfrac{1}{n+1}$

(b) $(-1)^n \dfrac{n}{n+1}$

(c) $\dfrac{(-1)^{n+1}}{n^2}$

5. Verify that the following series are convergent or divergent as indicated.

(a) $u_n = \dfrac{n+2}{2^n}$ (convergent)

(b) $u_n = \dfrac{n!}{8^n}$ (divergent)

(c) $u_n = \dfrac{n!}{3 \cdot 5 \cdot 7 \cdot \ldots \cdot (2n+1)}$ (convergent)

(d) $u_n = \dfrac{1}{(n-1)!}$ (convergent)

(e) $u_n = \dfrac{(-1)^{n+1}}{(2n-2)!}$ (convergent)

(f) $u_n = \dfrac{(-1)^{n+1}}{(2n-1)!}$ (convergent)

(g) $u_n = \dfrac{3^{n+1}}{n2^n}$ (divergent)

■ 4.10 Power Series

An infinite series of the form

(1) $c_0 + c_1(x-a) + c_2(x-a)^2 + \cdots + c_n(x-a)^n + \cdots$

in which x is a *variable* and the c_i and a are *constants* is called a *power series*. Since (1) converges to c_0 for $x = a$, every power series converges for at least one value of x. It may converge for a range of values, or for all values of x, depending on the values of the constants. The totality of values of x for which a power series converges is called the *interval of convergence*. The tests of Section 4.9 may be applied to find the interval.

Example 1. Find the interval of convergence of the power series,

$$x + \frac{x^2}{2} + \frac{x^3}{3} + \cdots + \frac{x^n}{n} + \cdots$$

By the *ratio test*,

$$\lim_{n \to \infty} \left| \frac{u_{n+1}}{u_n} \right| = \lim_{n \to \infty} \left| \left(\frac{x^{n+1}}{n+1} \right) \left(\frac{n}{x^n} \right) \right| = \lim_{n \to \infty} \left| x \frac{n}{n+1} \right| = |x|$$

and the series converges for $|x| < 1$ and diverges for $|x| > 1$. When $x = \pm 1$, the ratio test fails. However, the harmonic series diverges ($x = 1$) by Section 4.7, and the alternating harmonic series converges ($x = -1$) by Section 4.9. Hence the interval of convergence is $-1 \le x < 1$.

Similarly, the interval of convergence of

$$(x - a) + \frac{(x - a)^2}{2} + \frac{(x - a)^3}{3} + \cdots + \frac{(x - a)^n}{n} + \cdots$$

is given by $a - 1 \le x < a + 1$.

Example 2. Find the interval of convergence of

$$x - \frac{x^2}{2^2} + \frac{x^3}{3^2} - \frac{x^4}{4^2} + \cdots + (-1)^{n+1} \frac{x^n}{n^2} + \cdots$$

$$\lim_{n \to \infty} \left| \frac{u_{n+1}}{u_n} \right| = \lim_{n \to \infty} \left| \left(\frac{n^2}{(n+1)^2} \right) x \right| = |x|$$

The series is convergent for $|x| < 1$ and divergent for $|x| > 1$. When $x = 1$, the series is

$$1 - \frac{1}{2^2} + \frac{1}{3^2} - \frac{1}{4^2} + \cdots + \frac{(-1)^{n+1}}{n^2} + \cdots$$

which is an alternating series. Since the nth term approaches zero it converges. When $x = -1$, we have

$$-1 - \frac{1}{2^2} - \frac{1}{3^2} - \frac{1}{4^2} - \cdots - \frac{1}{n^2} - \cdots$$

which is convergent by comparison with the k-series for $k = 2$. The interval of convergence of the original series is $-1 \le x \le 1$.

Example 3.   Operations involving infinite series must be carried out carefully.   The series

$$\frac{2}{1} - \frac{3}{2} + \frac{4}{3} - \frac{5}{4} + \cdots$$

diverges, for the nth term does not approach zero.   Yet by inserting parentheses

$$(\frac{2}{1} - \frac{3}{2}) + (\frac{4}{3} - \frac{5}{4}) + (\frac{6}{5} - \frac{7}{6}) + \cdots$$

and performing the subtractions we obtain

$$\frac{1}{1 \cdot 2} + \frac{1}{3 \cdot 4} + \frac{1}{5 \cdot 6} + \cdots$$

which by the comparison test, using the k-series ($k = 2$), is *convergent*.

Exercises for Chapter 4

1. Find the sum of the first 10 terms of the following arithmetic and geometric series:

(a) $a = 100, d = -12$
(b) $a = 10, r = \frac{1}{2}$

2. (a) A firm earns $1000 per year and the rate of interest is 10% per year. Find the present value of this income flow.

(b) A firm earns $1000 the first year, 0.9($1000) in the second year, 0.9^2($1000) in the third year, etc.   Find the present value of this income flow for a rate of interest of 10% per year.

(c) A firm wishes to accumulate $10,000 at the end of 10 years.   It deposits into a capital equipment fund, $a per year at a rate of return of 20% per year. Find a.

3. Find the following limits:

(a) $\lim\limits_{x \to \infty} (\sqrt{x + 1} - \sqrt{x})$

Hint:

$$\lim_{x \to \infty} \sqrt{x + 1} - \sqrt{x} = \lim_{x \to \infty} \frac{(\sqrt{x + 1} - \sqrt{x})(\sqrt{x + 1} + \sqrt{x})}{\sqrt{x + 1} + \sqrt{x}}$$

$$= \lim_{x \to \infty} \frac{1}{\sqrt{x + 1} + \sqrt{x}} = 0$$

(b) $\lim\limits_{x \to 0} \dfrac{ax + b}{cx + d}, \quad \lim\limits_{x \to \infty} \dfrac{ax + b}{cx + d}$

Hint:

$$\lim_{x \to \infty} \frac{ax + b}{cx + d} = \lim_{x \to \infty} \frac{a + b/x}{c + d/x}$$

(c) $\lim\limits_{x \to 0} \dfrac{ax^2 + bx + c}{dx^2 + ex + f}, \quad \lim\limits_{x \to \infty} \dfrac{ax^2 + bx + c}{dx^2 + ex + f}$

4. For each of the following functions find

$$\lim_{h \to 0} \left[\frac{f(x + h) - f(x)}{h} \right]$$

(a) $f(x) = \text{constant} = c$
(b) $f(x) = x$
(c) $f(x) = cx$
(d) $f(x) = cx + d$
(e) $f(x) = ax^2 + bx + c$
(f) $f(x) = 1/x$
(g) $f(x) = \sqrt{x}$

Hint: use a method similar to 3(a).

5. Graph the following functions:

(a) $y = \dfrac{3x + 1}{x - 2}$ for $0 \leq x \leq 4$

(b) $y = \dfrac{x + 1}{x - 1}$ for $0 \leq x \leq 2$

(c) $y = \dfrac{2x^2 + 3x + 1}{3x^2 - 4x + 1}$ for $0 \leq x \leq 2$

6. Test the following series for convergence or divergence:

(a) $x_n = \dfrac{1}{n(n + 2)}$ (d) $x_n = \dfrac{n + 1}{n + 2}$

(b) $x_n = \dfrac{n}{n^3 - 1}$ (e) $x_n = \dfrac{(n + 1)(n + 2)}{2n^2}$

(c) $x_n = \dfrac{\sqrt{n}}{n + 1}$ (f) $x_n = \dfrac{2n^2 + 3n + 1}{n^2 + 5}$

7. Find the sum of the following convergent series:

(a) $x_n = \dfrac{1}{n(n + 1)}$

Hint: $\dfrac{1}{n(n + 1)} = \dfrac{1}{n} - \dfrac{1}{n + 1}$

(b) $x_n = \dfrac{2}{3^{n-1}}$

(c) $x_n = (-1)^{n-1} \dfrac{5}{2^{n-1}}$

8. Verify that the intervals of convergence for the following power series are as given

(a) $x_n = \dfrac{x^n}{\sqrt{n}}$ $\qquad\qquad\qquad$ $-1 \le x < 1$

(b) $x_n = (-1)^{n+1} \dfrac{x^{2n-1}}{(2n-1)!}$ $\qquad$ all values of x

(c) $x_n = nx^n$ $\qquad\qquad\qquad$ $-1 < x < 1$

(d) $x_n = \dfrac{(-1)^{n+1}(x-1)^n}{n}$ $\qquad$ $0 < x < 2$

(e) $x_n = \dfrac{x^n}{n!}$ $\qquad\qquad\qquad$ all values of x

9. Determine the intervals of convergence of the following power series:

(a) $x_n = \dfrac{(-1)^{n+1}x^n}{n(3^{n-1})}$

(b) $x_n = \dfrac{x^n}{n(3^{n-1})}$

(c) $x_n = \dfrac{x^n}{na^n}$

10. There are many management problems where we have to find a policy which will be used every month for some long period to come. Suppose the result of using policy P in month r is a profit $s_r(P)$. If we know the process will terminate in n months, we may choose P so as to maximize $\sum_{r=1}^{n} s_r(P)$. If we expect the process to continue indefinitely, we might try to maximize $\sum_{r=1}^{\infty} s_r(P)$. Unfortunately there is no reason to suppose that $s_r(P) \to 0$ as $r \to \infty$, so that the series will not converge, and it is meaningless to talk of maximization. There are two ways out of this dilemma.

(a) We can argue that since s_r is not received for r months, it should be discounted by a factor v^r, and the sum to be maximized is

$$\sum_{r=1}^{\infty} v^r s_r, \qquad 0 < v < 1$$

(b) We can argue that we wish to maximize *average* profits and that we are interested in

$$\lim_{n \to \infty} \frac{1}{n} \sum_{r=1}^{n} s_r$$

Show that as long as s_r is bounded (i.e., there exist $m \le M$ such that for all r, $m \le s_r \le M$), the series $\sum_{r=1}^{\infty} v^r s_r$ converges. The limit in (b) usually exists in practice, but it is difficult to state necessary and sufficent conditions on s_r.

11. If we are given a series $u_0, u_1, u_2, \ldots$ and if the power series $\sum_{0}^{\infty} u_r z^r$ converges for $0 \le |z| < \rho$, we say that the function $U(z) = \sum_{0}^{\infty} u_r z^r$ is the

generating function for the series. Show that the generating function exists if there exist $m < M$ such that $m < u_r < M$ for all r.

(In order to determine the sum of a sequence we may be able to find a generating function first and then expand it in a power series; see Chapter 8.)

12. Show that if for all r, $u_r \geq 0$, and we know that $\sum_0^\infty u_r = 1$, then the generating function $U(z)$ exists. Show that the series for $U(z)$ always converges for $0 \leq |z| \leq 1$, and find an example to show that $U(z)$ need not converge if $z > 1$.

13. If two series u_0, u_1, u_2, ... and v_0, v_1, v_2, ... have generating functions $U(z)$ and $V(z)$, show that a third series w_0, w_1, w_2, ... defined by $w_r = \sum_{i=0}^r u_i v_{r-i}$ has the generating function $W(z) \equiv U(z)V(z)$. (W_r is called the *convolution* of $\{u_r\}$ and $\{v_r\}$ and has frequent use in the theory of probability.)

14. If $\sum_0^\infty u_r z^r$ converges for $|z| < \rho_1$ and $\sum_0^\infty v_r z^r$ converges for $|z| < \rho_2$, show that $\sum_0^\infty w_r z^r$ converges for $|z| < \rho$, where ρ is the smaller of ρ_1 and ρ_2.
Hint:

$$
\begin{aligned}
\sum_{r=0}^n w_r z^r = \ & v_0(u_0 + zu_1 + z^2 u_2 + \cdots + z^n u_n) \\
& + v_1 z(u_0 + zu_1 + z^2 u_2 + \cdots + z^{n-1} u_{n-1}) \\
& \vdots \\
& + v_n z^n u_0
\end{aligned}
$$

Show that if $u_r \geq 0$, and $0 \leq z \leq \rho_1$, then

$$
\sum_{r=0}^n w_r z^r \leq U(z)(v_0 + v_1 z + v_2 z^2 + \cdots)
$$

Hence show that if $0 \leq z \leq \rho$, $\sum_{r=0}^n w_r z^r$ is bounded. The result follows.

15. We define a sequence u_r by the equations

$$
-\lambda_0 u_0 + \mu_1 u_1 = 0
$$

$$
\lambda_{r-1} u_{r-1} - (\lambda_r + \mu_r) u_r + \mu_{r+1} u_{r+1} = 0, \qquad r = 1, 2, 3, \ldots
$$

Show that the series $\sum_0^\infty u_r$ will converge provided $|\lambda_r / \mu_{r+1}| < 1$.
Hint: First show

$$
u_r = \left(\frac{\lambda_0 \cdot \lambda_1 \cdot \lambda_2 \cdot \ \cdots \ \cdot \lambda_{r-1}}{\mu_1 \cdot \mu_2 \cdot \ \cdots \ \cdot \mu_r} \right) u_0
$$

This series occurs in the theory of queues.

16. If in exercise 15, $\lambda_r = \lambda$ for all r and $\mu_r = r\mu$, show that the series $\sum_0^\infty u_r$ converges for all values of λ and μ.

17. Imagine that at time zero we start a system with a large number, u_0, of identical new parts. Suppose that failures of parts can only occur at times 1, 2, 3, ... and that as failures occur they are immediately replaced by new parts. Let $u_r(r = 0, 1, 2, \ldots)$ be the number of new parts inserted in the system at time r, and suppose that out of k new parts, a number kp_t fail at exact age t ($t = 1, 2, \ldots$). Show that the sequence $\{u_r\}$ satisfies the relationship

$$
u_r = u_0 p_r + u_1 p_{r-1} + u_2 p_{r-2} + \cdots + u_{r-1} p_1, \qquad r = 1, 2, 3, \ldots
$$

By multiplying this relationship by z^r, and adding over the values $r = 1$, $r = 2$, ..., show that

$$\sum_1^\infty u_r z^r = u_0(p_1 z + p_2 z^2 + p_3 z^3 + \cdots)$$
$$+ u_1 z(p_1 z + p_2 z^2 + \cdots)$$
$$\vdots$$
$$+ u_r z^r(p_1 z + p_2 z^2 + \cdots)$$
$$\vdots$$

Hence, if we define

$$+$$

$$P(z) = \sum_1^\infty p_r z^r$$

and

$$U(z) = \sum_0^\infty u_r z^r$$

prove that

$$U(z) = \frac{u_0}{1 - P(z)}$$

What is the interpretation of $U(1)$? Why would you expect it to diverge?

Hint: Since all items must fail at some age, $P(1) = \sum_1^\infty p_r = 1$. To test the convergence, recall that

$$\frac{u_0}{1 - P(z)} = u_0[1 + P(z) + P^2(z) + P^3(z) + \cdots]$$

and this series converges as long as $|P(z)| < 1$.

18. In exercise 17 suppose $p_r = qp^{r-1}$ where $p + q = 1$. Show that $P(z) = qz/(1 - pz)$. Hence find $U(z)$ and the sequence $\{u_r\}$.

19. Suppose the sequence $u_0, u_1, u_2, \ldots$ is such that $\lim_{n\to\infty} u_n = u$, and that $U(z) = \sum_0^\infty u_n z^n$ is the corresponding generating function. Show that

$$\lim_{z\to 1} (1 - z)U(z) = u$$

where the limit is over values of z less than unity.

Hint: Since $u_n \to u$, we can find N such that for any $\epsilon > 0$, and any $n > N$, $|u_n - u| < \epsilon$.

Use this to show that we can make $|(1 - z)U(z) - u|$ as small as we please by taking z close enough to unity.

$$|(1 - z)U(z) - u| = \left| (1 - z)\sum_{n=0}^N u_n z^n + (1 - z)\sum_{n=N+1}^\infty (u_n - u + u)z^n - u \right|$$

$$= \left| (1 - z)\sum_{n=0}^N u_n z^n + (1 - z)\sum_{N+1}^\infty (u_n - u)z^n \right.$$

$$\left. + (1 - z)\sum_{N+1}^\infty uz^n - u \right|$$

$$\leq \left| (1 - z) \sum_{n=0}^{N} u_n z^n \right| + \left| (1 - z) \sum_{N+1}^{\infty} \left| u_n - u \right| z^n \right.$$

$$+ \left| (1 - z) \frac{u z^{N+1}}{1 - z} - u \right|$$

$$\leq \left| (1 - z) \sum_{n=0}^{N} u_n z^n \right| + (1 - z) \frac{\epsilon z^{N+1}}{1 - z} + \left| u z^{N+1} - u \right|$$

$$= \left| (1 - z) \sum_{n=0}^{N} u_n z^n \right| + \epsilon z^{N+1} + \left| u z^{N+1} - u \right|$$

The result follows by considering what happens to each term separately.

20. Show, by using an example of a sequence which does not tend to a limit, that it is not necessarily true that if $\lim_{z \to 1} (1 - z) U(z) = u$, then $\lim_{n \to \infty} u_n = u$. [Consider, for example, $u_n = (-1)^n$.]

21. In exercise 17 we had $U(z) = u_0/[1 - P(z)]$, where $P(z) = \sum_1^{\infty} p_n z^n$ and $P(1) = \sum_1^{\infty} p_n = 1$. By long division show that

$$\frac{1 - z}{1 - P(z)} = [1 + (1 - p_1)z + (1 - p_1 - p_2)z^2 + \cdots]^{-1}$$

and hence by writing $1 = p_1 + p_2 + \cdots$, $1 - p_1 = p_2 + p_3 + \cdots$ show that if u_n tends to a limit, the limit must be $[u_0(p_1 + 2p_2 + 3p_3 + 4p_4 + \cdots)]^{-1}$. Interpret this in terms of the average life of the parts.

5

Coordinate Geometry

In solving problems it is often necessary to express costs and profits as a function of such variables as advertising budgets, production quantities, and inventory levels. These relationships may be expressed in graphical, tabular, or analytic form. This chapter will develop the graphical methods and their relationships with the analytic methods. It will be demonstrated that it is possible to analyze business problems from both analytic and graphical points of view.

It often happens that one branch of mathematics can be used to solve problems in other areas. This can be done whenever two areas have the same mathematical structure. The easiest way to picture the situation is to imagine that we take a statement in English and translate it into French. The two statements are then equivalent although their appearance is quite different. If they are mathematical problems, we can state the problem in English, translate it to French and get a French mathematician to find the solution. The solution would then be translated for the benefit of the English mathematician who cannot read French. There would be little point to all this unless the Frenchman had an insight into the problem that the Englishman did not.

It happens that there are many problems in geometry which can be translated into algebra, solved as algebraic problems, and translated back into geometry. Frequently such problems are difficult or impossible to solve by geometric reasoning alone. The converse is also true; frequently our geometric insight (because we can often draw pictures) enables us to solve algebraic problems. Probably there are a few business problems of a purely geometric nature, but there are many whose solution is facilitated by an ability to switch to and fro between geometric and algebraic reasoning. Mathematical systems that have the same structure are called *isomorphic*.

In this chapter we discuss the relationship between algebra and geometry. It is mostly a theoretical chapter, but it will provide the necessary tools for our discussion of calculus and linear programming later.

We will build up the isomorphism between algebra and geometry in exactly the same way as we translate from English into French, that is, we will first compile a dictionary that tells us which "words" correspond to which. Then we will need to compare the "grammars" or rules for making sentences out of words.

■ 5.2 Points on a Line

In geometry we start with the concept of a *point*, but we cannot say very much of interest about a single point. In order to have a nontrivial discussion we next introduce the idea of a line (straight line). A *line* is determined by any two points on it. Suppose we have a line and mark a particular point on it, which we will call the *origin O*. Any other point P can be designated by its distance from O, measured positively if P is to the right of O and negatively if P is to the left; O itself is designated by zero (see Figure 5.1). We would say that $OP = x$ is the *coordinate* of P.

The following consequences are immediate and the student should verify them for himself.

1. If P and Q, whose respective coordinates are x and y [written $P(x)$ and $Q(y)$], are two points, then the distance d between them is given by

$$d = \sqrt{(x - y)^2}$$

Since d is always a positive quantity, we take the positive root, and this takes care of the two cases, $x \geq y$, $x \leq y$.

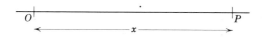

Figure 5.1

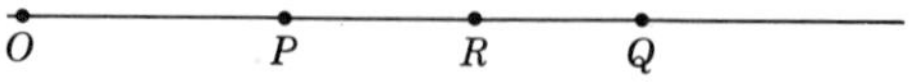

Figure 5.2

2. If $P(x)$ and $Q(y)$ are any two points and R is a point between P and Q (see Figure 5.2), then the coordinate, u, of R is always expressible as

$$u = \alpha x + \beta y$$

where $\quad\quad\quad \alpha \geq 0, \quad \beta \geq 0, \quad$ and $\quad \alpha + \beta = 1$

3. Two points P and Q determine the set of points S which lies between them (including P and Q themselves). Such a set is said to be *convex* because if X and Y are two points of S, then every point of the segment XY also belongs to S. The notion of *convexity* is important and will be generalized later. We take the set of points defined by statement 2 above to be an algebraic definition of a convex set, as follows:

The convex set S determined by x and y is the set of all numbers expressible as

$$u = \alpha x + \beta y$$

where $\quad\quad\quad \alpha \geq 0, \quad \beta \geq 0, \quad$ and $\quad \alpha + \beta = 1$

Along a line, convexity is a rather trivial idea, but we will see that the idea is readily extended to higher dimensional spaces, such as planes and solids.

4. If $P_1(x_1)$, $P_2(x_2)$, $\ldots$, $P_n(x_n)$ are any points along a line, then any point U which lies between two of them has a coordinate u expressible as

$$u = \alpha_1 x_1 + \alpha_2 x_2 + \cdots + \alpha_n x_n$$

where $\quad\quad\quad \alpha_1 \geq 0, \quad \alpha_2 \geq 0, \ldots, \alpha_n \geq 0$

and $\quad\quad\quad\quad \alpha_1 + \alpha_2 + \cdots + \alpha_n = 1$

This, of course, is a trivial consequence of statement 2 because if U lies between P_i and P_j, then $u = \alpha_i x_i + \alpha_j x_j$, and we can take the remaining α's to be zero. The α's are not unique, and they can be determined in many ways if $n > 2$.

Again, we will see that this concept can be extended to planes and solids.

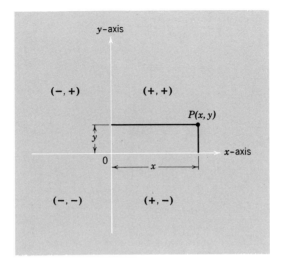

Figure 5.3

■ 5.3 Points in a Plane

The geometry of a line is not very exciting, but our ideas are readily extended to planes. In order to designate a point in a plane, we need two mutually perpendicular lines * (known as *axes*). Any point P is denoted by two coordinates—its distances from each of the lines—measured according to an agreed sign convention.

Of course any convention would do, but it is customary to draw the picture as in Figure 5.3; the two lines are labeled *x-axis* and *y-axis*, and in stating the coordinates of P as (x, y) we mean P lies a distance x along the x-axis to the right of the y-axis and a distance y along the y-axis, measured upward from the x-axis. The point 0 of intersection of the axes has coordinates $(0, 0)$ and is called the *origin*.

In Figure 5.3 we see that the plane is divided into four *quadrants* by the axes. The signs in the figure are those of the coordinates in each quadrant. The top right quadrant in which both coordinates are positive is of particular importance in business because many business variables cannot take negative values.

We will now find the two dimensional analogs of statements 1, 2, 3, and 4 in Section 5.2 made about points on a line.

* Actually any two nonparallel lines will do, but the situation becomes unnecessarily complicated if they are not perpendicular.

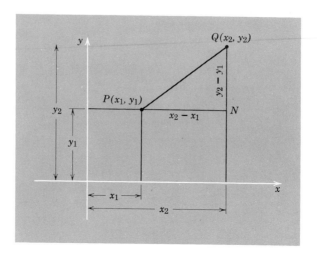

Figure 5.4

1. If $P(x_1, y_1)$ and $Q(x_2, y_2)$ are two points, the distance d between them is given by

$$d = \sqrt{(x_1 - x_2)^2 + (y_1 - y_2)^2}$$

This can easily be verified with the use of Pythagoras' Theorem. In Figure 5.4 we see $d = PQ$, and

$$PQ^2 = PN^2 + QN^2$$

$$= (x_2 - x_1)^2 + (y_2 - y_1)^2$$

$$= (x_1 - x_2)^2 + (y_1 - y_2)^2$$

The reader should sketch the cases where some or all of the coordinates are negative.

2. If $P(x_1, y_1)$ and $Q(x_2, y_2)$ are any two points and $R(u, v)$ is any point on the line between them, then

$$u = \alpha_1 x_1 + \alpha_2 x_2$$

$$v = \alpha_1 y_1 + \alpha_2 y_2$$

where $\qquad \alpha_1 \geq 0, \quad \alpha_2 \geq 0, \quad$ and $\alpha_1 + \alpha_2 = 1$

This can be seen by examining the similar triangles in Figure 5.5. Since triangles PRR'' and PQQ'' are similar, we have

$$\frac{RR''}{QQ''} = \frac{PR''}{PQ''}$$

or

$$\frac{v - y_1}{y_2 - y_1} = \frac{u - x_1}{x_2 - x_1}$$

From the figure, each of these ratios is less than one, say each is equal to α_2.

Hence

$$u = (1 - \alpha_2)x_1 + \alpha_2 x_2$$

$$v = (1 - \alpha_2)y_1 + \alpha_2 y_2$$

Note that by similar reasoning the coordinates (x, y) of *any* point on the line PQ must satisfy the equation

$$\frac{x - x_1}{x_2 - x_1} = \frac{y - y_1}{y_2 - y_1}$$

This relationship is called the *equation of the line PQ*. However, if the point is not between P and Q, these ratios will no longer be between zero and one. We will return to this topic later.

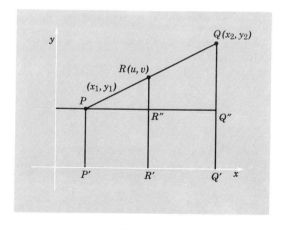

Figure 5.5

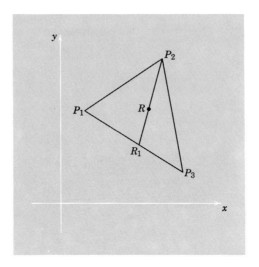

Figure 5.6

3. Three points $P_1(x_1, y_1)$, $P_2(x_2, y_2)$, and $P_3(x_3, y_3)$ determine a set of points S which lie in the triangle * $P_1P_2P_3$.

The set S is convex (i.e., if X, Y are two points of S, all the points of the segment XY belong to S), and the coordinates (u, v) of any point R of S can be written

$$u = \alpha_1 x_1 + \alpha_2 x_2 + \alpha_3 x_3$$

$$v = \alpha_1 y_1 + \alpha_2 y_2 + \alpha_3 y_3$$

where $\alpha_1 \geq 0$, $\alpha_2 \geq 0$, $\alpha_3 \geq 0$,   and $\alpha_1 + \alpha_2 + \alpha_3 = 1$

The convexity of S is geometrically obvious. In order to see the second statement, examine Figure 5.6.

Let P_2R meet P_1P_3 at $R_1(u_1, v_1)$. Since R_1 lies between P_1 and P_3, we know

$$u_1 = \beta_1 x_1 + \beta_3 x_3 \Big] \ \beta_1 \geq 0, \quad \beta_3 \geq 0$$

$$v_1 = \beta_1 y_1 + \beta_3 y_3 \Big/ \ \beta_1 + \beta_3 = 1$$

Since R lies between P_2 and R_1, we have

$$u = \gamma_1 u_1 + \gamma_2 x_2 \Big] \ \gamma_1 \geq 0, \quad \gamma_2 \geq 0$$

$$v = \gamma_1 v_1 + \gamma_2 y_2 \Big/ \ \gamma_1 + \gamma_2 = 1$$

* This section is trivial if the three points are on a line.

The result follows with

$$\alpha_1 = \beta_1\gamma_1, \quad \alpha_2 = \gamma_2, \quad \alpha_3 = \beta_3\gamma_1$$

4. We can easily extend statement 3, as we did for several points on a line. If $P_1(x_1, y_1)$, $P_2(x_2, y_2)$, ..., $P_n(x_n, y_n)$ are the corners of a convex figure S, then any point R within or on the boundary of S has coordinates (u, v), where

$$\left.\begin{aligned} u &= \alpha_1 x_1 + \alpha_2 x_2 + \cdots + \alpha_n x_n \\ v &= \alpha_1 y_1 + \alpha_2 y_2 + \cdots + \alpha_n y_n \end{aligned}\right\} \quad \begin{aligned} &\alpha_1 \geq 0, \quad \alpha_2 \geq 0, \ldots, \alpha_n \geq 0 \\ &\alpha_1 + \alpha_2 + \cdots + \alpha_n = 1 \end{aligned}$$

To verify these equations note that S must look like Figure 5.7a and not like Figure 5.7b.

Divide S into triangles $P_1P_2P_3$, $P_1P_3P_4$, ..., $P_1P_rP_{r+1}$, ..., $P_1P_{n-1}P_n$. The point R must lie in one of these triangles, and we can apply statement 3 to it.

As it happens, any point within a nonconvex figure can also be represented by coordinates that satisfy relationships like those of u and v. However, for a nonconvex figure, it is no longer true that *all* relationships of this type represent a point inside the figure (see Figure 5.7b).

The reader may now be wondering if there is any algebraic method of defining the set S, without reference to geometry. The answer is Yes, but first we must study the equation of a line in more detail.

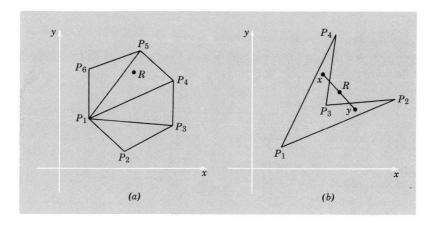

Figure 5.7   (a) $P_1P_2P_3P_4P_5P_6$ convex.   (b) $P_1P_2P_3P_4$ not convex.

Exercises

1. Plot the following pairs of points and compute the distances between them:

   (a) $(1, 0)$ and $(-2, 3)$
   (b) $(0, 3)$ and $(-1, -2)$
   (c) $(5, 6)$ and $(6, 0)$
   (d) $(8, 9)$ and $(7, -3)$

2. Find the coordinates of the point half way between $(3, 2)$ and $(6, 9)$.

3. Plot the three points $(3, 2)$, $(6, 6)$, and $(12, 4)$, and sketch the convex set formed by these points. Which of the following points belong to the convex set: $(7, 5)$, $(7, 3)$, $(8, 3)$, $(10, 5)$?

4. The three principal customers of a manufacturing firm are located at the coordinates $(4, 4)$, $(9, 7)$, and $(14, 2)$, where the origin is the center of a city and the coordinates are measured from the center of the city. The firm wishes to locate a warehouse at the site that is equally distant from all customers. Show that the warehouse site location is $(8.75, 1.75)$. Draw the diagram showing the locations of the customers and warehouse.

■ 5.4   The Equation of a Line

We have already seen that any point R on the line $P(x_1, y_1)$, $Q(x_2, y_2)$ must have coordinates (x, y) that satisfy

$$(1) \qquad \frac{x - x_1}{x_2 - x_1} = \frac{y - y_1}{y_2 - y_1}$$

Equation (1) is sometimes called the *two-point* equation of the line. A little manipulation shows that this can be written as *

$$(2) \qquad\qquad ax + by + c = 0$$

where

$$a = \frac{1}{x_2 - x_1}, \quad b = \frac{-1}{y_2 - y_1}$$

and

$$c = \frac{-x_1}{x_2 - x_1} + \frac{y_1}{y_2 - y_1}$$

so that a, b, c are independent of x and y. Such an equation is called

---

* We are assuming $x_1 \neq x_2$ and $y_1 \neq y_2$. If $x_1 = x_2$, then $b = 0$ and $c/a = x_1$; similarly, if $y_1 = y_2$. Of course, if $x_1 = x_2$ and $y_1 = y_2$, the points coincide and do not define a line.

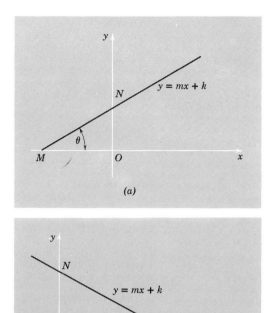

Figure 5.8 (a) $m > 0$. (b) $m < 0$.

linear and is the general expression that represents a line. By putting $x = 0$, we see the line meets the y-axis (along which $x = 0$) at the point $(0, -c/b)$ and by setting $y = 0$, it meets the x-axis at $(-c/a, 0)$. Of course, if $a = 0$, the line is $y = -c/b$, which is parallel to the x-axis, a distance $-c/b$ from it. If $b = 0$, the line is parallel to the y-axis, a distance $-c/a$ from it. Now, if $b \neq 0$, we may solve equation (2) for y and write

(3) $$y = mx + k$$

where $$m = -\frac{a}{b}, \quad k = -\frac{c}{b}$$

This form has the advantage of a physical interpretation. In Figure 5.8a let θ be the angle between the line and the positive direction of the

x-axis. Then we define * the *slope of the line* as tan θ,

$$\tan \theta = \frac{NO}{MO}$$

and M is the point $(-k/m, 0)$, N is the point $(0, k)$. Thus the distance OM is equal to k/m, and ON is equal to k.

Hence
$$\tan \theta = k \div \frac{k}{m} = m$$

In Figure 5.8b, $\tan \theta = - \tan (\pi - \theta) = - \frac{ON}{OM}$

However, it is not difficult to see that if the line slopes as in Figure 5.8b, $m < 0$. Thus

$$OM = \frac{-k}{m}, \quad ON = k$$

and, again, tan $\theta = m$.

In both cases m is the slope of the line. Equation (3) is called the *slope-intercept* form of the line.

Exercises

1. Find the equation of a line passing through the points $(1, 2)$ and $(-1, 3)$.

2. Find the slope of the line joining the points $(7, 5)$ and $(9, 7)$. Find the equation of this line.

3. It costs a company \$200 to ship one of its products one mile and \$400 to ship 100 miles. What is the linear equation between cost and the number of mi'es shipped? What are the slope and intercept of this line? What would be the cost of shipping 200 miles?

4. A firm invests \$10 million in a new facility that has a net return of \$500,000 per year. An investment of \$20 million would yield net income of \$2 million per year. What is the linear relationship between investment and annual income? What would be the annual return on an investment of \$15 million?

5. It costs a mail order firm \$15,000 to process 1000 orders, and \$25,000 to process 2000 orders. Determine the linear equation between processing cost and order quantity. What is the cost of processing 3000 orders?

---

* For the definition of tan θ, read "tangent theta"; see an elementary book on plane trigonometry or Section 5.7 of this book.

■ 5.5   Distance of a Point from a Line

We now turn to the interpretation of the expression $ax + by + c$ for a point $P(x_1, y_1)$ not on the line $ax + by + c = 0$. Since the point is not on the line, either $ax_1 + by_1 + c > 0$ or $ax_1 + by_1 + c < 0$. The reader should satisfy himself that the sign of $ax + by + c$ is the same for every point on one side of the line and changes as we cross the line. A formal proof is not difficult, but it is tedious and we will not give one.

Example.   Consider the line $3x - 5y + 15 = 0$ and its graph as shown in Figure 5.9.

The values of $3x - 5y + 15$ at different points are presented in Table 5.1.

TABLE 5.1

Point	$3x - 5y + 15$	Point	$3x - 5y + 15$
$(4, 2)$	17	$(4, 2)$	17
$(4, 3)$	12	$(3, 2)$	14
$(4, 4)$	7	$(2, 2)$	11
$(4, 5)$	2	$(1, 2)$	8
$(4, 6)$	-3	$(0, 2)$	5
$(4, 7)$	-8	$(-1, 2)$	2
$(4, 8)$	-13	$(-2, 2)$	-1
$(4, 9)$	-18	$(-3, 2)$	-4

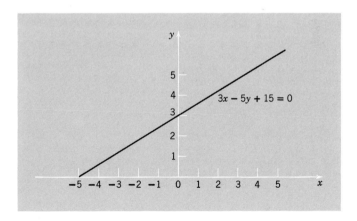

Figure 5.9

All points that have positive values of $3x - 5y + 15$ are to the right of the line, whereas all negative values are to the left. It may be noted that the origin is to the right of the line.

Exercise. Consider the line $2x + 3y - 12 = 0$. Draw the graph of the line and verify that the origin is to the left of the line. Determine which of the following points yields $2x_1 + 3y_1 - 12 > 0$: (2, 2), (2, 3), (2, 4), (3, 2), (4, 2), and (5, 2).

We are now in a position to answer a question posed earlier. *How can we designate a convex set S algebraically?* Let the boundary lines of a plane area such as P_1, P_2, ..., P_n in Figure 5.7a be given by equations

$$a_1 x + b_1 y + c_1 = 0$$

$$a_2 x + b_2 y + c_2 = 0$$

$$\cdot$$
$$\cdot$$
$$\cdot$$

$$a_n x + b_n y + c_n = 0$$

All points inside Figure 5.7a defined by P_1, P_2, ..., P_n are on the same side of a given line. For any point $R(x, y)$, inside the figure, one of each of the pairs of inequalities must hold:

either $\qquad a_1 x + b_1 y + c_1 > 0 \qquad$ or $\qquad a_1 x + b_1 y + c < 0$

and either $\quad a_2 x + b_2 y + c_2 > 0 \qquad$ or $\qquad a_2 x + b_2 y + c_2 < 0$

$$\cdot$$
$$\cdot$$
$$\cdot$$

and either $\quad a_n x + b_n y + c_2 > 0 \qquad$ or $\qquad a_n x + b_n y + c < 0$

By suitable choice of the a's, b's, and c's it is always possible to make all the inequalities "greater than." For example, suppose the plane area is a triangle $P_1 P_2 P_3$, with $P_1(0, 1)$, $P_2(-1, 0)$, and $P_3(1, 0)$ (Figure 5.10).

The boundary lines have equations

$$P_1 P_2: y = x + 1; \quad P_1 P_3: y = -x + 1; \quad P_2 P_3: y = 0$$

If we write these equations as

$$y - x - 1 = 0$$

$$y + x - 1 = 0$$

$$y = 0$$

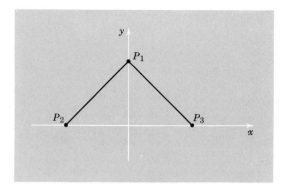

Figure 5.10

then the first and second expressions are negative inside the figure [for example, at the point $(0, \frac{1}{2})$] while the third is positive. We can make all three expressions positive by writing the equations as

$$x - y + 1 = 0$$
$$-x - y + 1 = 0$$
$$y = 0$$

In this case all points within and on the triangle $P_1 P_2 P_3$ satisfy

$$x - y + 1 \geq 0$$
$$-x - y + 1 \geq 0$$
$$y \geq 0$$

Thus an algebraic definition of a convex set S is those points (x, y) that satisfy a system of linear inequalities

$$a_1 x + b_1 y + c_1 \geq 0$$
$$a_2 x + b_2 y + c_2 \geq 0$$
$$\cdot$$
$$\cdot$$
$$a_n x + b_n y + c_n \geq 0$$

It may happen that it is impossible to find a point that satisfies all the inequalities; then S is said to be *null*.

It is easy enough to see that if $P(x_1, y_1)$ and $Q(x_2, y_2)$ satisfy the inequalities, then so do all points R lying between P and Q; thus S is indeed convex.

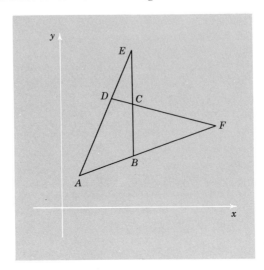

Figure 5.11

R has coordinates $(\alpha_1 x_1 + \alpha_2 x_2, \; \alpha_1 y_1 + \alpha_2 y_2)$, where $\alpha_1 \geq 0$, $\alpha_2 \geq 0$, $\alpha_1 + \alpha_2 = 1$, and direct substitution shows that if (x_1, y_1) and (x_2, y_2) satisfy the inequalities, so do the coordinates of R.

To make the analogy between algebra and geometry complete, we need an algebraic interpretation of the corners. Let us examine Figure 5.11. The quadrilateral $ABCD$ is a convex figure, and its corners are the inter-sections of pairs of lines out of the four lines AE, AF, BE, DF. Un-fortunately, not all such intersections are corners of the convex figure (E and F are outside the quadrilateral $ABCD$ in Figure 5.11); we need a criterion for distinguishing between them. Since a point of intersection lies on two lines, its coordinates must satisfy the equations of both. However, to be a corner, they must satisfy all the other inequalities de-fining the convex set.

Definition. We now give a formal definition of a *corner* (or vertex). Let u and v be values of x and y that simultaneously satisfy any two out of the n equations

$$a_1 x + b_1 y + c_1 = 0$$

$$a_2 x + b_2 y + c_2 = 0$$

$$\cdot$$

$$\cdot$$

$$\cdot$$

$$a_n x + b_n y + c_n = 0$$

If at the same time u and v also satisfy *all* inequalities

$$a_1 x + b_1 y + c_1 \geq 0$$

.

.

.

$$a_n x + b_n y + c_n \geq 0$$

then (u, v) is a *corner* of the convex set defined by the inequalities. It is now possible to give an algebraic proof of statement 4, in Section 5.3, which says that if (x_1, y_1), (x_2, y_2) ... (x_k, y_k) are corners of a convex set, any point of the set has coordinates

$$(\alpha_1 x_1 + \alpha_2 x_2 + \cdots + \alpha_k x_k, \quad \alpha_1 y_1 + \alpha_2 y_2 + \cdots + \alpha_k y_k)$$

where $\alpha_1 \geq 0$, $\alpha_2 \geq 0$ ... $\alpha_k \geq 0$, and $\alpha_1 + \alpha_2 + \cdots + \alpha_k = 1$

The reader may care to attempt such a proof. However, since we have a geometric proof, it is hardly necessary and we will not do so.

We will now show that the distance, d of the point $R(u, v)$ from the line whose equation is $ax + by + c = 0$ is given by

$$d = \frac{au + bv + c}{\pm \sqrt{a^2 + b^2}}$$

The sign is chosen so as to make $d > 0$. In Figure 5.12 the required distance $d = RN$. Draw RP and RQ parallel to the x- and y-axes so

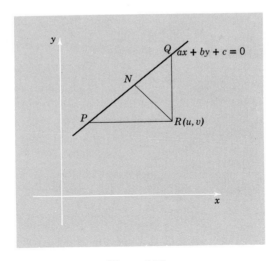

Figure 5.12

that their equations are

$$y = v$$

$$x = u$$

Since Q lies on RQ and QP, its coordinates must satisfy both equations at once so that P is the point

$$\left(\frac{-bv - c}{a}, v \right)$$

and similarly Q is the point

$$\left(u, \frac{-au - c}{b} \right)$$

Now triangles RPQ and RNP are similar. Therefore

$$\frac{RN}{RQ} = \frac{PR}{PQ} \quad \text{or} \quad RN = \frac{PR}{PQ} \cdot RQ$$

but

$$QR = -v + \left(\frac{-au - c}{b} \right) = -\frac{1}{b}(au + bv + c)$$

and

$$PQ = \left\{ \left[u - \left(\frac{-bv - c}{a} \right) \right]^2 + \left(\frac{-au - c}{b} - v \right)^2 \right\}^{1/2}$$

$$= (au + bv + c)\,[\pm \sqrt{1/a^2 + 1/b^2}]$$

$$PR = u - \left(\frac{-bv - c}{a} \right) = \frac{(au + bv + c)}{a}$$

Thus

$$RN = d = \frac{au + bv + c}{a} \cdot \frac{au + bv + c}{b} \cdot \frac{ab}{\pm(au + bv + c)\sqrt{a^2 + b^2}}$$

$$= \frac{au + bv + c}{\pm \sqrt{a^2 + b^2}}$$

and as $d > 0$, we choose the square root to make this quantity positive. Note that if R is on the line, $d = 0$, and $au + bv + c = 0$. Note also that the origin is a distance $\dfrac{c}{\pm\sqrt{a^2 + b^2}}$ from the line. We shall have occasion to use this fact when we discuss linear programming (Chapter 14).

Example 1. Find the equations of the bisectors of the angles between the lines

$$a_1 x + b_1 y + c_1 = 0$$

$$a_2 x + b_2 y + c_2 = 0$$

We use the fact that any point (x, y) on a bisector is equidistant from both lines. Thus any such point must satisfy

$$\frac{a_1 x + b_1 y + c_1}{\sqrt{a_1^2 + b_1^2}} = \frac{a_2 x + b_2 y + c_2}{\sqrt{a_2^2 + b_2^2}}$$

or

$$\frac{a_1 x + b_1 y + c_1}{\sqrt{a_1^2 + b_1^2}} = \frac{-a_2 x - b_2 y - c_2}{\sqrt{a_2^2 + b_2^2}}$$

Note that both of these lines pass through the intersection of the original lines, because whenever both of the original equations are satisfied, the equations of the bisectors are zero. The reader should consider what happens if the original lines are parallel, i.e.,

$$\frac{a_1}{b_1} = \frac{a_2}{b_2}$$

The reason that the bisectors pass through the point of intersection is that their equations have the form

$$f(x, y) = \lambda(a_1 x + b_1 y + c_1) + \mu(a_2 x + b_2 y + c_2) = 0$$

where

$$\lambda = \frac{1}{\sqrt{a_1^2 + b_1^2}}, \quad \mu = \pm \frac{1}{\sqrt{a_2^2 + b_2^2}}$$

It is clear that whatever the values of λ, μ, $f(x, y) = 0$ will represent a line through the intersection of the lines and, conversely, all lines through the intersection of the lines have this form.

Example 2. Find the equation of the line through the intersection of $2x + 3y - 1 = 0$ and $3x + y + 2 = 0$ which passes through the origin. Such a line has an equation

$$\lambda(2x + 3y - 1) + \mu(3x + y + 2) = 0$$

If the origin $(0, 0)$ is on the line, then

$$-\lambda + 2\mu = 0$$

or $\lambda = 2\mu$, say $\lambda = 2$, $\mu = 1$. The line has an equation

$$7x + 7y = 0$$

that is,

$$x + y = 0$$

Exercises

1. What is the distance of a point $(5, 3)$ from a line $2x + 3y - 1 = 0$?

2. What is the distance of a point $(-1, 2)$ from a line passing through the points $(2, 3)$ and $(1, 5)$?

3. Find the equation of a line passing through the intersection of $8x + 6y - 1 = 0$ and $x - y + 5 = 0$ which passes through the point $(0, 2)$.

4. The coordinates of the three vertices of a triangle ABC are $A(1, 6)$, $B(-2, 2)$, and $C(4, 2)$.   Find

  (a) the lengths of the three sides AB, BC, and AC.
  (b) the perpendicular distance of A from the line BC.
  (c) the area of the triangle ABC.
  (d) the slopes of the lines AB and AC.

5. The equations of the four sides of a parallelogram are $x - 2y + 5 = 0$; $x - 2y - 1 = 0$; $2y - 3x = 0$; and $2y - 3x - 2 = 0$.   Find the area.

6. Find the equation of a line parallel to the line $3x - 2y + 3 = 0$ and passing through the point of intersection of the lines $x - 2 = 0$ and $x + y + 1 = 0$.

7. A highway runs between two cities located at coordinates $(20, 10)$ and $(80, 90)$. A firm is located at the point $(40, 70)$. What is the shortest distance between the firm and the highway? If it costs the firm \$2 per mile per ton to truck a product to the highway, what would be the cost of shipping 100 tons?

■ **5.6   The Circle, Parabola, Ellipse, and Hyperbola** *

In most books on coordinate geometry the properties of the above curves are discussed at length. While these curves are of considerable interest to mathematicians, physicists, and engineers, they are not of great importance in the application of mathematics to business. We will content ourselves by defining them and giving the simplest equations that represent them.

All four curves are classed as *conic sections* because they can be obtained by slicing through a cone (Figure 5.13).

If we take a (double) cone and take a slice parallel to the axis of sym-

* May be omitted on first reading.

metry AB, we obtain an *hyperbola*; normal to the axis yields a *circle*; parallel to a *generator* (line lying on the surface) yields a *parabola.* Any other section that does not pass through the apex O gives an *ellipse.* A section through the axis yields a pair of straight lines. It can be shown that all these curves have the following property.

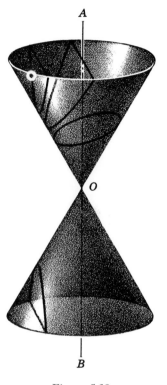

For any conic section there exists a line, called the *directrix*, and a point, called the *focus*, such that if P_1 and P_2 are any two points on the curve, with distances d_1 and d_2 from the directrix and distances f_1 and f_2 from the focus, then

$$\frac{f_1}{d_1} = \frac{f_2}{d_2}$$

Accordingly, we will define a *conic section* as the locus of a point that moves in such a way that the ratio of its distance from a fixed point to its distance from a fixed line is a constant e, called its *eccentricity.* We then classify conic sections according to the value of e,

Curve	Value of e
Circle *	0
Ellipse	$0 < e < 1$
Parabola	$e = 1$
Hyperbola	$e > 1$

Figure 5.13

General Equation of a Conic Section

Let the directrix be the line $x = -c$ and the focus the point $(-d, 0)$. Let $P(x, y)$ be any point of the curve and N the point on the directrix such that PN is perpendicular to the directrix (Figure 5.14).

Then $\qquad\qquad PN = x + c$

and $\qquad\qquad PF = [y^2 + (x + d)^2]^{\frac{1}{2}}$

* The line is infinitely far off and the distance from the point is fixed.

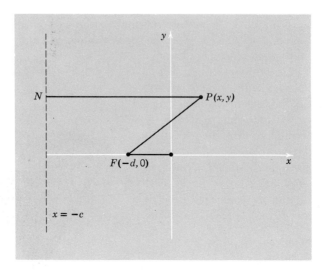

Figure 5.14

Therefore
$$\frac{PF}{PN} = \frac{[y^2 + (x + d)^2]^{\frac{1}{2}}}{x + c} = e$$

Therefore
$$\frac{PF^2}{PN^2} = \frac{y^2 + (x + d)^2}{(x + c)^2} = e^2$$

Therefore $y^2 + x^2 + 2xd + d^2 = e^2x^2 + e^2c^2 + 2e^2xc$

Therefore

(1) $y^2 + x^2(1 - e^2) + 2x(d - e^2c) = e^2c^2 - d^2$

This equation can be made simpler by suitable choice of c and d or, what amounts to the same thing, choice of the origin, relative to the cuve.

Case 1.   The ellipse. $0 < e < 1$.   Choose $d = e^2c$ (Figure 5.15).   Then equation (1) becomes

(2) $y^2 + x^2(1 - e^2) = e^2c^2(1 - e^2)$

Divide by $e^2c^2(1 - e^2)$.

(3) $\dfrac{y^2}{e^2c^2(1 - e^2)} + \dfrac{x^2}{e^2c^2} = 1$

or, if $a^2 = e^2c^2,\ \ b^2 = e^2c^2(1 - e^2) = a^2(1 - e^2)$

(4) $\dfrac{x^2}{a^2} + \dfrac{y^2}{b^2} = 1$

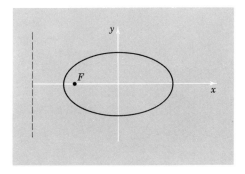

Figure 5.15   The ellipse.

Example 1. Sketch the curve and find the coordinates of the foci and vertices and the equation of the directrix represented by the following equation

$$\frac{x^2}{16} + \frac{y^2}{9} = 1$$

$$a^2 = 16, \quad a = 4$$

$$b^2 = 9, \quad b = 3$$

Now
$$9 = b^2 = a^2(1 - e^2) = 16(1 - e^2)$$

and
$$1 - e^2 = \frac{9}{16}$$

$$e^2 = \frac{7}{16}$$

$$e = \frac{\sqrt{7}}{4}$$

Also
$$16 = a^2 = e^2c^2 = \tfrac{7}{16}c^2$$

and
$$c = \frac{16}{\sqrt{7}}$$

and
$$d = e^2c = \frac{7}{16} \cdot \frac{16}{\sqrt{7}} = \sqrt{7}$$

The coordinates of the foci are $(-\sqrt{7}, 0)$ and $(\sqrt{7}, 0)$; the coordinates of the vertices are $(-4, 0)$ and $(4, 0)$; and the equation of the

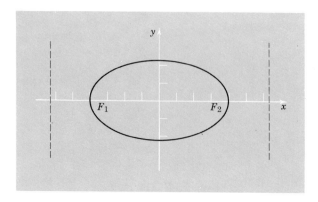

Figure 5.16   The foci of an ellipse.

directrix is $x = -16/\sqrt{7}$ or $x = 16/\sqrt{7}$. (Notice that because of the symmetry of the curve there are two foci, each with a corresponding directrix.)

The graph of the ellipse is shown in Figure 5.16.

Example 2.   Find the equation of the ellipse where the coordinates of the foci are $(2, 0)$ and $(-2, 0)$ and $a = 6$.

$$\frac{36}{2} = \frac{a^2}{d} = \frac{e^2 c^2}{e^2 c} = c, \qquad c = 18$$

$$36 = a^2 = e^2 c^2 = 324 e^2, \qquad e = \tfrac{1}{3}$$

$$b = a\sqrt{1 - e^2} = 6\sqrt{\tfrac{8}{9}} = 4\sqrt{2}$$

The equation of the ellipse is

$$\frac{x^2}{36} + \frac{y^2}{32} = 1$$

Case 2.   The Parabola. (Figure 5.17.) $e = 1$.   In this case equation (1) becomes

$$y^2 = 2x(c - d) + c^2 - d^2$$

Choose $d = -c$ (or the origin midway between the focus and the directrix), and we have

$$y^2 = 4cx$$

It is customary to write a instead of c and obtain the standard form

(5) $$y^2 = 4ax$$

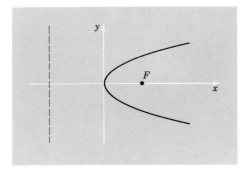

Figure 5.17   The parabola.

Example 3. Sketch the curve and find the equation of the directrix and the coordinates of the focus represented by the following equation.

$$y^2 = 8x$$

$4c = 8$, $c = 2$, and the equation of the directrix is $x = -2$.

Since the origin is midway between the focus and the directrix, the coordinates of the focus are $(2, 0)$. The parabola is sketched in Figure 5.18.

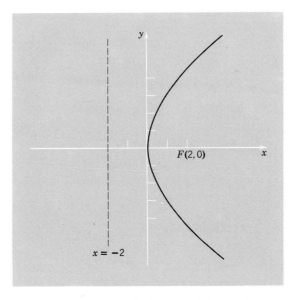

Figure 5.18   The parabola $y^2 = 8x$

Case 3. Hyperbola. $e > 1$.   We proceed, as in the case of the ellipse, as far as equation (2).   Now, since $e > 1$, $e^2c^2(1 - e^2) < 0$, and we write $e^2c^2(1 - e^2) = -b^2$ and obtain the standard form for the hyperbola

(6)
$$\frac{x^2}{a^2} - \frac{y^2}{b^2} = 1$$

Exercise.   Sketch the curve represented by the following equation:

$$\frac{x^2}{16} - \frac{y^2}{4} = 1$$

and find the coordinates of the foci and equation of the directrix.   (Note that as in the case of an ellipse the curve is symmetric, with two foci and two directrices.   However the hyperbola has two nonintersecting branches.)

If in equation (6) we have $a^2 = b^2$, the curve is called a *rectangular hyperbola* (in Figure 5.19) with equation

$$x^2 - y^2 = a^2$$

or
$$(x + y)(x - y) = a^2$$

Now $(x + y)/\sqrt{2}$ is the distance of the point $P(x, y)$ from the line $x + y = 0$, and $(x - y)/\sqrt{2}$ is its distance from the line $x - y = 0$. Thus if we write

$$u = \frac{x - y}{\sqrt{2}}$$

$$v = \frac{x + y}{\sqrt{2}}$$

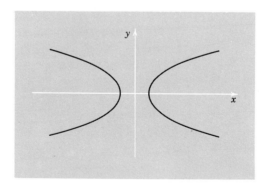

Figure 5.19   The rectangular hyperbola.

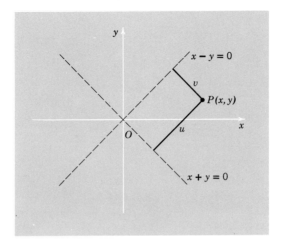

Figure 5.20   Change of axes.

we can regard (u, v) as the coordinates of P referred to axes at $45°$ to the original axes (see Figure 5.20). In this case the equation of the rectangular hyperbola becomes

$$uv = \frac{a^2}{2}$$

or simply

$$uv = k$$

Replacing u and v by x and y, we see that the equation $xy = k$ also represents a rectangular hyperbola (see Figure 5.21).

Case 4.   The Circle. (Figure 5.22). $e = 0$. The easiest way to obtain the standard equation for a circle is to place the center at the origin and assume the radius is r. The distance of the point $P(x, y)$ from the origin is $\sqrt{x^2 + y^2}$, and if P is on the circle, we must have

(7) $$x^2 + y^2 = r^2$$

We can compare this with equation (4) for the ellipse by writing it as

$$\frac{x^2}{r^2} + \frac{y^2}{r^2} = 1$$

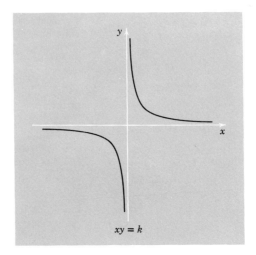

Figure 5.21   Rectangular hyperbola.

We see that the circle is obtained from the ellipse by setting

$$a^2 = b^2 = r^2, \quad \text{that is,} \quad a^2 = e^2c^2 = r^2$$

so that as $e = 0$, c must be infinite, in such a way that $ec = r$. Thus the directrix of a circle lies at an infinite distance from the center.

   Returning to equation (1), we see that when $e = 0$, to obtain the standard form (no term in x), we must set $d = 0$. Thus the center and focus of a circle coincide.

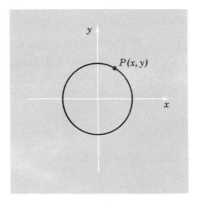

Figure 5.22   The circle.

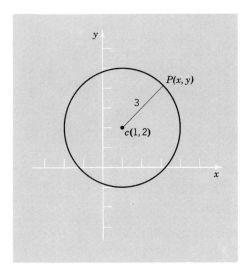

Figure 5.23   The circle.

Example 4.   Find the equation of the circle with center at $(1, 2)$ and radius, $r = 3$ (Figure 5.23).   Find also the points where this circle meets the x-axis.

The distance from $P(x, y)$ to the center $C(1, 2)$ is 3 units or

$$(x - 1)^2 + (y - 2)^2 = 9$$

$$x^2 - 2x + 1 + y^2 - 4y + 4 = 9$$

$$x^2 + y^2 - 2x - 4y - 4 = 0$$

The intersections of the circle and the x-axis are given by $y = 0$, and

$$x^2 - 2x - 4 = 0$$

$$x = \frac{2 \pm \sqrt{4 + 16}}{2} = 1 \pm \sqrt{5}$$

and the points of intersection are $(-1.24, 0)$ and $(3.24, 0)$.

Exercises

1. Show that the rectangular hyperbola can degenerate into two straight lines, and determine the values of the constants that are required for this.

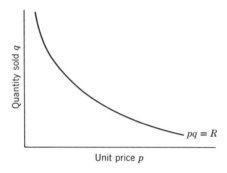

Figure 5.24   Price-sales relationship.

2. A firm sells its products in a market where the total revenue obtainable is a constant. Letting p = unit price and q = quantity sold, the total revenue is given by

$$R = pq = \text{constant}$$

The graph of this relationship is a rectangular hyperbola as shown in Figure 5.24.

Show that the quantity sold for a total revenue of \$100,000 and unit prices of \$5, \$10, and \$20 is 20,000 units, 10,000 units, and 5000 units, respectively.

■ 5.7   Special Functions and Their Properties

Introduction

In analyzing any business problem with the aid of mathematics, a basic step is to formulate a model which in some sense duplicates the behavior of the real world variables we are investigating. We might start by plotting a graph of the relationship observed between two variables and sketching a smooth curve through the points. Two typical graphs are shown in Figure 5.25.

In Figure 5.25a we have a curve which rises steeply and flattens out, eventually approaching a horizontal line, but never quite reaching it. It is called the *learning curve* because if y represents the amount learned up to the time x, the curve closely reproduces observed behavior. For example suppose we start production of a new radio set and plot the number of sets produced in successive hours. Production steadily rises as operators learn the intricacies of the new model and as minor "bugs" are removed. Eventually it settles down to a steady rate, indicated by the horizontal line.

In Figure 5.25*b* we have a *periodic* function, that is to say if *x* represents time, the curve from time T to $2T$ is exactly the same as from 0 to T, and is merely repeated in successive time intervals. The interval T is called the *period*. There are many business phenomena which exhibit this pattern of behavior. Any seasonal sales data can be represented by this type of curve, where T is one year. Many production figures, particularly those relating to agriculture are seasonal. Other examples can be found in sickness and absentee rates, commodity prices, and perhaps in accident rates.

It is all very well to plot graphs but for purposes of analysis and optimization we need functions which can be represented mathematically. Unfortunately none of the functions, presently at our disposal, exhibit the behavior we require, and it is necessary to develop new functions which do. Before doing so we will briefly review the ways in which functions have been defined so far.

In Chapter 3 we investigated the linear function $y = ax + b$ and the quadratic function $y = ax^2 + bx + c$. We can introduce higher powers of *x* and obtain the general *polynomial*

$$y = a_n x^n + a_{n-1} x^{n-1} + \cdots + a_1 x + a_0$$

and by dividing one polynomial by another we obtained the general *rational* function

$$y = \frac{a_n x^n + a_{n-1} x^{n-1} + \cdots + a_0}{b_m x^m + b_{m-1} x^{m-1} + \cdots + b_0}$$

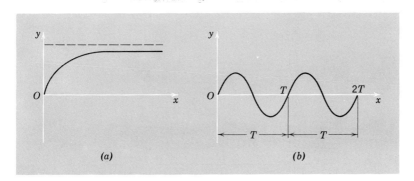

Figure 5.25 Two common business curves. (a) The learning curve. (b) A periodic function.

Other functions may be obtained by introducing non-integral powers of x such as $x^{1/2}$ or $x^{4/5}$. To summarize, all the functions we have used, can be obtained by means of a finite number of the following operations:

(a) addition (subtraction)
(b) multiplication (including integral powers)
(c) division
(d) taking roots (fractional powers).

In this section we will consider some functions which cannot be obtained in this manner.

The Exponential Function

The functions $y = 2^x$ and $y = 3^x$ are graphed in Figure 5.26. These functions have the common characteristic of monotonicity, where increasing values of x yield increasing values of y. The general form, called the exponential function, is

$$y = a^x$$

Here a is said to be the *base* of the function. It will be seen in Section

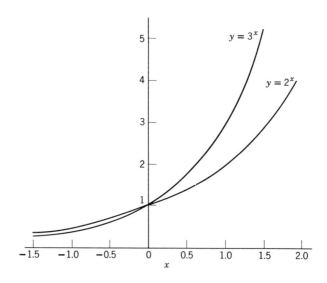

Figure 5.26 $y = 2^x$ and $y = 3^x$.

6.8 that a particularly important base is e, defined either by

$$e = \lim_{n \to \infty} \left(1 + \frac{1}{n}\right)^n$$

or

$$e = 1 + 1 + \frac{1}{2!} + \frac{1}{3!} + \cdots = \sum_{n=0}^{\infty} \frac{1}{n!}$$

which can be shown to be equivalent.

The numerical value of e is 2.71828....

Example 1. We know that $\left(1 + \frac{1}{n}\right)^n$ is the amount of \$1 at the end of one year when interest is compounded at the rate of 100% per year, n times in a year. Consider the amount for different values of n:

TABLE 5.2 $(1 + 1/n)^n$

n	1	2	4	10	100	1000	10,000
$\left(1 + \dfrac{1}{n}\right)^n$	2	2.25	2.43	2.59	2.70	2.717	2.718

Exercise. Show that the limit used to define e exists. *Hint:* Let $f(n) = \left(1 + \frac{1}{n}\right)^n$. Proceed as follows.

  (a) Show that $f(n+1)/f(n) > 1$.
  (b) Expand $f(n)$ by the Binomial Theorem to show that

$$f(n) < \sum_{n=0}^{\infty} (1/n!) = g(n)$$

  (c) $g(n)$ is convergent by comparison with the geometric series.
  (d) Use rule (5), Section 4.4.

The Logarithm Function

If we begin with the exponential function, $y = a^x$, we say that $x = \log_a y$ (read x = logarithm of y to the base a). If $y_1 = a^{x_1}$ and $y_2 = a^{x_2}$, then

$$y_1 y_2 = a^{x_1} a^{x_2} = a^{x_1 + x_2}$$

and thus $\log_a (y_1 y_2) = \log_a y_1 + \log_a y_2$. Two important bases are $a = 10$ and $a = e$. The symbol $\log y$ will be used instead of $\log_e y$.

Exercises

1. Prove that

   (a) $\log_a 1 = 0$
   (b) $\log_a a = 1$
   (c) $\log_a (y_1/y_2) = \log_a y_1 - \log_a y_2$
   (d) $\log_a y^n = n \log_a y$

2. Graph $y = \log_a x$ for $a = 2$, e, and 10.

The Learning Curve

We started this section by recognizing the need for a curve which rises steeply to begin with, then flattens out, and ultimately approaches as close as we please to a horizontal line, without ever reaching it (Figure 5.25a). A convenient representation for such a curve is

$$y = f(x) = a(1 - e^{-bx})$$

where $a > 0$, $b > 0$. We have $f(0) = 0$ and $\lim\limits_{x \to \infty} f(x) = a$, i.e., as $x \to \infty$ the curve approaches the horizontal line $y = a$.

Example 2. The number of items manufactured per day x days after the beginning of a production run, y, is given by

$$y = 100(1 - e^{-0.2x})$$

The graph of this function is represented below (Figure 5.27). The production rate is an increasing function of x, with a maximum value

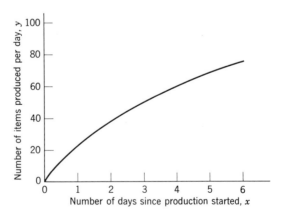

Figure 5.27   Production rate.

of 100 units per day, and reaches 63% of the maximum after one week ($x = 5$).

Example 3.   A company has product sales, S, given by

$$S = 5000 + 10,000(1 - e^{-0.002x})$$

where $x =$ the advertising effort, in $ thousands.   Plot this function (see Figure 5.28).

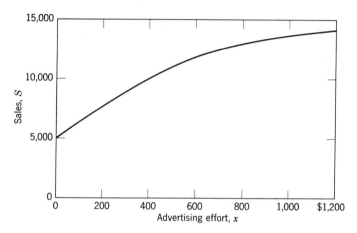

Figure 5.28   Advertising effectiveness.

Exercises

1. If the interest rate is $i\%$ per year payable k times per year, an amount x after n years becomes $x\left(1 + \dfrac{i}{100k}\right)^{nk}$.   Sometimes when k is large it is simpler to use the approximation $xe^{(in/100)}$.
Compare the two functions for $i = 5$, $n = 5$, $k = 1, 2$ and 4, $x = 500$.
2. If $y = 5x^2$, plot $\log_e y$ in terms of x.
Hint:

$$\log_e y = 2 \log_e 5x$$

$$= 2 \log_e 5 + 2 \log_e x$$

3. Solve the equation $5x = 3e^{-2x}$.
Hint: Plot the two curves $y = 5x$ and $y = 3e^{-2x}$.   The point of intersection of these two curves is the solution.
4. In Example 1, plot y in terms of x, if $y = 500(1 - e^{-0.4x})$.

Trigonometric Functions

Trigonometric functions were originated for the use of surveyors and map-makers; later they were used in astronomy, which found practical application in navigation. Today they have their uses in the business world because of two remarkable properties:

(i) The graphs of the sine and cosine repeat themselves at intervals of 2π. (We say "have a *period* of 2π".)

$$\sin (x + 2k\pi) = \sin x$$

$$\cos (x + 2k\pi) = \cos x$$

where k is any integer.

(ii) There is a theorem in advanced analysis, due to Fourier, which states that *any* periodic function can be represented as the (infinite) sum of sine and cosine functions, i.e., if $f(x)$ is such that $f(x + 2k\pi) = f(x)$ then

$$f(x) = a_0 + a_1 \sin x + a_2 \sin 2x + a_3 \sin 3x + \cdots$$

$$+ b_1 \cos x + b_2 \cos 2x + b_3 \cos 3x + \cdots$$

If the period is T instead of 2π all we need is a change of scale, i.e., replace x by $y\dfrac{T}{2\pi}$ and $f(x) = f\left(\dfrac{Ty}{2\pi}\right) = g(y)$ so that g has a period of 2π.

Thus in order to analyze the behavior of periodic systems we need to study trigonometric functions. In elementary books on trigonometry the following definitions are given:

Let ABC be a triangle with a right angle at A, and let the angle at B be x *radians; BC* is called the *hypotenuse* of the triangle, AB is the side *adjacent* to angle B and AC is the side *opposite* to angle B (see Figure 5.29). Then:

$$\sin x = \frac{AC}{BC} = \frac{\text{opposite side}}{\text{hypotenuse}}$$

$$\cos x = \frac{AB}{BC} = \frac{\text{adjacent side}}{\text{hypotenuse}}$$

$$\tan x = \frac{AC}{AB} = \frac{\text{opposite side}}{\text{adjacent side}}$$

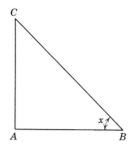

Figure 5.29   Right triangle.

The following table of values for the trigonometric functions should be graphed as an exercise ($\pi = 3.14$, 2π radians $= 360°$) (see Figure 5.30).

TABLE 5.3   TRIGONOMETRIC VALUES

x	0	$\pi/6$	$\pi/4$	$\pi/3$	$\pi/2$	π	$3\pi/2$	2π
$\sin x$	0	.50	.71	.87	1	0	-1	0
$\cos x$	1	.87	.71	.50	0	-1	0	1

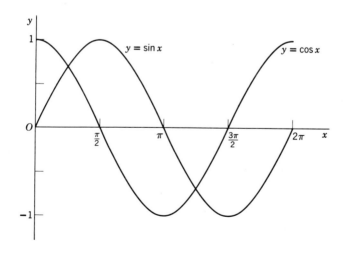

Figure 5.30   Trigonometric functions.

Example 4.   An appliance manufacturer has the following monthly sales.

Month	Apr.	May	June	July	Aug.	Sept.	Oct.	Nov.	Dec.	Jan.	Feb.	Mar.
Sales	500	600	673	700	673	600	500	400	327	300	327	400

Show that the monthly sales are given by

$$S = 500 + 200 \sin x$$

where $x = 0$, $\pi/6$, $\pi/3$, correspond to the months, April, May, June, ...

Sales are plotted for each month as 12 discrete points and connected by a smooth curve in Figure 5.31.

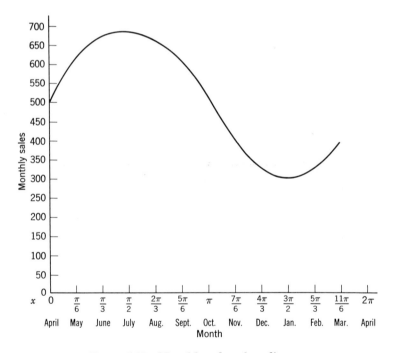

Figure 5.31   Monthly sales of appliances.

Exercises

1. As in Example 4, plot monthly sales for $S = 500 + 100 \cos x$.

2. Sometimes, instead of representing a curve by an equation between x and y, i.e., $f(x, y) = 0$, it is more convenient to use a *parametric form*. We express x and y separately in terms of a third variable, t, which is called a *parameter*. For example $x = 5 \cos t$, $y = 3 \sin t$ represents a curve. Each point (x, y) on it may be found by giving t an appropriate value. Sketch the curve and state what it is. Also by eliminating t show that the relationship between x and y is an ellipse. *Hint:* $\sin^2 t + \cos^2 t = 1$.

Exercises for Chapter 5

1. Find the equations of the following lines:

   (a) passing through $(2, 3)$ and $(1, -4)$.
   (b) slope of $-\frac{1}{2}$ and $y -$ intercept of 3.
   (c) $x -$ intercept of 3 and $y -$ intercept of 5.

2. Take each possible pair of lines in exercise 1 and find the coordinates of their points of intersection.

3. What is the distance of each of the lines in exercise 1 from the point $(5, 8)$?

4. Find the center and radius of the circle given by the equation

$$x^2 + y^2 - 6x + 4y + 4 = 0$$

Hint: The above equation can be written as

$$(x - 3)^2 + (y + 2)^2 = 9 + 4 - 4 = 9$$

5. Find the equation of the circle whose center is at the point $(2, 3)$ and which touches the x-axis. Find the two points of intersection of the circle and the y-axis.

6. Sketch the parabola $(y + 2)^2 = 4(x - 1)$.
Hint: Draw the lines $y + 2 = 0$ and $x - 1 = 0$, and consider these as new coordinate axes.

7. Plot the curves:

   (a) $x = 8 \sec t$, $y = 5 \tan t$
   (b) $y = \log_e x^2$
   (c) $y = 1 - e^{-0.5x}$

8. An ellipse can also be defined as the locus of a point that moves so that the sum of the distances from two fixed points (foci) is a constant.

   (a) Prove this.
   (b) The coordinates of the two foci are $(-2, 0)$ and $(2, 0)$, and the sum of the distances is 12. Show that this yields the same ellipse as in Example 2, Section 5.6.

9. A hyperbola is the locus of a point that moves so that the absolute difference of its distances from two fixed points is a constant; prove it.

10. A firm has a manufacturing cost of $1000 per setup, independent of the number x of items produced. Graph the rectangular hyperbola that expresses the cost of setup per unit manufactured, c, as a function of x. At what production quantity is c equal to $10?

11. It costs $5000 to purchase a new truck, and the cumulative operating costs after x months is given by $8x^2$, in dollars. The total cost per month of acquisition and operation for x months is

$$y = \frac{5000}{x} + \frac{8x^2}{x}$$

$$= \frac{5000}{x} + 8x$$

(a) Graph y as a function of x for various values of x.
(b) Show that y is minimum at $x = 25$ months.

12. A company has product sales given by

$$S = 1000 + 5000(1 - e^{-0.5x})$$

where $x = $ the advertising effort in $ thousands. Plot this function.

13. The number of items manufactured per day, x days after the beginning of a production run, y, is given by

$$y = 500(1 - e^{-0.5x})$$

(a) Graph y as a function of x.
(b) Find the value of x for which $y = 400$.

14. Two firms F_1 and F_2, located $2d$ miles apart, manufacture the same product. Each firm prices the product on the same basis of a fixed price plus a variable price dependent on the distance between the consumer and manufacturer. Let P_i be the price charged by manufacturer i so that

$$P_i = a_i + b_i d_i, \qquad i = 1, 2$$

where a_i, b_i are constants and d_i is the distance from firm F_i to the consumer.

We assume that consumers buy from the firm with the lower price. The general equation of the curve separating the market areas supplied by the two firms has the equation

$$a_1 + b_1 d_1 = a_2 + b_2 d_2$$

It is convenient to select axes so that the origin is midway between the two firms, and so that both firms lie on the x-axis, at the points $(-d, 0)$ and $(d, 0)$ (see Figure 5.32).

Let $P(x, y)$ be a point on the curve separating the market areas. Then

$$d_1 = \sqrt{(x + d)^2 + y^2}$$

$$d_2 = \sqrt{(x - d)^2 + y^2}$$

and the equation of the boundary is

$$a_1 + b_1\sqrt{(x + d)^2 + y^2} = a_2 + b_2\sqrt{(x - d)^2 + y^2}$$

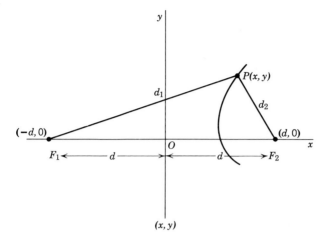

Figure 5.32   Market regions of two firms.

Show that when $a_1 = a_2$, the boundary is a circle whose equation is

$$x^2 + y^2 - 2d \left\{ \frac{b_2{}^2 + b_1{}^2}{b_2{}^2 - b_1{}^2} \right\} x + d^2 = 0$$

Find the center and radius.

15. Show that when $b_1 = b_2$ the boundary curve is a hyperbola whose equation is

$$\frac{x^2}{a^2} - \frac{y^2}{b^2} = 1$$

where $a = \dfrac{a_2 - a_1}{2b_1}$ and $b^2 = d^2 - a^2$. What happens when $a_1 = a_2$ and $b_1 = b_2$?

16. Suppose a third firm F_3, located a distance $2d$ from F_1 and F_2, enters the market, and that F_3 prices its product in the same way

$$P_3 = a_3 + b_3 d_3$$

If we use the same coordinate system as before, what are the coordinates of F_3?

If $a_1 = a_2 = a_3 = a$ and $b_1 = b_2 = b_3 = b$, find the equations of the boundary curves separating the areas supplied by each firm and show that they are all straight lines. Draw a sketch to illustrate your results.

17. Suppose that we generalize exercise 16 by allowing b_1, b_2, and b_3 to differ, but keeping $a_1 = a_2 = a_3 = a$. Show the market areas are separated by circles. Draw a sketch to show the market areas for the case where $b_1 > b_2 > b_3$.

Part Two

Deterministic Systems

6

The Derivative of a Function

■ 6.1 Introduction

We saw in Chapter 5 that a relationship between two variables may be represented in graphical form. In many business problems we are interested in the rate of change of a function and, in particular, in the range of values of the control variable for which the rate of change may be positive or negative. Of significant importance are the particular values, called *extreme values*, where the rate of change is zero.

For example, production costs per unit decrease with increasing production quantities but stocking costs increase. This means that *total* costs start by decreasing but later increase. The value of the production quantity that yields no additional change in total costs, that is where the rate of change in total costs with respect to production quantity is zero, is the optimal amount to produce.

Another example is the case where the number of units sold depends on the advertising effort. We are interested in determining the effect of changes in advertising effort on total profits, given by sales revenue less cost of sales and advertising costs. We continue to increase advertising effort as long as the rate of change of profits with advertising effort is positive. However, at the point where the rate of change of profits with respect to advertising effort becomes zero, we have obtained the optimal advertising effort.

To develop the rate of change of a function we introduce the concept of the difference operator applied to a function and then find the limit of successive differences. This limit is called the derivative and various operational rules are determined.

113

The derivative operation is applied to production, replacement, pricing, and other management decision problems.

■ 6.2 Differences

Suppose that the variable u is a function of n and that we determined u corresponding to $n = 0, 1, 2, \ldots$. Instead of writing $u = f(n)$, we frequently write simply u_n to indicate the functional relationship. We now ask what is the change in u_n corresponding to a change in n from n to $n + 1$. The change in u_n, or *first difference* of u_n, is $u_{n+1} - u_n$, which is a function of n, just as is u_n. It is of sufficient importance to be given a symbol of its own. We write

$$\Delta u_n = u_{n+1} - u_n \quad \text{(Read ``Delta } u_n.\text{'')}$$

We have given a new meaning to two symbols (Δ and u_n) in juxtaposition. Unlike elementary algebra, where juxtaposition indicates a product, Δu_n is really a single entity. Δ is called an *operator*. It tells us how to compute the quantity Δu_n from the sequence $u_0, u_1, u_2, \ldots$. We will see later that certain operators, including Δ, obey algebraic rules, not unlike those obeyed by numbers, but for the time being Δ should be thought of as an instruction, just as $+$, $-$, $\times$, and $\div$ are instructions. Δ differs from the more familiar instructions of arithmetic because it operates on one symbol (u_n) which must be a function, whereas $+$, $-$, $\times$, and $\div$ operate on two symbols (e.g., $a + b$).

Having applied the operator Δ once to u_n, we can apply it to the resulting differences, i.e., we can compute $\Delta(\Delta u_n)$. The result is called the *second difference of* u_n and is written $\Delta^2 u_n$. We can now apply Δ a third time, i.e., $\Delta(\Delta^2 u_n)$ and obtain the *third difference*, or $\Delta^3 u_n$. In fact, Δ may be applied as often as we wish, and in general we write the kth *difference of* u_n as $\Delta^k u_n$.

Definition. $\Delta^1 u_n = \Delta u_n = u_{n+1} - u_n$

$$\Delta^k u_n = \Delta(\Delta^{k-1} u_n) \quad k = 2, 3, \ldots .$$

The following consequences of the definitions should be noted.

$$\Delta^r(\Delta^s u_n) = \Delta^r \Delta^s u_n = \Delta^{r+s} u_n, \quad r, s = 1, 2, 3, \ldots$$

$$\Delta(u_n \pm v_n) = \Delta u_n \pm \Delta v_n$$

$$\Delta a u_n = a \Delta u_n, \quad \text{(where } a \text{ is any constant)}$$

$$\Delta u_n v_n = u_{n+1} v_{n+1} - u_n v_n$$

$$= u_{n+1}(v_{n+1} - v_n) + v_n(u_{n+1} - u_n)$$

$$= u_{n+1} \, \Delta v_n + v_n \, \Delta u_n$$

$$\Delta\left(\frac{u_n}{v_n}\right) = \frac{u_{n+1}}{v_{n+1}} - \frac{u_n}{v_n} = \frac{v_n u_{n+1} - u_n v_{n+1}}{v_n v_{n+1}}$$

$$= \frac{v_n(u_{n+1} - u_n) - u_n(v_{n+1} - v_n)}{v_n v_{n+1}}$$

$$= \frac{v_n \, \Delta u_n - u_n \, \Delta v_n}{v_n v_{n+1}}$$

Just as we introduced the operator Δ, we can also introduce an operator E by the following definition:

Definition. $Eu_n = u_{n+1}$ (i.e., E increases the subscript by 1).
The two operators Δ and E have a simple interrelationship for

$$\Delta u_n = u_{n+1} - u_n = Eu_n - 1(u_n) = (E - 1)u_n$$

where $1(u_n)$ is the operator defined by the ordinary multiplication by 1. Furthermore,

$$Eu_n = u_n + (u_{n+1} - u_n) = (1 + \Delta)u_n$$

We write symbolically

$$E \equiv 1 + \Delta \qquad \text{or} \qquad \Delta \equiv E - 1$$

meaning that the operations on both sides of the identity sign yield the same result when applied to u_n. If $k > 1$ and $E^k u_n = E(E^{k-1}u_n)$, then

$$E^r E^s u_n = E^{r+s} u_n, \qquad \text{for } r, s = 1, 2, \ldots.$$

$$E(u_n \pm v_n) = Eu_n \pm Ev_n$$

$$E(au_n) = aEu_n$$

It follows that *

$$\Delta^k \equiv (E - 1)^k \equiv E^k - \binom{k}{1} E^{k-1}$$

$$+ \binom{k}{2} E^{k-2} - \binom{k}{3} E^{k-3} \cdots + (-1)^{k-1} kE + (-1)^k$$

where

$$\binom{k}{r} = \frac{k!}{r!(k-r)!} \qquad \text{and} \qquad k! = k(k-1)(k-2) \ldots (3)(2)(1)$$

and further

$$E^k \equiv (1 + \Delta)^k \equiv 1 + \binom{k}{1} \Delta + \binom{k}{2} \Delta^2 + \cdots \binom{k}{k-1} \Delta^{k-1} + \Delta^k$$

Example 1. Let $u_n = n^2$; tabulate u_n for $n = 0, 1, 2, \ldots, 5$, and find Δu_n for $n = 0, 1, \ldots, 4$. The result is a matter of simple arithmetic, and we obtain Table 6.1.

TABLE 6.1

n	u_n	Δu_n
0	0	
		1
1	1	
		3
2	4	
		5
3	9	
		7
4	16	
		9
5	25	

Note that Δu_0 is written on the line between u_0 and u_1, Δu_1 is written between u_1 and u_2, etc. This is merely a convenient way of indicating the relationships between first differences and the originals.

* We are using the Binomial Theorem, which will be discussed later, to expand $(E - 1)^k$ in powers of E.

Example 2. Find the second and third differences of $u_n = n^2$.
We extend Table 6.1 and obtain Table 6.2. Note that all differences

TABLE 6.2

n	u_n	Δu_n	$\Delta^2 u_n$	$\Delta^3 u_n$
0	0			
		1		
1	1		2	
		3		0
2	4		2	
		5		0
3	9		2	
		7		0
4	16		2	
		9		
5	25			

higher than the second yield zero values.

Example 3. Consider the example $u_n = n^2$, for $n = 0, 1, 2, \ldots, 5$.
Find $E u_n = u_{n+1}$. The result is shown in Table 6.3.

TABLE 6.3

n	0	1	2	3	4	5
u_n	0	1	4	9	16	25
$E u_n$	1	4	9	16	25	

Exercises

1. Find Δu_n and $\Delta^2 u_n$ for $n = 1, 2, \ldots, 5$ when $u_n = 1/n$.
2. A company has determined that the price P of its principal product is directly proportional to the total demand D and inversely proportional to the total industry supply S, where

$$P = k\frac{D}{S}, \qquad k \text{ is a positive constant}$$

Show that for an increase ΔD in D and ΔS in S, the corresponding change in price is given by

$$\Delta P = k \frac{S \, \Delta D - D \, \Delta S}{S(S + \Delta S)}$$

3. For the relationship in exercise 2, $D = 10{,}000$ units, $S = 20{,}000$ units, and $P = \$10$. Find the value of k, and find the change in price for an increase of 2000 units in D, 2000 units in S, 2000 units in D and S.

4. Consider $u_n = n^3$, for $n = 0, 1, 2, \ldots, 5$. Find $E^k u_n$ for $k = 1, 2, 3$.

■ **6.3 Computation of u_n**

If we wish to tabulate u_0, u_1, u_2, $\ldots$, we could do so by first tabulating u_0, Δu_0, $\Delta^2 u_0$, $\ldots$ and then computing u_k from the relationship $E^k u_0 = (1 + \Delta)^k u_0 = u_k$. The formula is only of practical importance for integral values of k when we can find a number r such that $\Delta^r u_n$ is constant for all values of n (i.e., does not depend on the value chosen for n). In this case $\Delta^{r+1} u_n = \Delta^r u_{n+1} - \Delta^r u_n = 0$, and all higher order differences are also zero, so that the formula involves relatively few terms. In practice, when k is not too large and we can find r such that $\Delta^r u_n$ is nearly constant, we can apply the formula, ignoring differences above the rth.

We note that

$$\Delta^k u_n = \Delta^{k-1} u_{n+1} - \Delta^{k-1} u_n, \qquad k = 1, 2, \ldots$$

(We define $\Delta^0 \equiv 1$.)

or
$$\Delta^{k-1} u_{n+1} = \Delta^k u_n + \Delta^{k-1} u_n$$

If we know $\Delta^k u_0$ and $\Delta^{k-1} u_0$, we may find $\Delta^{k-1} u_1$ by addition. Knowing $\Delta^k u_1$ and $\Delta^{k-1} u_1$, we can find $\Delta^{k-1} u_2$ and so on until we have computed as many terms as we wish. All we need is the appropriate values of $\Delta^k u_n$. If we know $\Delta^r u_n$ is constant for all n (or nearly so), we can successively compute $\Delta^{r-1} u_n$, $\Delta^{r-2} u_n$, $\ldots$ until we have tabulated u_n itself. The scheme of computation is shown in Table 6.4.

If differences were only useful for tabulating functions at integral values of the argument, they probably would not have received the attention they have. It can be shown* that if $E^k u_n$ is defined by $E^k u_n = u_{n+k}$ for all k, positive or not, integral or not, then the following result

* Proof requires the use of the Binomial Theorem, which will be discussed in Chapter 8.

TABLE 6.4 *

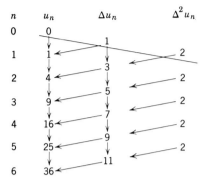

n	u_n	Δu_n	$\Delta^2 u_n$
0	0		
1	1	1	2
2	4	3	2
3	9	5	2
4	16	7	2
5	25	9	2
6	36	11	

* We start with the observation that for all values of n, we have

$$\Delta^2 u_n = 2,$$
$$u_0 = 0,$$
$$\Delta u_0 = 1,$$

and obtain

$$\Delta u_1 = \Delta u_0 + \Delta^2 u_0 = 1 + 2 = 3$$
$$\Delta u_2 = \Delta u_1 + \Delta^2 u_1 = 3 + 2 = 5$$

.

.

.

We then obtain

$$u_1 = u_0 + \Delta u_0 = 0 + 1 = 1$$
$$u_2 = u_1 + \Delta u_1 = 1 + 3 = 4$$

holds, provided higher order differences than the rth are small enough to be neglected.

$$u_{n+k} = \left[1 + k\Delta + \frac{k(k-1)}{2!} \Delta^2 \right.$$
$$\left. + \frac{k(k-1)(k-2)}{3!} \Delta^3 + \cdots + \binom{k}{r} \Delta^r \right] u_n$$

This is called Newton's interpolation formula and is extremely useful for inserting fractional entries into a table.

Example 1. Compute 19^2 from Table 6.2.

$$19^2 = u_{19} = E^{19} u_0 = \left(1 + 19\Delta + \frac{19 \cdot 18}{2} \Delta^2 \right) u$$

$$= u_0 + 19\Delta u_0 + 171\Delta^2 u_0$$

$$= 0 + 19 + 171 \cdot 2$$

$$= 361$$

There is another way of using tables of differences to tabulate functions, which is particularly useful when we require several consecutive entries.

Example 2. The following is an extract from a table of insurance premiums. Neglecting fourth and higher differences, compute the premium at age 32.

Age	30	35	40	45	50
Annual premium ($) per $2000 of face value	18.50	21.77	25.94	31.47	38.58

We first compute the table of differences.

Age	n	u_n	Δu_n	$\Delta^2 u_n$	$\Delta^3 u_n$	$\Delta^4 u_n$
30	0	18.50				
			3.27			
35	1	21.77		0.90		
			4.17		0.46	
40	2	25.94		1.36		−0.24
			5.53		0.22	
45	3	31.47		1.58		
			7.11			
50	4	38.58				

We require the premium at age 32; $32 = 30 + 0.4(35 - 30)$;

$$u_{0.4} = u_0 + 0.4\Delta u_0 + \frac{0.4(-0.6)}{2}\Delta^2 u_0 + \frac{0.4(-0.6)(-1.6)}{3!}\Delta^3 u_0$$

$$= 19.73$$

(The actual premium was $19.74.)

Exercises

1. Compute $u_n = n^5$ for $n = 0, 1, 2, 3, 4, 5$. Find Δu_0, $\Delta^2 u_0$, $\Delta^3 u_0$, $\Delta^4 u_0$, and $\Delta^5 u_0$. Assuming that $\Delta^5 u_n$ is constant, use addition only to extend your tabulation of u_n for $n = 6, 7, 8$.

2. Show that if $x^{(r)} = x(x - 1)(x - 2) \ldots (x - r + 1)$ and $x^{(1)} = x$, $x^{(0)} = 1$, then $\Delta x^{(r)} = rx^{(r-1)}$; and if $x_{(r)} = x^{(r)}/r!$, then $\Delta x_{(r)} = x_{(r-1)}$.

3. Using the results of exercise 2, show that

$$\Delta^r x^{(r)} = r!, \quad \Delta^r x_{(r)} = 1$$

and that

$$\Delta^s x^{(r)} = \Delta^s x_{(r)} = 0 \qquad \text{for all } s > r$$

4. Show that any polynomial of the form

$$P_r(x) = a_r x^r + a_{r-1} x^{r-1} + \cdots + a_1 x + a_0$$

can be expressed uniquely in the form

$$P_r(x) = b_r x^{(r)} + b_{r-1} x^{(r-1)} + \cdots + b_1 x^{(1)} + b_0$$

and hence

$$\Delta^r P_r(x) = a_r r!, \quad \Delta^s P_r(x) = 0 \qquad \text{for all } s > r$$

5. Show $\Delta a^n = (a - 1)a^n$, and hence $\Delta^r a^n = (a - 1)^r a^n$.

6. A company has found that total production costs, C, vary with the amount produced, D, as given below.

D	5000	10,000	15,000	20,000	25,000
C	$20,000	$30,000	$40,000	$50,000	$60,000

Use Newton's interpolation formula to find the production costs for a production quantity of 7000 units; 12,000 units.

7. Another firm has found that its production costs for the same product varied as shown below.

D	5000	10,000	15,000	20,000	25,000
C	$17,500	$35,000	$57,500	$85,000	$117,500

Use Newton's interpolation formula to find the production costs for a production quantity of 7000 units; 12,000 units. Compare the costs in exercises 6 and 7.

■ 6.4   Rate of Change—Derivatives

In Example 2, Section 6.3, on insurance premiums, the tabulation was at intervals of 5 rather than 1. We found it convenient to change the scale to perform calculations. However, we may define the operator Δ more generally by

$$\Delta u_x = u_{x+h} - u_x$$

Here h is any arbitrary interval (positive or negative). In this case the effect of Δ will depend on the value of h. We might wish to ascertain how the change in u_x compares with h. Such a comparison is described as the *rate of change* in u_x over the interval x to $x + h$.

Definition. The *rate of change* of u_x over the interval x to $x + h$ is

$$\frac{u_{x+h} - u_x}{h} = \frac{\Delta u_x}{h}$$

In the insurance example, if x is the age and $h = 5$, the annual rates of change of premium are $\frac{3.27}{5}$, $\frac{4.17}{5}$, $\frac{5.33}{5}$, and $\frac{7.11}{5}$, i.e., 0.65, 0.83, 1.07, and 1.42 per year. If we took 10-year intervals, the rates per year would be different. For example, the increase in premiums between 30 and 40 is \$7.44 and the rate of increase is \$0.74 per year. As another example, consider $u_x = x^2$. Here $u_{x+h} = (x + h)^2$, so that

$$\Delta u_x = (x + h)^2 - x^2$$

$$= 2hx + h^2$$

and the rate of change is

$$\frac{\Delta u_x}{h} = \frac{2hx + h^2}{h} = 2x + h$$

Thus the rate of change depends on two variables, x and h. For many purposes it is desirable to have a measure of *rate of change* which is a function of x only. One way of doing this might be to agree on some value of h which would always be used when we compute rates of change. For instance, we might agree that h should always be given the value one, and it would then be unnecessary to specify h on any particular occasion. If the reader will think for a moment about the use of the term *rate of change* in ordinary language, he will realize that specifications of $h = 1$ is contrary to everyday usage. When we think of speed, which is the change in distance divided by the change in time, we do not normally have a particular change in time in mind. We talk of the speed of an automobile at any given instant of time; we are really thinking of the distance traveled in a *short* interval of time divided by the interval.

What do we mean by *short?* Empirically we probably mean as small an interval as our instruments permit us to measure. Conceptually, as opposed to empirically, there is no limit to how small an interval we choose. In our example where we found the rate of change of x^2 to be $2x + h$ we can decrease h until it vanishes; we say that in the limit, as h tends to zero, the rate of change tends to $2x$. We have *not* said that the rate of change over an interval of zero is $2x$. We cannot measure such a quantity, because if Δ operates over a zero interval $\Delta x^2 = x^2 - x^2 = 0$ and if we attempt to divide by the interval, we obtain $0/0$, which is meaningless. What we have said is that we can make $\Delta x^2/h$ as close to $2x$ as we please by taking sufficiently small values of h. In symbols:

$$\lim_{h \to 0} \frac{\Delta x^2}{h} = \lim_{h \to 0} \frac{2xh + h^2}{h}$$

$$= \lim_{h \to 0} (2x + h)$$

$$= 2x$$

These concepts may be illustrated graphically. In Figure 6.1 we show the graph of $y = x^2$.

Let P be a fixed point on the graph, Q a moving point, and $Q_1, Q_2, \ldots$ a sequence of points that becomes closer and closer to P. The slope of the chord PQ_1 is $\dfrac{(x + h_1)^2 - x^2}{h_1}$, that of PQ_2 is $\dfrac{(x + h_2)^2 - x^2}{h_2}$, and so

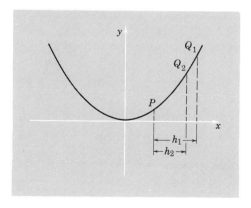

Figure 6.1 $y = x^2$.

on.   We see that as Q moves past Q_1, Q_2, $\ldots$ two things happen:

1. The interval h decreases to zero and P and Q coincide.
2. The chord PQ becomes the tangent to the curve at P.

To summarize, the rate of change at the point P, measured by $\lim\limits_{h \to 0} \dfrac{\Delta x^2}{h}$, is the slope of the tangent to the curve at the point P.   We might observe, in passing, that at the *minimum* value of x^2, i.e., when $x = 0$, the rate of change is zero.   We will see in the next chapter that one important use of rates of change is to find minimum points.   A very frequent business problem is to find a way of achieving minimum costs.   The concept of the limiting value of a rate of change is of sufficient importance to be given a special name.   It is called the *derivative* or *derived function*.   The process of finding this limit is called *differentiation*.   If we use the notation $f(x)$, the derived function is defined by

$$f'(x) = \lim_{h \to 0} \frac{f(x + h) - f(x)}{h}$$

Note that, just as in the discussion of limits in Chapter 4, nothing is said about the *sign* of h.

Other common notations are

$$f'(x) = \frac{df}{dx} = \frac{d}{dx} f(x) = Df(x)$$

If $y = f(x)$, we also write

$$f'(x) = \frac{dy}{dx}$$

Here d/dx and D can be regarded as operators, conveying instructions, in the same way as Δ and E are operators.

The second derivative of a function is defined as

$$f''(x) = \frac{d}{dx}\left(\frac{df}{dx}\right) = \lim_{h \to 0}\left(\frac{\Delta f'(x)}{h}\right)$$

Example.   A firm has a revenue function given by

$$R = 10D$$

where R is the gross revenues and D is the quantity sold, and a production cost function given by

$$C = 100{,}000 + 50\left(\frac{D}{1000}\right)^2$$

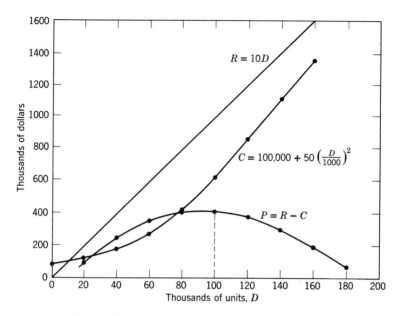

Figure 6.2   Revenue, cost, and profit functions.

Graph the total profit function, $P = R - C$, as a function of D. What is the rate of change of P with respect to D? Find the value of the rate of change at $D = 100,000$ units. Refer to Figure 6.2.

To determine the net profit function, we have

$$P = R - C = 10D - 100,000 - 50\left(\frac{D}{1000}\right)^2$$

The rate of change of the revenues with respect to demand is given by *

$$\frac{dP}{dD} = 10 - \frac{50}{(1000)^2}\,2D$$

$$= 10 - 0.0001D$$

At $D = 100,000$ units we have that

$$\frac{dP}{dD} = 10 - 0.0001(100,000)$$

$$= 10 - 10$$

$$= 0$$

---

* The reader should show that the derivative of $ax + bx^2$ is $a + 2bx$.

The values of revenues, costs, and profits may be calculated as shown in Table 6.5.

TABLE 6.5

D	20	40	60	80	100	120	140	160	180
R	200	400	600	800	1000	1200	1400	1600	1800
C	120	180	280	420	600	820	1080	1380	1720
P	80	220	320	380	400	380	320	220	80

D is shown in thousands; R, C and P are shown in thousands of dollars.
The rate of change is zero at the value of $D = 100,000$ units. We will demonstrate in the following chapter that the value of the derivative is always zero at the maximum point of a function.

Exercises

1. If $y = x^2$, calculate $\Delta y / h$ for $x = 2$ and $h = 1, 0.1, 0.01$, and 0.001.
2. If $y = x^3$, find Δy over the interval x to $x + h$. Hence find

$$\frac{dy}{dx} = \lim_{h \to 0} \frac{\Delta y}{h}$$

3. Show that if $f(x) = k$, where k is constant, then $f'(x) = 0$.
4. Show that if u and v are each functions of x, then

   (a) If $f(x) = ku(x)$, then $f'(x) = ku'(x)$.
   (b) If $f(x) = u(x) \pm v(x)$, then $f'(x) = u'(x) \pm v'(x)$.

5. Use the results of exercises 2, 3, and 4 to differentiate the following:

   (a) $3x^3$
   (b) $2x^2 + 3x$
   (c) $x^3 - 3x^2 + 5$
   (d) $3x^2 - 7$
   (e) $2x - x^3 - 3x^2$

6. In the example of Section 6.4, if

$$R = aD \quad \text{and} \quad C = b + mD^2$$

what is the rate of change of the profits P with respect to the demand D?

■ 6.5   Differentiating Products and Quotients

We have already discussed differencing functions expressible as the product or quotients of other functions. Let us now see what happens when we take these differences over an interval h, divide them by h, and let h tend to zero.

Let $f(x) = u(x) \cdot v(x)$; then if Δ refers to the interval h, we have, by the reasoning of Section 6.2

$$\Delta f(x) = \Delta u(x) \cdot v(x) = u(x+h)\Delta v(x) + v(x)\Delta u(x)$$

Therefore $$\frac{\Delta f(x)}{h} = u(x+h)\frac{\Delta v(x)}{h} + v(x)\frac{\Delta u(x)}{h}$$

Therefore

$$\lim_{h \to 0} \frac{\Delta f(x)}{h} = \left[\lim_{h \to 0} u(x+h)\right]\left[\lim_{h \to 0} \frac{\Delta v(x)}{h}\right] + \left[\lim_{h \to 0} v(x)\right]\left[\lim_{h \to 0} \frac{\Delta u(x)}{h}\right]$$

Therefore

(1) $$\frac{d}{dx} u(x)v(x) = u(x)v'(x) + v(x)u'(x)$$

In a very similar fashion, if $f(x) = \dfrac{u(x)}{v(x)}$, $v(x) \neq 0$,

$$f'(x) = \lim_{h \to 0} \left[\frac{v(x)\dfrac{\Delta u(x)}{h} - u(x)\dfrac{\Delta v(x)}{h}}{v(x)v(x+h)}\right]$$

Therefore

(2) $$\frac{d}{dx}\frac{u(x)}{v(x)} = \frac{v(x)u'(x) - u(x)v'(x)}{[v(x)]^2}$$

Exercise.   Differentiate with respect to x

(a) $y = \dfrac{x}{x+1}$

(b) $y = (x^2 + 2x)(x^3 + 4x^2 + x - 5)$

■ 6.6   Derivative of a Monomial

We are now in a position to differentiate x^n for all integral values of n. We have already seen the following results, or obtained them in exercises.

If $y = k$, then $\dfrac{dy}{dx} = 0$

$y = kx$, then $\dfrac{dy}{dx} = k$

$y = kx^2$, then $\dfrac{dy}{dx} = 2kx$

These are consistent with the general formula:

(3) If $y = x^n$, then $\dfrac{dy}{dx} = nx^{n-1}$

Let us assume that this is true for $n = 0, 1, 2, \ldots, r$. We have $y = x^{r+1} = x \cdot x^r$. Put $u(x) = x$, $v(x) = x^r$ in equation (1) in Section 6.5. Then

$$\frac{dy}{dx} = x\,\frac{d}{dx}\,x^r + x^r\,\frac{d}{dx}\,x$$

$$= x \cdot rx^{r-1} + x^r \cdot 1$$

$$= (r+1)x^r$$

Thus if our formula is true for $n = r$, it is true for $n = r + 1$. But it is true for $n = 0$, so it is true for $n = 1$ and hence for $n = 2, 3, \ldots$ Next, consider negative indices. Let $y = x^{-n}$. Therefore

$$y = \frac{1}{x^n}$$

Let $u(x) = 1$, $v(x) = x^n$ in equation (2) of Section 6.5.

$$\frac{dy}{dx} = \frac{d}{dx}\left(\frac{1}{x^n}\right) = \frac{x^n(0) - 1(nx^{n-1})}{x^{2n}} = \frac{-n}{x^{n+1}} = -nx^{-n-1}$$

Thus we have proved equation (3) for all integral values of n.

From now on we will assume that equation (3) is true for *all* values of n whether integral or not. A proof for n equal to a rational fraction will be given in exercise 2 at the end of this chapter, but a proof for an arbitrary n, including irrationals such as $\sqrt{2}$ or π, is beyond the scope of this text.

■ **6.7   Differentiating a Function of a Function**

We now know enough to differentiate any polynomial or ratio of two polynomials. Consider, for example, $y = (x + 1)^5$. This is a polynomial, and by multiplication we obtain

$$y = x^5 + 5x^4 + 10x^3 + 10x^2 + 5x + 1$$

Therefore $$\frac{dy}{dx} = 5x^4 + 20x^3 + 30x^2 + 20x + 5$$

$$= 5(x + 1)^4$$

Surely this is not a coincidence.

If $y = x^5$, then $\dfrac{dy}{dx} = 5x^4$

If $y = (x + 1)^5$, then $\dfrac{dy}{dx} = 5(x + 1)^4$

This suggests that there may be a simpler method of differentiating $(x + 1)^5$ than by expansion as a polynomial and subsequent differentiation.

Let $f(x) = g[u(x)]$; i.e., to obtain the value of $f(x)$ we first compute $u(x)$ and then use this as the argument in g. In the above example, $u(x) = x + 1$ and $g(u) = u^5$.

$$\frac{f(x + h) - f(x)}{h} = \frac{g[u(x + h)] - g[u(x)]}{h}$$

If we assume $u(x + h) \neq u(x)$,

$$\frac{f(x + h) - f(x)}{h} = \frac{g[u(x + h)] - g[u(x)]}{u(x + h) - u(x)} \times \frac{u(x + h) - u(x)}{h}$$

Now let $u(x + h) - u(x) = k$, and write u as an abbreviation for $u(x)$. It should be clear that if $u(x)$ is a continuous function, k will tend to zero as h tends to zero. We have

$$\frac{f(x + h) - f(x)}{h} = \frac{g(u + k) - g(u)}{k} \times \frac{u(x + h) - u(x)}{h}$$

Therefore

$$f'(x) = \lim_{h \to 0} \frac{f(x + h) - f(x)}{h} = \lim_{k \to 0} \frac{g(u + k) - g(u)}{k} \lim_{h \to 0} \frac{u(x + h) - u(x)}{h}$$

$$= g'(u)u'(x)$$

$$= g'[u(x)]u'(x)$$

If $u(x + h) - u(x) = 0$ for all small h, the above proof is invalid. However, in this case $f(x + h) = f(x)$ and $f'(x) = 0$; also, $u'(x) = 0$, so in all cases

(4) $$f'(x) = g'[u(x)]u'(x)$$

As an example of the use of this formula let us differentiate $y = (x + 1)^5$. Put $g(u) = u^5$, $u = x + 1$. Therefore

$$g'(u) = 5u^4, \quad u'(x) = 1$$

Therefore $$\frac{dy}{dx} = 5u^4 \times 1 = 5(x + 1)^4$$

Example. Let $y = (2x^3 + 3x^2 - x + 5)^4$

$$g(u) = u^4$$

$$u = 2x^3 + 3x^2 - x + 5$$

Therefore $$\frac{dy}{dx} = 4(2x^3 + 3x^2 - x + 5)^3(6x^2 + 6x - 1)$$

Equation (4) is often written in the following suggestive way. Let y be a function of z and z a function of x. Then

$$\frac{dy}{dx} = \frac{dy}{dz} \cdot \frac{dz}{dx}$$

The implication is that the dz may be cancelled from the product on the right. However, while this is a useful mnemonic device, it is hardly a proof of the result. After all, we have never even defined the symbol dz, let alone arithmetic operations on it.

■ 6.8   Differentiation of Special Functions

The Logarithm Function

We wish to find the derivative of the function

$$y = \log x$$

introduced in Section 5.7.   We will show $dy/dx = 1/x$.

$$\frac{dy}{dx} = \lim_{h \to 0} \frac{\log (x + h) - \log x}{h}$$

$$= \lim_{h \to 0} \frac{1}{h} \log \left(\frac{x + h}{x} \right)$$

$$= \lim_{h \to 0} \frac{1}{h} \frac{x}{x} \log \left(1 + \frac{h}{x} \right)$$

$$= \frac{1}{x} \lim_{h \to 0} \frac{x}{h} \log \left(1 + \frac{h}{x} \right)$$

$$= \frac{1}{x} \lim_{h \to 0} \log \left(1 + \frac{h}{x} \right)^{\frac{x}{h}}$$

$$= \frac{1}{x} \log e \ *$$

$$= \frac{1}{x}$$

Example.   For $z = \log y$, find dz/dx where y is a function of x.   We have that

$$\frac{dz}{dx} = \frac{dz}{dy} \frac{dy}{dx} \qquad \text{by Section 6.7}$$

$$= \frac{1}{y} \frac{dy}{dx}$$

* It may be observed from the definition of the exponential function in Section 5.7 that by substituting $n = x/h$, $\displaystyle\lim_{h \to 0} \log \left(1 + \frac{h}{x} \right)^{\frac{x}{h}} = \log e = 1$.

Exercise. Show that

$$\frac{d \log (a + bx)}{dx} = \frac{b}{a + bx}$$

The Exponential Function

We wish to find the derivative of the function,

$$y = a^x$$

introduced in Section 5.7. We will show that $dy/dx = a^x \log a$.

Taking the logarithm of both sides, to the base e, we have that

$$\log y = x \log a \ *$$

Using the result of the previous example to differentiate both sides of this equation with respect to x we have

$$\frac{1}{y}\frac{dy}{dx} = \log a$$

$$\frac{dy}{dx} = a^x \log a$$

For $a = e$, $\log e = 1$, and

$$\frac{d(e^x)}{dx} = e^x$$

Exercises

1. Show that $\dfrac{d(ae^{bx})}{dx} = abe^{bx}$.

2. Find $\dfrac{d(x^2 e^{-3x})}{dx}$.

The Derivative of Trigonometric Functions

To differentiate $\sin x$, let us write $f(x) = \sin x$. We will show that $f'(x) = \cos x$.

* See exercise 1(d), Section 5.7.

Now $f(x + h) = \sin(x + h)$, and

$$\frac{f(x + h) - f(x)}{h} = \frac{\sin(x + h) - \sin x}{h}$$

$$= \frac{2 \cos\left(x + \dfrac{h}{2}\right) \sin h/2}{h}$$

$$= \cos\left(x + \frac{h}{2}\right) \frac{\sin h/2}{h/2}$$

Therefore $f'(x) = \left[\lim_{h \to 0} \cos\left(x + \frac{h}{2}\right)\right] \left[\lim_{h \to 0} \frac{\sin h/2}{h/2}\right]$

$$= [\cos x][1]$$

$$= \cos x$$

We will prove, using geometric principles that $\lim_{x \to 0} \dfrac{\sin x}{x} = 1$.   Refer to Figure 6.3.

POR is the angle x and S is the point where the circle, with center O, and radius OP, meets OR. PT is the tangent at P and is thus perpendicular to the radius OP.   From triangle ORP we have $\sin x = \dfrac{PR}{OP}$.

By definition, the radian measure of an angle is $x = \dfrac{\text{arc } PS}{OP}$ and from triangle OPT we have $\tan x = \dfrac{PT}{OP}$.   Comparison of PR with arc PS and PT shows that $PR < \text{arc } PS < PT, \dfrac{PR}{OP} < \dfrac{\text{arc } PS}{OP} < \dfrac{PT}{OP}$, whence

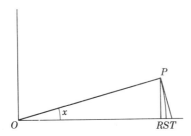

Figure 6.3   Lim (six x/x) = 1.

$\sin x < x < \tan x$. Since $\tan x = \dfrac{\sin x}{\cos x}$ by dividing, we have that

$$1 < \frac{x}{\sin x} < \frac{1}{\cos x}$$

Replacing each term by its reciprocal and reversing this inequality, $1 > \dfrac{\sin x}{x} > \cos x$. As $x \to 0$ we find that $\dfrac{\sin x}{x}$ lies between 1 and a quantity very close to 1. We conclude $\lim\limits_{x \to 0} \dfrac{\sin x}{x} = 1$.

Exercise. Show that

(a) $\dfrac{d(\cos x)}{dx} = -\sin x$

(b) $\dfrac{d(\tan x)}{dx} = \sec^2 x$

Exercises for Chapter 6

1. Differentiate the following:

(a) $\dfrac{x^2}{x^2 + 1}$

(b) $\dfrac{2x^3 - 3x^2 + 2x}{x^2 + 2x - 1}$

(c) $\dfrac{(x^2 + x)^3}{x + 1}$

(d) $(x + 5)^2(x^2 + 1)$

(e) $(x^2 + 2x)(5x^2 - 2x^3)(x^2 - 3)$

(f) $\cos(x^2 + 1)$

(g) $x \sin x$

(h) $\log\left(\dfrac{x}{x + 1}\right)$

(i) xe^{-ax}

(j) $(\sin ax)e^{-bx}$

2. Generalize the formula that gives the derivative of $y = x^n$ as $dy/dx = nx^{n-1}$ to the case where the index is a rational fraction, i.e., $n = r/q$ where $q \neq 0$ and r, q are integers.

   Hint: $y = x^{r/q} = z^r$ where $z^q = x$; use $dy/dx = dy/dz \cdot dz/dx$. We can easily find dx/dz. Show that in general $dz/dx = 1/\dfrac{dx}{dz}$ provided $dx/dz \neq 0$.

3. Graph the functions and their derivatives:

(a) $y = \sqrt{x}$

(b) $y = e^x + e^{-x}$

(c) $y = xe^{-2x}$

(d) $y = e^{-x^2}$

(e) $y = 100(1 - e^{-0.5x})$

(f) $y = x^2(1 - x)$

(g) $y = \log(1 + x^2)$

(h) $y = \tan x$

4. Show that the intersection of the circle $x^2 + y^2 - 6x - 8y + 23 = 0$ and the line $y = x + 3$ is a single point $(2, 5)$.

5. Find dy/dx for the circle in exercise 4 at the intersection point $(2, 5)$ and show that this value is equal to 1, which is also the slope of the line $y = x + 3$. The line is called *the tangent to the circle at the point* $(2, 5)$.

6. Generalize the product formula by induction, i.e., assume that if

$$f(x) = \prod_{i=1}^{n} u_i(x)$$

$$= u_1(x)u_2(x) \ldots u_n(x)$$

then $$f'(x) = u_1'(x)u_2(x) \ldots u_n(x)$$

$$+ u_1(x)u_2'(x)u_3(x) \ldots u_n(x)$$

$$+ u_1(x)u_2(x)u_3'(x)u_4(x) \ldots u_n(x)$$

$$\vdots$$

$$+ u_1(x) \ldots u_{n-1}(x)u_n'(x)$$

$$= f(x) \sum_{i=1}^{n} \frac{u_i'(x)}{u_i(x)} \quad \text{(provided } f(x) \neq 0.)$$

and hence show that if

$$f(x) = \prod_{i=1}^{n+1} u_i(x) \qquad \text{then} \qquad f'(x) = f(x) \sum_{i=1}^{n+1} \frac{u_i'(x)}{u_i(x)}$$

(with suitable interpretation if $f(x) = 0$). Since the result is true for $n = 1$, it will thus be proved true for all n.

7. A company has observed the following cost data in its manufacturing operations:

Quantity produced per week, q	1000	2000	3000	4000
Cost per unit, C/q	$7.00	$8.50	$10.33	$12.25

(a) What *total* cost can be expected for a production run of 2500? 3300?

(b) Graph the total costs as a function of quantity produced. If the total costs are expressible by a formula

$$C = aq^2 + bq + c \qquad [1000 \leq q \leq 6000]$$

find a, b, c.

(c) What is the rate of change of cost per unit, dC/dq, when production is running at 2000, 3500, 3800 units per week?

(d) The rate of change of cost per unit is called the marginal cost, and there is a formula in economics that says profit is maximized by producing a quantity q such that marginal cost equals marginal revenue, the latter being sales price per unit.

If the sales price is $9.00 per unit, what is the optimal value of q? What will the total profit be?

In this exercise we have deliberately avoided specifying the nature of the units. If the units are, for example, gallons, then the product may well be infinitely divisible so that it makes obvious sense to talk of dC/dq. However, if the product is machine bearings, changes in production can only take place in steps of a unit each. Why, then, should we be concerned with dC/dq, which implies continuous changes in q? Strictly speaking, we should only be interested in ΔC where Δ refers to differences over an interval of one. However, if q is large enough, the difference between ΔC and dC/dq is negligible, and the latter may be simpler to compute. In pure mathematics we often work numerical problems by using $\Delta f(x)/h$ as an approximation to $f'(x)$. In business problems it is frequently convenient to regard $f'(x)$ as an approximation to $\Delta f(x)/h$. The reader should verify that the approximation error is negligible in the above exercise.

8. In a pricing experiment, the following data were obtained.

Price per unit, p	$0.10	$0.11	$0.12	$0.13	$0.14
Total sales volume, S (Units)	98,000	85,000	76,000	63,000	56,000

(a) Plot the coordinates of revenue $R = pS$ against price p, and sketch in the straight line that appears to fit the data best. From the graph, estimate the relationship between R and p in the form $R = \alpha + \beta p$.

(b) Find S as a function of p, and hence find R as a function of S.

(c) The average cost c of producing and marketing, per unit sold, is given by

$$c = 0.018 + 10^{-6}S$$

and the total cost is $C = Sc$. What is the marginal cost of producing and marketing (dC/dS)?

(d) If profit is maximized when marginal cost is equal to marginal revenue, what sales will maximize profit? What is the corresponding price?

9. A trucking firm has an average engine overhaul cost of $1000 and a routine maintenance cost (in dollars) of

$$c = 0.03m + 10^{-7}m^2$$

where m is the interval, in miles, between engine overhauls.

(a) Show that the total engine maintenance cost (dollars per mile) is given by

$$C = \frac{1000}{m} + 0.03 + 10^{-7}m$$

(b) Find the rate of change of the total maintenance cost with respect to the engine overhaul interval, dC/dm.

(c) Find the value of m at which the derivative in (b) is equal to zero.

(d) Evaluate and compare C for $m = 50{,}000$, $100{,}000$, and $200{,}000$ miles.

10. A refrigerator manufacturer produces q units in a production run at a total cost of manufacturing and stocking given by

$$C = 25q + 1000\,\frac{S}{q}$$

where S is the total annual sales.

(a) For a fixed value of S, find the rate of change of C with respect to q, dC/dq.

(b) Find the values of q at which $dC/dq = 0$ for $S = 100{,}000$ units and $S = 200{,}000$ units.

(c) Graph dC/dq versus q for $S = 100{,}000$ units and $S = 200{,}000$ units.

11. A company records sales of a new product in successive years following commercialization. For the first 5 years of a product's life, the annual sales, S_n, may be approximated by the formula

$$S_n = S_0(1 + a)^n$$

where n is the number of years since the product was introduced, $n = 0, 1, 2, \ldots, 5$. For each value of n, find S_n and $\Delta(S_n)$.

12. The sales, S, for a product of price, p, is given by

$$S = 10{,}000e^{-0.5p}$$

Find

(a) Total revenues, $R = pS$.

(b) Marginal revenues, $\dfrac{dR}{dp}$.

(c) If the total costs of sales are $C = 0.5S$, the net profits, $P = R - C$, for $p = \$1, \$2, \$3,$ and $\$4$.

(d) Graph P as a function of p.

13. A chemical firm has noted that the annual sales S of new products depend on the amounts invested in research and development R, improved plant and facilities P, and marketing and promotion M, given by the formula

$$S = R^a P^b M^c, \quad 0 < a, b, c < 1$$

(a) Find the rate of change of sales (dS/dR, dS/dP, and dS/dM) with respect to each of the control variables. (*Hint*: Assume other variables are held constant.)

(b) Show that

$$S = \frac{R}{a}\frac{dS}{dR} = \frac{P}{b}\frac{dS}{dP} = \frac{M}{c}\frac{dS}{dM}$$

7

The Problem of Optimization

■ 7.1 Criteria of Optimization: Single Variable

We have already mentioned that many business problems amount to choosing the best of the available alternatives. Some of the exercises at the end of Chapter 6 illustrated one rule that can be used to maximize profits. In this chapter we will consider more general rules that can be applied in a wide variety of situations.

It should be noted that there is little real difference between the problems of finding the maximum or minimum of a function, for the value of

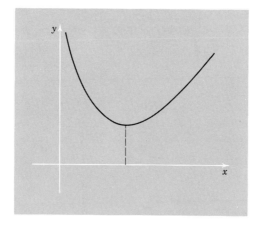

Figure 7.1   Single minimum.

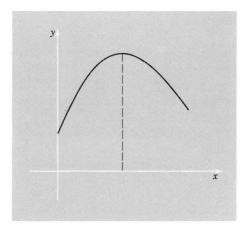

Figure 7.2   Single maximum.

x that maximizes $y = f(x)$ also minimizes $z = -f(x)$. If we are concerned with profits, the best alternative will be the one that yields the largest profit.   If we are interested with costs, the best alternative minimizes them.

In Figures 7.1, 7.2, and 7.3 we show some possible situations.   In the case of a minimum, the function $y = f(x)$ starts by decreasing, reaches a minimum, and then increases. Thus, just before the minimum, $dy/dx <$

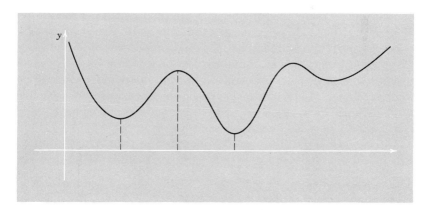

Figure 7.3   Maxima and minima.

0; just after the minimum, $dy/dx > 0$. We conclude * that a necessary condition for a minimum is that $dy/dx = 0$.

Examination of Figure 7.2 suggests that just before a maximum, $dy/dx > 0$ and just after, $dy/dx < 0$. At the maximum we have $dy/dx = 0$. We can summarize by saying that a necessary condition for a *turning point* or *extremum* is $dy/dx = 0$. However, this condition is not sufficient, and as yet we have no way of deciding whether we have a maximum or minimum.

The arguments we have used could also be applied to Figure 7.3. The only difference is that we would first have to break the figure into parts, each of which only contains one turning point. Thus if we find the values of x at which $f'(x) = 0$, all we have done is to discover where the curve $y = f(x)$ has *local* maxima and minima; we will need some way of finding whether a given turning point is *a* maximum or *a* minimum. Further, we will usually be interested in *the* maximum or *the* minimum. Before we discuss these problems, let us consider some simple examples, where only one turning point exists and its nature is obvious.

■ 7.2   The Economic Lot-size Formula

Suppose that we have a contract to supply 1000 items a month at a uniform daily rate, and that each time we start a production run it costs us $50. In order to avoid high production costs we decide to produce a large quantity at a time and to store it until the contract calls for delivery. Unfortunately, it costs money to store goods (warehouse rent, insurance, interest on capital, and so on); hence we do not want to store so many that storage costs per item exceed the savings due to large production runs. If the cost of storage is 1 cent per item per month, how many should be made per run so as to minimize total average costs?

Let us start by assuming we make q items in each run and that a graph of inventory against time will look like Figure 7.4. (Of course, inventory is not depleted in a smooth fashion. It cannot change by less than an item at a time, but the figure shown is usually accurate enough.)

The average inventory is $q/2$ and the average cost of holding inventory is $q/2 \times 0.01 = q/200$ dollars per month.

The batches of q will last $q/1000$ months and the average setup cost will be $50 \div q/1000 = 50,000/q$ dollars per month. Thus the total

---

* We have used geometrical intuition here. Strictly speaking, our conclusion only follows if we specify that $dy/dx = f'(x)$ is continuous. In fact, $f'(x)$ may not even exist at a minimum. A more rigorous discussion will be given at the end of this chapter.

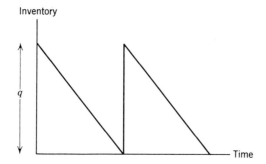

Figure 7.4 Production cycle, instantaneous production, no shortages.

average cost per month, say K, is given by

$$K = \frac{q}{200} + \frac{50,000}{q}$$

To minimize costs we set $dK/dq = 0$, i.e.,

$$\frac{1}{200} - \frac{50,000}{q^2} = 0$$

$$q^2 = 10^7$$

so $q = 3160$

This means we should make a little over 3 months supply at a time. The associated cost will be

$$\frac{3160}{200} + \frac{50,000}{3160} \simeq 31.6 \text{ dollars per month}$$

How do we know that we have a minimum? We observe that as $q \to 0$, $K \to \infty$, and as $q \to \infty$, $K \to \infty$. In between, K is finite. Thus for small q, K decreases as q increases, and for large q, K increases. Since there is only one turning point in between, it must be a minimum. The reader should sketch a rough graph of K against q.

Exercise. Find general formulas for optimum q and minimum K when the demand rate is R, the cost of holding inventory is c_1, and the setup cost is c_3 per run.

(*Answer:* $q = \sqrt{2c_3 R/c_1}, \quad K = \sqrt{2c_1 c_3 R}$)

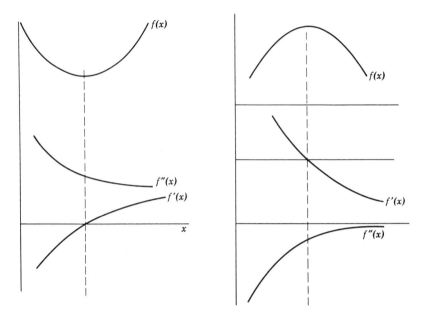

Figure 7.5   Graphical illustration of maximum and minimum.

■ 7.3   Some Ways of Distinguishing Between Maxima and Minima

Let $y = f(x)$ be a function whose turning points we wish to study, and let x_0 be a point such that

$$f'(x_0) = 0$$

If x_0 yields a minimum, then for small $h > 0$ we must have

$$f'(x_0 - h) < 0 \quad \text{and} \quad f'(x_0 + h) > 0$$

Thus

$$\frac{f'(x_0 - h) - f'(x_0)}{-h} > 0 \quad \text{and} \quad \frac{f'(x_0 + h) - f'(x_0)}{h} > 0$$

But if we let h tend to zero in both inequalities, then, provided it exists at x_0, we will obtain the derivative * of $f'(x)$ at $x = x_0$. This is usually denoted by $f''(x_0)$ and is called the *second derivative of $f(x)$*. We conclude that at a minimum, $f''(x_0)$ cannot be negative. In other words, if $f'(x_0)$

_____

* If the derivative of $f'(x)$ exists, then both expressions tend to the same limit, which, of course, is the derivative of $f'(x)$. If $y = f(x)$, we often write $f''(x) = d^2y/dx^2$.

$= 0$ *and* $f''(x_0) > 0$, we must have a minimum. Very similar reasoning shows that if $f'(x_0) = 0$ *and* $f''(x_0) < 0$, we must have a maximum. Figure 7.5 shows the above reasoning graphically.

Of course, if $f'(x_0) = f''(x_0) = 0$, we might have either or we might even have a "shoulder," which is neither. This is shown in Figure 7.6 for $y = x^3$.

We have seen that there may be several maxima or minima. Usually we wish to find *the* maximum or *the* minimum. The only way to do so is to examine the value of the function at *all* of the local maxima (or local minima).

Example 1. Find *the* minimum of the function $y = x^4 - 14x^2 + 24x + 9$, and sketch the curve.

$$f(x) = x^4 - 14x^2 + 24x + 9$$

$$f'(x) = 4x^3 - 28x + 24$$

For a turning point, $f'(x) = 0$, so

$$4x^3 - 28x + 24 = 0$$

$$x^3 - 7x + 6 = 0$$

$$(x - 1)(x - 2)(x + 3) = 0$$

Thus $x = 1, 2$ or -3

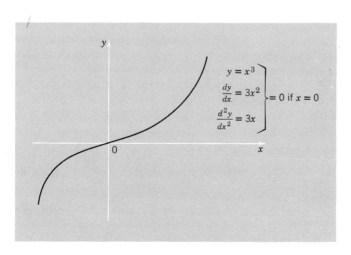

Figure 7.6 $y = x^3$.

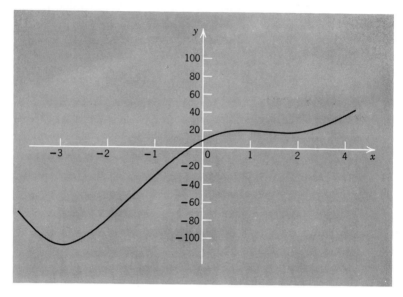

Figure 7.7 $y = x^4 - 14x^2 + 24x + 9.$

Now

$$f''(x) = 12x^2 - 28$$

$$f''(1) = -16$$

$$f''(2) = 20$$

$$f''(-3) = 80$$

Thus $x = 1$ is a maximum; $x = 2$ and $x = -3$ are minima. We have $f(-\infty) = \infty$. (The curve has no absolute maximum * in the sense that values of x can be found to make y as large as we please.) Also, $f(2) = 17, f(-3) = -108$, so that *the* minimum occurs when $x = -3$. Finally, $f(0) = 9$. The curve is shown in Figure 7.7.

Example 2. By finding the second derivative of the cost function, show that the economic lot-size formula in Section 7.2 yields a minimum cost.

---

* It should be noted that y does have an absolute maximum if we restrict the range of x. For example, if $0 \le x \le 2$, y has an absolute maximum when $x = 1$. If $0 \le x \le 5$, y has an absolute maximum for $x = 5$. In general, when searching for *the* maximum or *the* minimum of $f(x)$, where $a \le x \le b$, we must examine all points in the range for which $f'(x) = 0$, together with $f(a)$ and $f(b)$.

We had

$$K = \frac{q}{200} + \frac{50{,}000}{q}$$

Therefore

$$\frac{dK}{dq} = \frac{1}{200} - \frac{50{,}000}{q^2}$$

$$\frac{d^2K}{dq^2} = \frac{2 \times 50{,}000}{q^3} > 0 \qquad \text{for all } q > 0$$

Therefore we have a minimum.

Example 3. Show that the rule of equating marginal cost to marginal revenue does maximize profit.

Let $C(x)$ be the cost of producing x items and let $R(x)$ be the revenue obtained by selling x items. The profit is $P(x) = R(x) - C(x)$. For a turning point

$$P'(x) = 0, \qquad \text{that is,} \qquad R'(x) - C'(x) = 0$$

or
$$R'(x) = C'(x)$$

But $R'(x)$ is the rate of change of revenue with volume or the marginal revenue; $C'(x)$ is the marginal cost (the revenue produced by the last item sold, the cost of making the last item) so that equating marginal cost and marginal revenue does give a turning point. It is reasonable to suppose that costs of production will increase indefinitely as x increases, but that income will not. (The market is limited; prices can be dropped to zero without selling infinite quantities.) Hence $P(x) \rightarrow -\infty$ as $x \rightarrow \infty$. Therefore, if there is a turning point, it will yield a maximum. If $R'(x)$ is always less than $C'(x)$, the best procedure is to make nothing; otherwise we lose money! (Presumably $P(0) = 0$.)

Exercises

1. Find the minimum of the function $y = 3x^4 + 8x^3 - 90x^2$, and sketch the curve.

2. The relationship between sales S and advertising cost x is given by the formula

$$S = \frac{20{,}000x}{500 + x}$$

The gross profit is 20% of sales revenue. Express net profit P as a function of sales S and advertising cost x. Also, find x so as to maximize net profit.

Hint: $P = \frac{1}{5}S - x$

3. In the above exercise, by finding the second derivative of the net profit function, show that we do get maximum profit.

4. Find the maximum of the function

$$3x^4 - 10x^3 + 3x^2 + 12x + c$$

and sketch the curve.

5. It costs $10,000 to buy a new truck, and the running cost in dollars for each year is:

Year	1	2	3	4	5	6	7
Running cost	1000	1500	2000	2500	3000	3500	4000

Find when the truck should be replaced so as to minimize average cost. (Assume there is no resale value.)

6. In exercise 5, if the resale value is not zero and its dollar value is given by

Year	1	2	3	4
Resale value	7000	4900	3430	2401

find when the truck should be replaced to minimize average annual costs.

7. If the initial cost of buying a truck is C, and the total running cost for x years is

$$\sum_{t=1}^{x} [a + b(t - 1)], \qquad \text{that is,} \qquad ax + \frac{bx(x - 1)}{2}$$

find the average cost per year. Also, find x so as to minimize the average cost.

Hint:

$$\text{Total average annual cost} = \frac{C + ax + bx(x - 1)/2}{x}$$

$$= C/x + a + b(x - 1)/2$$

(*Note:* Exercises 5 and 7 refer to the same economic replacement problem with $C = 10{,}000$, $a = 1000$, $b = 500$.)

■ 7.4 Problems with Several Variables

We have seen that if cost, y, can be expressed as a function of one independent variable, say batch size x, then to minimize cost we need to
examine those values of x for which $dy/dx = 0$. Usually reality is not
so simple, and we find that cost is a function of several variables, for
example, marketing expenditure, rate of production, batch size, amount
of overtime, and so on. Let us imagine that cost, y, can be expressed
by an equation:

$$y = f(x, z)$$

and that someone asks us to determine the optimal value of x for all
choices of z. We would start by differentiating $f(x, z)$ with respect to x,
forgetting about possible changes in z, and equating the result to zero.
For example, let

$$y = 5x^2 + 5z^2 - 2xz - 16x + 8z + 14$$

Then
$$\frac{dy}{dx} = 10x - 2z - 16 = 0$$

Therefore, for a turning point, $x = 0.2z + 1.6$.

In a similar fashion we could find the value of z (ignoring possible
changes in x) that results in a turning point.

$$\frac{dy}{dx} = 10z - 2x + 8 = 0 \qquad \text{or} \qquad z = 0.2x - 0.8$$

Furthermore,
$$\frac{d^2y}{dx^2} = 10 \qquad \text{and} \qquad \frac{d^2y}{dz^2} = 10$$

and we see that in both cases we have minima.

The obvious question to ask is: Can we find a pair of values for x and z
such that y is now smaller than for any other values? We might consider the case where we simultaneously make both derivatives equal to
zero, that is,

$$10x - 2z - 16 = 0$$

$$10z - 2x + 8 = 0$$

or
$$x = 1.5, \quad z = -0.5$$

It is intuitively reasonable that these values should yield a minimum;
a proof must be deferred until Section 7.8.

■ 7.5 Partial Derivatives

We have implied that it is legitimate to use the notation dy/dx for the derivative of y with respect to x, whether or not other variables are present in y. Unfortunately, this is not always the case; it may be ambiguous. In the example above, suppose that x is itself equal to z^2. There are now two possible derivatives with respect to z.

1. The derivative we considered above, which assumed there was no relationship between x and z.
2. The derivative we would obtain if we first expressed y in terms of z and then differentiated the result.

The former is called the *partial derivative* of y with respect to z, whereas the latter is the *total derivative*. It is customary to use the notation dy/dz for total derivatives and $\partial y/\partial z$ for partial derivatives. Of course, if y is a function of one variable only, say x, we could write either dy/dx or $\partial y/\partial x$. However, it is customary to use dy/dx in this case. Let us now find the total derivative of y with respect to z. We have, on replacing x by z^2 in the example of Section 7.4,

$$y = 5z^4 + 5z^2 - 2z^3 - 16z^2 + 8z + 14$$

$$= 5z^4 - 2z^3 - 11z^2 + 8z + 14$$

The *total* derivative is

$$\frac{dy}{dz} = 20z^3 - 6z^2 - 22z + 8$$

This could also have been obtained by a general formula, which will be proved later

$$\frac{dy}{dz} = \frac{\partial y}{\partial x} \cdot \frac{dx}{dz} + \frac{\partial y}{\partial z}$$

We have

$$\frac{\partial y}{\partial z} = 10z - 2x + 8$$

$$\frac{\partial y}{\partial x} = 10x - 2z - 16$$

$$\frac{dx}{dz} = 2z$$

Therefore $\quad \dfrac{dy}{dz} = 2z(10x - 2z - 16) + (10z - 2x + 8)$

$$= 2z(10z^2 - 2z - 16) + (10z - 2z^2 + 8)$$

$$= 20z^3 - 6z^2 - 22z + 8$$

We now give a formal definition of a partial derivative.

Definition. If $y = f(x, z)$, then the *partial derivative* of y with respect to x is given by

$$\frac{\partial y}{\partial x} = \lim_{h \to 0} \frac{f(x + h, z) - f(x, z)}{h}$$

To evaluate the partial derivative of y with respect to x, $\partial y/\partial x$, the variable z is considered to be a constant.

The partial derivative with respect to z is defined analogously, and the concept is readily extended to any number of variables. The notation $\dfrac{\partial y}{\partial x} = f_x$ is also common.

The rules stated in Chapter 6 for ordinary derivatives are valid for partial derivatives. For any constant k, and functions y, y_1, and y_2, we have

$$\frac{\partial(ky)}{\partial x} = k \frac{\partial y}{\partial x}$$

$$\frac{\partial(y_1 + y_2)}{\partial x} = \frac{\partial y_1}{\partial x} + \frac{\partial y_2}{\partial x}$$

$$\frac{\partial(y_1 y_2)}{\partial x} = y_1 \frac{\partial y_2}{\partial x} + y_2 \frac{\partial y_1}{\partial x}$$

$$\frac{\partial \left(\dfrac{y_1}{y_2} \right)}{\partial x} = \frac{y_2 \dfrac{\partial y_1}{\partial x} - y_1 \dfrac{\partial y_2}{\partial x}}{y_2{}^2}$$

Example 1. Find the partial derivatives of $y = ax^2 + bxz + cz^2$.

$$\frac{\partial y}{\partial x} = \lim_{h \to 0} \frac{a(x + h)^2 + b(x + h)z + cz^2 - ax^2 - bxz - cz^2}{h}$$

$$= \lim_{h \to 0} \frac{2ahx + ah^2 + bhz}{h}$$

$$= 2ax + bz$$

It should be observed that the partial derivative of y with respect to x may be found by considering z to be held constant and calculating the ordinary derivative.

$$\frac{\partial y}{\partial z} = \lim_{k \to 0} \frac{ax^2 + bx(z + k) + c(z + k)^2 - ax^2 - bxz - cz^2}{k}$$

$$= \lim_{k \to 0} \frac{bkx + 2ckz + ck^2}{k}$$

$$= bx + 2cz$$

Example 2. Find the partial derivatives of $y = (a + bx)/z$.

$$\frac{\partial y}{\partial x} = \lim_{h \to 0} \frac{1}{h} \left[\frac{a + b(x + h)}{z} - \frac{a + bx}{z} \right]$$

$$= \lim_{h \to 0} \frac{1}{h} \left(\frac{bh}{z} \right)$$

$$= \frac{b}{z}$$

$$\frac{\partial y}{\partial z} = \lim_{k \to 0} \frac{1}{k} \left(\frac{a + bx}{z + k} - \frac{a + bx}{z} \right)$$

$$= \lim_{k \to 0} \frac{1}{k} \left[\frac{-k(a + bx)}{z(z + k)} \right]$$

$$= -\frac{a + bx}{z^2}$$

Exercises

1. Find $\partial y/\partial x$ and $\partial y/\partial z$ for the following:

(a) $y = \dfrac{x}{z} + \dfrac{z}{x}$

(b) $y = (x - z)^2 + x^3 - 3z$

(c) $y = ax^n z^m$

(d) $y = x \log z + z \log x$

(e) $y = (x^2 + z^2)e^z$

(f) $y = \sin (2x + 3z)$

2. At a gasoline station the annual profits p have been determined to be

$$p = a_1 xy + a_2 xz + a_3 yz - b_1 x^2 - b_2 y^2 - b_3 z^2$$

where x is the number of employees,

   y is the number of gasoline pumps,

   z is the inventory of automobile supplies (tires, oil, etc.), and

   a_1, a_2, a_3, b_1, b_2, and b_3 are positive constants.

Find $\partial p/\partial x$, $\partial p/\partial y$, and $\partial p/\partial z$ and interpret the solutions.

■ **7.6   Second and Higher Orders of Partial Derivatives**

The concept of a second partial derivative is similar to that of the second ordinary derivative, i.e.,

$$\frac{\partial^2 y}{\partial x^2} = \frac{\partial}{\partial x}\left(\frac{\partial y}{\partial x}\right) \quad \text{and} \quad \frac{\partial^2 y}{\partial z^2} = \frac{\partial}{\partial z}\left(\frac{\partial y}{\partial z}\right)$$

or the second derivative is the first derivative of the first derivative. Also

$$\frac{\partial^2 y}{\partial x \partial z} = \frac{\partial}{\partial x}\left(\frac{\partial y}{\partial z}\right) \quad \text{and} \quad \frac{\partial^2 y}{\partial z \partial x} = \frac{\partial}{\partial z}\left(\frac{\partial y}{\partial x}\right)$$

Under certain conditions of continuity of the function $y = f(x, z)$, it may be demonstrated that the order in which the partial derivative is taken is not important, or

$$\frac{\partial^2 y}{\partial x \partial z} = \frac{\partial^2 y}{\partial z \partial x}$$

The proof requires use of the Mean Value Theorem (see R. Courant, *Differential and Integral Calculus*, vol. II (1936), pp. 55–57).   This fact is illustrated in the following examples.

Example 1

$$y = x^3 + xz^2 + z^3$$

$$\frac{\partial y}{\partial x} = 3x^2 + z^2, \quad \frac{\partial y}{\partial z} = 2xz + 3z^2$$

$$\frac{\partial^2 y}{\partial z \partial x} = 2z, \quad \frac{\partial^2 y}{\partial x \partial z} = 2z$$

Example 2

$$y = \frac{x}{x+z}$$

$$\frac{\partial y}{\partial x} = \frac{x+z-x}{(x+z)^2} = \frac{z}{(x+z)^2}, \quad \frac{\partial y}{\partial z} = \frac{-x}{(x+z)^2}$$

$$\frac{\partial^2 y}{\partial z \partial x} = \frac{(x+z)^2 - 2z(x+z)}{(x+z)^4} = \frac{x-z}{(x+z)^3}$$

$$\frac{\partial^2 y}{\partial x \partial z} = \frac{-(x+z)^2 + 2x(x+z)}{(x+z)^4} = \frac{x-z}{(x+z)^3}$$

Higher order derivatives are obtained by an obvious extension; for example

$$\frac{\partial^3 y}{\partial z^3} = \frac{\partial}{\partial z}\left(\frac{\partial^2 y}{\partial z^2}\right), \quad \frac{\partial^3 y}{\partial x \partial z^2} = \frac{\partial}{\partial x}\left(\frac{\partial^2 y}{\partial z^2}\right)$$

The subscript notation can also be extended so that

$$f_{xx} = \frac{\partial f_x}{\partial x}, \quad f_{xy} = \frac{\partial f_y}{\partial x}, \quad f_{yy} = \frac{\partial f_y}{\partial y}$$

However, while this notation is common, it is not universal and should be explained whenever there is a possibility of ambiguity.

■ **7.7 Total Derivative**

We now prove the following result.

If $y = f(x, z, t)$ and x, z are themselves functions of t, then y can be expressed as a function of t only, and the *total derivative* of y with respect to t is given by the formula

$$\frac{dy}{dt} = \frac{\partial y}{\partial x}\frac{dx}{dt} + \frac{\partial y}{\partial z}\frac{dz}{dt} + \frac{\partial y}{\partial t}$$

Proof. Suppose an increase of h in t produces an increase of k in x and l in z (and assume that if $h \neq 0$, then $k \neq 0, l \neq 0$).

$$\frac{y(t+h) - y(t)}{h} = \frac{f(x+k, z+l, t+h) - f(x, y, t)}{h}$$

$$= \frac{f(x+k, z+l, t+h) - f(x, z+l, t+h)}{k} \times \frac{k}{h}$$

$$+ \frac{f(x, z+l, t+h) - f(x, z, t+h)}{l} \times \frac{l}{h}$$

$$+ \frac{f(x, z, t+h) - f(x, z, t)}{h}$$

Now let $h \to 0$, so that

$$\frac{k}{h} = \frac{x(t+h) - x(t)}{h} \to \frac{dx}{dt}$$

$$\frac{l}{h} = \frac{z(t+h) - z(t)}{h} \to \frac{dz}{dt}$$

and we have, for example,

$$\frac{f(x+k, z+l, t+h) - f(x, z+l, t+h)}{k} \to \frac{\partial y}{\partial x}$$

The result follows except when either k or l is zero for all sufficiently small h. Suppose, for example, $k = 0$; then x is not dependent on t, and $dx/dt = 0$. It is easy enough to show that if x does not depend on t,

$$\frac{dy}{dt} = \frac{\partial y}{\partial z} \frac{dz}{dt} + \frac{\partial y}{\partial t}$$

and so our result is generally true. The reader should compare this result with the formula in Section 6.7,

$$\frac{dy}{dx} = \frac{dy}{dz} \frac{dz}{dx}$$

Example. In placing spot commercials on television, a given sum of money x will buy so many spots. Each spot produces a certain size audience (number of exposures). If we know the relationship between exposures and sales and between sales and gross profit, then we could express net profit (after allowing for the cost of commercials) as a function of both sales and cost of advertising.

For example, suppose that spots cost \$500 each and yield an average audience of 100,000 apiece. Suppose sales S are related to exposures E by the formula

$$S = \frac{20,000E}{100,000 + E}$$

and that gross profit is 20% of sales.

Express net profit P as a function of sales S and advertising cost x. Find $\partial S/\partial E$ and hence dP/dx.

Now $P = \frac{1}{5}S - x$ and $E = 200x$

$$\frac{\partial S}{\partial E} = \frac{20,000(100,000 + E) - 20,000E}{(100,000 + E)^2} = \frac{2 \times 10^9}{(100,000 + E)^2}$$

$$\frac{dP}{dx} = \frac{1}{5}\frac{dS}{dx} - 1$$

$$= \frac{1}{5}\frac{\partial S}{\partial E}\frac{dE}{dx} - 1 = \frac{1}{5}\left(\frac{2 \times 10^9}{(100,000 + E)^2}\right)200 - 1$$

$$= \frac{8 \times 10^{10}}{(100,000 + E)^2} - 1$$

Exercises

1. In each of the exercises below, find all partial derivatives of the first and second order with respect to x and z.

(a) $y = 2x^2 + 3xz + 4z^2$

(b) $y = 3x^3 - 8x^2z - xz^4 + z^3$

(c) $y = \dfrac{x^2 + z^2}{x + z}$

(d) $y = ax + bz + \dfrac{c}{x} + \dfrac{d}{z}$

(e) $y = e^{5x-3z}$

(f) $y = \log{[2z/(3x + z)]}$

(g) $y = x \cos{(x + z)}$

(h) $y = (x + z)e^{-(x+z)}$

2. Find the total derivative of y with respect to t by using the total derivative formula,

$$\frac{dy}{dt} = \frac{\partial y}{\partial x}\frac{dx}{dt} + \frac{\partial y}{\partial z}\frac{dz}{dt}$$

for exercise 1, where $x = t$ and $z = t^2$.

3. The total cost of ordering and holding two products is given by

$$y = C_{11}x + C_{12}z + \frac{C_{21}}{x} + \frac{C_{22}}{z}$$

where x and z are the quantities of items ordered of types 1 and 2. Find and interpret

$$\frac{\partial y}{\partial x} \quad \text{and} \quad \frac{\partial y}{\partial z}$$

4. The sales of a firm's product S are related to the number of spot commercials per day, E, and the length of each commercial, L, in minutes,

$$S = \frac{20,000EL^{\frac{1}{2}}}{100,000 + EL^{\frac{1}{2}}}$$

Find and interpret

$$\frac{\partial S}{\partial E} \quad \text{and} \quad \frac{\partial S}{\partial L}$$

■ **7.8   Maximization and Minimization with Several Variables**

Now that we understand partial derivatives we are in a position to extend the first part of this chapter to the case of several variables. We will work with two variables although the reasoning for three or more is very similar. We start by defining a local maximum (minimum) of a function.

Definition.   The point (x', y') is a local maximum with respect to the function $f(x, y)$ if and only if, for all sufficiently small h, k,

$$f(x' + h, y' + k) \leq f(x', y')$$

It is a local minimum if $f(x' + h, y' + k) \geq f(x', y')$. Of course, we have *the* maximum (or *the* minimum) if the inequality remains true for all values of h and k.

In order to see the difference between the maximum and a local maximum, consider the contour map in Figure 7.8. We have drawn curves in the xy-plane, along each of which $f(x, y)$ is constant. At point A we may suppose $f = 75$ and at B, $f = 120$. A is the top of a "hill," and if we move in the neighborhood of A, we only find values less than 75. However, there are points far away from A (such as B) where f takes on values in excess of 75. A is a local maximum, but B is *the* maximum.

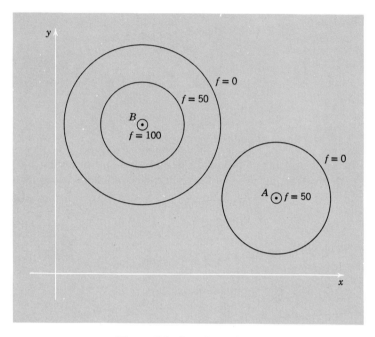

Figure 7.8   Local maxima.

Theorem.   A necessary condition for a local maximum or minimum is that the partial derivatives shall simultaneously vanish.

By definition of a maximum we must have for $h > 0$,

$$f(x' + h, y') \leq f(x', y')$$

and

$$f(x' - h, y) \leq f(x', y')$$

Therefore

$$\frac{f(x' + h, y') - f(x', y')}{h} \leq 0$$

and

$$\frac{f(x' - h, y') - f(x', y')}{-h} \geq 0$$

It follows that as $h \rightarrow 0$, we obtain

$$\frac{\partial f}{\partial x} = 0$$

Similarly,

$$\frac{\partial f}{\partial y} = 0$$

The same result is obtained for a minimum by reversing both inequalities.

A problem of major importance is to distinguish between the various possibilities when the partial derivatives vanish. In many practical cases the nature of the point is apparent; however, we must defer the mathematical discussion until we have described Taylor's Theorem in the next chapter (Section 8.8).

The condition $\partial f/\partial x = \partial f/\partial y = 0$ is necessary for a maximum or minimum, but it is not sufficient. Consider $f(x, y) = x^2 - y^2$, when $x = y = 0$. For this function $\partial f/\partial x = 2x$, $\partial f/\partial y = 2y$, so that both derivatives vanish at the origin. However, if we keep $x = 0$ and change the value of y, we find f decreases, but if we keep $y = 0$ and change x, we find f increases. In fact, f has a *saddle-point* at the origin. Figure 7.9 is a contour map, showing curves along which $f(x, y)$ has fixed values.

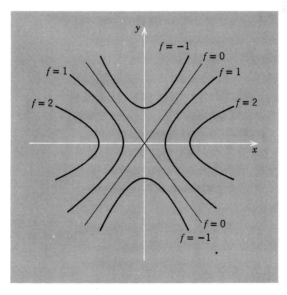

Figure 7.9 $f(x, y) = x^2 - y^2$.

■ 7.9 Criteria for Maximum and Minimum Value

We have seen that a necessary condition for a maximum or minimum value of the function $y = f(x, z)$ at the point $x = a$, $z = b$ is that

$$\frac{\partial y}{\partial x} = 0 \quad \text{and} \quad \frac{\partial y}{\partial z} = 0$$

To distinguish maximum from minimum values we must examine the second partial derivative, for we may have three cases:

1. The function is a maximum at $x = a$, $z = b$.
2. The function is a minimum at $x = a$, $z = b$.
3. The function has a saddle-point at $x = a$, $z = b$, where deviations from this pair of values may yield greater or smaller values.

Each of these cases is illustrated in Figure 7.10.

For the function to have a maximum value at the point $x = a$, $z = b$, we must have

$$\frac{\partial^2 y}{\partial x^2} < 0 \quad \text{and} \quad \frac{\partial^2 y}{\partial z^2} < 0$$

as in the case of ordinary derivatives. However, as will be demonstrated in Chapter 8, we must also have

$$\frac{\partial^2 y}{\partial x^2} \frac{\partial^2 y}{\partial z^2} - \left(\frac{\partial^2 y}{\partial x \partial z}\right)^2 > 0$$

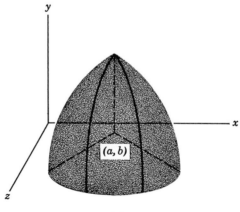

(a)

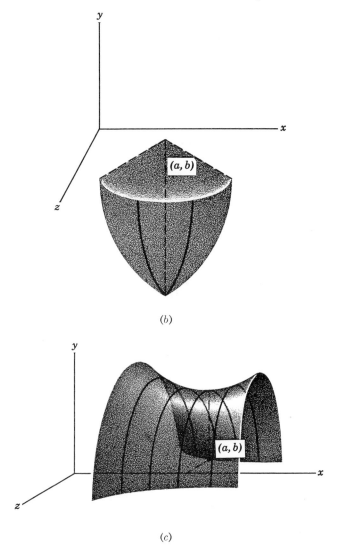

Figure 7.10 (a) Case 1: y is a maximum at $x = a$, $z = b$. (b) Case 2: y is a minimum at $x = a$, $z = b$. (c) Case 3: y is a saddle point at $x = a$, $z = b$.

The latter condition must also hold for a minimum point, where

$$\frac{\partial^2 y}{\partial x^2} > 0 \qquad \text{and} \qquad \frac{\partial^2 y}{\partial z^2} > 0$$

Example 1.   Find the extreme values for $y = x^2 + z^2$.

$$\frac{\partial y}{\partial x} = 2x, \quad \frac{\partial y}{\partial z} = 2z$$

$$\frac{\partial^2 y}{\partial x^2} = 2, \quad \frac{\partial^2 y}{\partial z^2} = 2, \quad \frac{\partial^2 y}{\partial x \partial z} = 0$$

The value $x = 0$, $z = 0$ yields an extreme value for y, $y = 0$, for

$$\frac{\partial^2 y}{\partial x^2}\frac{\partial^2 y}{\partial y^2} - \left(\frac{\partial^2 y}{\partial x \partial y}\right)^2 = 4 - 0 = 4 > 0$$

Since $\partial^2 y/\partial x^2 > 0$ and $\partial^2 y/\partial z^2 > 0$, this is a minimum value.

Example 2.   Consider the spot commercial example in Section 7.7.   We know that the rate of change of profits per dollar of advertising cost is given by

$$\frac{dP}{dx} = \frac{8 \times 10^{10}}{(100,000 + E)^2} - 1$$

For an optimal advertising effort, $dP/dx = 0$,

$$(100,000 + E)^2 = 8.10^{10}$$

$$100,000 + E = 2\sqrt{2} \times 10^5$$

$$E = (2\sqrt{2} - 1)10^5 = 182,000$$

$$x = \frac{E}{200} = \frac{182,000}{200} = \$910$$

Since spots cost $500 each, two spots are optimal ($x = 500$, $P = 1500$; $x = 1000$, $P = 1667$).

■ **7.10   Generalization of the Economic Lot-size Formula**

Before reading this section the reader should review the discussion of the economic lot-size formula, Section 7.2.

Consider a manufacturer with an annual demand of R units.   Holding cost is $\$C_1$ per unit per year, shortage cost is $\$C_2$ per unit short per year, and setup cost is $\$C_3$ per production batch.   Production orders are fulfilled with no delay and demand is at a constant rate.

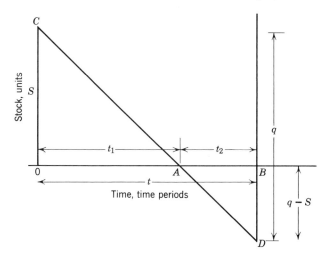

Figure 7.11 Production cycle, instantaneous production, shortages permitted.

(i) How often should production be scheduled?

(ii) What should the production quantity be?

    Let t = interval between production orders,

        q = production quantity.

The production cycle is illustrated in Figure 7.11.

The stock on hand, or short, is given by a point on the line CD.

Let S = planned inventory level on completion of one production batch.

    t_1 = duration of that part of the cycle during which stock is on hand.

    t_2 = duration of remainder of the cycle during which no stock is on hand.

    Shortages are assumed to be backlogged and not lost.

Now triangle COA is similar to triangle DBA, and thus

$$\frac{t_1}{S} = \frac{t_2}{q - S} = \frac{t_1 + t_2}{q} = \frac{t}{q}$$

or

$$t_1 = \frac{S}{q}\,t$$

$$t_2 = \frac{q - S}{q}\,t$$

The cost of holding is

$$C_1 \left(\frac{1}{2} St_1 \right) = \frac{1}{2} C_1 \frac{S^2}{q} t$$

The cost of shortages is

$$C_2 \left(\frac{1}{2} (q - S) t_2 \right) = \frac{1}{2} C_2 \frac{(q - S)^2}{q}$$

The cost of setups is C_3. The total cost per cycle is

$$C_3 + \frac{1}{2} C_1 \frac{S^2}{q} t + \frac{1}{2} C_2 \frac{(q - S)^2}{q} t$$

The number of cycles per year is R/q, and the length of each cycle is $t = \dfrac{1}{R/q} = q/R$. The total annual cost K is

$$K = \left[C_3 + \frac{1}{2} C_1 \frac{S^2}{q} t + \frac{1}{2} C_2 \frac{(q - S)^2}{q} t \right] \frac{R}{q}$$

$$= \frac{RC_3}{q} + \frac{1}{2} C_1 \frac{S^2}{q} + \frac{1}{2} C_2 \frac{(q - S)^2}{q}$$

We wish to find the values of q and S that minimize K. For minimum K we must have

$$\frac{\partial K}{\partial S} = 0 \quad \text{and} \quad \frac{\partial K}{\partial q} = 0$$

$$\frac{\partial K}{\partial S} = C_1 \frac{S}{q} - C_2 \frac{(q - S)}{q} = 0$$

$$S = \frac{C_2}{C_1 + C_2} q$$

$$\frac{\partial K}{\partial q} = \frac{-RC_3}{q^2} - \frac{C_1 S^2}{2 q^2} - \frac{C_2 (q - S)^2}{2 q^2} + C_2 \frac{(q - S)}{q} = 0$$

Substituting the value of S,

$$\frac{RC_3}{q^2} = -\frac{C_1}{2}\left(\frac{C_2}{C_1+C_2}\right)^2 - \frac{C_2}{2}\left(1 - \frac{C_2}{C_1+C_2}\right)^2 + C_2\left(1 - \frac{C_2}{C_1+C_2}\right)$$

$$= \frac{1}{2(C_1+C_2)^2}\left[-C_1 C_2{}^2 - C_2 C_1{}^2 + 2C_2 C_1(C_1 + C_2)\right]$$

$$= \frac{C_1 C_2}{2(C_1+C_2)}$$

$$q = \sqrt{2RC_3(C_1+C_2)/C_1 C_2}$$

The optimal interval between production orders is

$$t = \frac{q}{R} = \sqrt{2C_3(C_1 + C_2)/RC_1 C_2}$$

In the event that shortages are not permitted, $C_2 = \infty$, and the results reduce to the economic lot-size formula of Section 7.2

$$q = \sqrt{2RC_3/C_1}$$

$$t = \sqrt{2C_3/RC_1}$$

Exercises

1. Find the optimum values of x and z:

(a) $y = \dfrac{(x-\alpha)^2}{z^2} + \dfrac{(x-\beta)^2}{z^2} + \log z$

(b) $y = x^2 + xz + z^2$

(c) $y = (2x + z)e^{-(2x+z)}$

2. Show that the coordinates of the point such that the sum of the squares of the distances from the n points (x_1, y_1), (x_2, y_2), $\ldots$, (x_n, y_n) is a minimum is given by

$$\left(\frac{1}{n}\sum_{i=1}^{n} x_i, \frac{1}{n}\sum_{i=1}^{n} y_i\right)$$

3. For the generalized economic lot size formula find the values of t and q where

$$R = 10{,}000 \text{ units}$$

$$C_1 = 2 \text{ per unit per year}$$

$$C_2 = 8 \text{ per unit short per year}$$

$$C_3 = 500$$

4. A firm manufactures two different sized packages of soap at a cost of 10 and 20¢ per package. The annual demand for each product is given by

$$x_1 = 3p_2 - 3p_1$$
$$x_2 = 55 + 2p_1 - 4p_2$$

where x_i is the demand, in thousands, for package i and p_i is the price, in cents, of package $(i = 1, 2)$.

Find the package prices that maximize the total annual profits.

■ 7.11 Maximization and Minimization Subject to Constraints: Lagrange Multipliers

We have previously referred to the economic lot-size formula Sections 7.2 and 7.10 for determining economic batch sizes. It will be recalled that we considered how much to produce of a single item so as to minimize the average cost of setup and inventory holding. Suppose now that we are concerned with two items and that because of production and storage limitations there is an upper limit on the sum of the batch sizes. How shall we proceed?

Let us take a specific example. A manufacturer produces two items, A and B. Given the following data, what are the optimal batch sizes if the two batches must not exceed 2500 items together?

	Item A	*Item B*
Monthly demand R	1000	1500
Setup cost C_3, in dollars	50	100
Monthly holding cost per item C_1, in dollars	0.10	0.06

First of all, we attempt to solve the problem as if there were no batch size restriction. If the resulting batch sizes add up to less than 2500, we will have the optimal solution. We can use the economic lot-size formula for each item separately, and we have

$$q = \sqrt{2C_3 R/C_1}$$

For item A $$q_A = \sqrt{\frac{2 \times 50 \times 1000}{0.1}} = 1000$$

For item B $$q_B = \sqrt{\frac{2 \times 100 \times 1500}{0.06}} = 2240$$

The items cannot be treated separately because the total is too large. (1000 + 2240 > 2500.) We must assume that exactly 2500 will be made (since any amount less than 2500 yields greater costs) and solve the problem accordingly.

Instead, suppose that we produce x of item A and y of item B. Then, arguing as we did in Section 7.2, the total monthly cost K is given by

$$K = \frac{x}{2} \times 0.1 + 50 \div \frac{x}{1000} + \frac{y}{2} \times 0.06 + 100 \div \frac{y}{1500}$$

$$= 0.05x + \frac{50{,}000}{x} + 0.03y + \frac{150{,}000}{y} \quad \text{(See Exercise 3, Section 7.7)}$$

K is to be minimized subject to the condition

$$x + y - 2500 = 0$$

Let us add an arbitrary multiple of this condition to K and consider

$$L = K + \lambda(x + y - 2500)$$

$$= x(0.05 + \lambda) + \frac{50{,}000}{x} + y(0.03 + \lambda) + \frac{150{,}000}{y} - 2500\lambda$$

So long as we preserve the condition, L will not differ in value from K. It is a fact that if we minimize L with respect to all three variables x, y, λ, we will obtain values of x and y that minimize K subject to the conditions (see proof below).

We have

$$\frac{\partial L}{\partial x} = 0.05 + \lambda - \frac{50{,}000}{x^2} = 0$$

$$\frac{\partial L}{\partial y} = 0.03 + \lambda - \frac{150{,}000}{y^2} = 0$$

$$\frac{\partial L}{\partial \lambda} = x + y - 2500 = 0$$

The last equation, of course, is the original constraint. Thus

$$x = \sqrt{\frac{50{,}000}{0.05 + \lambda}}, \quad y = \sqrt{\frac{150{,}000}{0.03 + \lambda}}$$

We can now find λ by trial and error. Setting $\lambda = 0$ is equivalent to ignoring the constraint * and yields $x = 1000$, $y = 2240$.

Since these are too big, we try positive values of λ. We start with $\lambda = 0.01$ and obtain

$$x = \sqrt{\frac{50,000}{0.06}} = \sqrt{833,000} = 913$$

$$y = \sqrt{\frac{150,000}{0.04}} = \sqrt{3,750,000} = 1937$$

These are still too big, but now we form the array

λ	$x + y - 2500$
0	740
0.01	350

This suggests we try $\lambda = 0.02$ and we obtain

$$x = 845 \qquad y = 1732$$

and
$$x + y = 2577$$

We could carry on with additional values of λ, but if we took $x = 800$, $y = 1700$, we would be near enough for practical purposes.

A general proof of the validity of what we have done is not difficult. Suppose that we wish to minimize (maximize) $f(x, y)$ subject to $g(x, y) = 0$. We can imagine that we have solved for x and obtained x as a function of y. We now require the total derivative df/dy, which we will equate to zero.

We have

$$\frac{df}{dy} = \frac{\partial f}{\partial x} \cdot \frac{dx}{dy} + \frac{\partial f}{\partial y} = 0$$

Differentiating $g(x, y)$ with respect to y yields

$$\frac{dg}{dy} = \frac{\partial g}{\partial x} \cdot \frac{dx}{dy} + \frac{\partial g}{\partial y} = 0$$

* The first two equations have only one nonnegative solution, and thus there is only one turning point. If these solutions add to more than 2500, we will have to reduce the batch sizes until they add to exactly 2500.

and hence

$$\frac{df}{dy} + \lambda \frac{dg}{dy} = \frac{dx}{dy}\left(\frac{\partial f}{\partial x} + \lambda \frac{\partial g}{\partial x}\right) + \frac{\partial f}{\partial y} + \lambda \frac{\partial g}{\partial y} = 0$$

Now choose λ such that the coefficient of the unknown quantity dx/dy vanishes, i.e.,

$$\frac{\partial f}{\partial x} + \lambda \frac{\partial g}{\partial x} = 0$$

Then we must also have

$$\frac{\partial f}{\partial y} + \lambda \frac{\partial g}{\partial y} = 0$$

and the original constraint $g(x, y) = 0$. Thus there are three equations for determining the three unknowns x, y, and λ.

The method works quite generally for several variables and several constraints. Thus to find the turning points of $f(x, y, z)$, subject to $g(x, y, z) = 0$, $h(x, y, z) = 0$, we would define $L = f + \lambda g + \mu h$ and solve the equations

$$\frac{\partial L}{\partial x} = 0, \quad \frac{\partial L}{\partial y} = 0, \quad \frac{\partial L}{\partial z} = 0$$

together with $g = 0$, $h = 0$. λ and μ are called *Lagrange multipliers*.

Exercise

In the above example find the value of x and y for the restriction that

$$x + y \leq 2000$$

Exercises for Chapter 7

1. Graph the following function between $x = -3$ and $x = +6$,

$$y = 3x^4 - 8x^3 - 78x^2 - 120x + 20$$

and identify all local maximum and minimum points.

2. Find the partial derivatives of the first and second orders of

(a) $y = \dfrac{x^2 - z^2}{x^2 + z^2}$

(b) $y = (x^3 - x^2z + z^3)e^{2x-z}$

3. Find the values of x and z that minimize

$$y = ax^2 + bz^2$$

subject to $x + z = B$.

4. Maximize the function
$$y = 3xz$$
subject to the restriction
$$x^2 + z^2 = 9$$

5. Consider the function
$$y = ax + \frac{b}{x}, \quad a > 0, \quad b > 0$$

Find dy/dx, d^2y/dx^2 and the value of x, say x_0, for which dy/dx vanishes. Show that x_0 yields a minimum for y and that the two terms of y are equal when $x = x_0$.

6. Consider the functions
$$y_1 = ax + \frac{b}{x^2}$$

$$y_2 = ax^2 + \frac{b}{x}$$

$$y_3 = ax^2 + \frac{b}{x^2}$$

(a) Draw the graphs of each function for $a = 1$, $b = 1$.
(b) Determine the optimal values of x for each function and the corresponding minimum values.
(c) Compare the minimum functional values with the values obtained by substituting the x-value that equates both terms in each function.
(d) What are the relative values of the terms in (c) at the optimal x?

7. The total cost of sampling information for accounting purposes is
$$C = C_1 n + \frac{C_2}{\sqrt{n}}$$
where C_1 is the unit cost of sampling an item
C_2 is the cost of a unit error in estimation
and n is the number of items in the sample.

Find the optimum number of items to be sampled that minimizes the total cost of sampling.

8. A firm has a budget $\$B$ to invest in developing and marketing n new products. If x_i is devoted to research and y_i to marketing product i the net profit will be $f_i(x_i, y_i)$. Show that, in general, the total profit $E = f_1 + f_2 + \cdots + f_n$ is maximized when

(1)
$$\frac{\partial E}{\partial x_1} = \frac{\partial E}{\partial x_2} = \cdots = \frac{\partial E}{\partial x_n} = \frac{\partial E}{\partial y_1} = \frac{\partial E}{\partial y_2} = \cdots = \frac{\partial E}{\partial y_n}$$

and

(2)
$$x_1 + x_2 + \cdots + x_n + y_1 + y_2 + \cdots + y_n = B$$

Under what circumstances would condition (1) be violated; under what circumstances would (2) be violated?

9. Two chemical firms located 2 miles and 5 miles from a river and 5 miles apart desire to construct a common sewage disposal plant on the river at minimum cost. Find the location of the plant such that the total pipe used in both firms is a minimum if they are on the same side of the river.

10. A chemical firm has noted that the annual sales of new products S depend on the amount invested in research and development R, improved plant and facilities P, and marketing and promotion M, given by the formula

$$S = R^{0.2}P^{0.6}M^{0.5}, \text{ in millions of dollars}$$

Find the values of R, P, and M that maximize the net profits

$$S - R - P - M$$

11. In exercise 10, find the values of R, P, and M that maximize the net profits and such that

$$R + P + M = 20 \text{ million}$$

12. The number N of a certain product sold is a function of the unit selling price s and the amount of advertising t given by

$$N = \frac{1 + bt}{1 + t}(\alpha - \beta s)$$

If c is the unit cost of production, then the total profits P is given by

$$P = N(s - c) - t$$

(a) Show that the values of s and t that maximize P are

$$s = \frac{\alpha + \beta c}{2\beta}$$

$$t = (\alpha - \beta c)\sqrt{(b - 1)/4\beta} - 1$$

(b) Find optimal s and t for $\alpha = 4 \times 10^6$, $\beta = 2 \times 10^6$, $b = 5000$, and $c = 1$.

13. There are two media of advertisements. If the amounts x_1 and x_2 are spent on each media, the total sales S is given by

$$S = \frac{20{,}000x_1}{500 + x_1} + \frac{10{,}000x_2}{200 + x_2}$$

The gross profit is 20% of the sales. Because of the financial limitations there is a limit of $1000 on the sum of the advertisement costs. Find x_1 and x_2 so as to maximize the total net profit $P = \frac{1}{5}S - x_1 - x_2$.

14. There are n media of advertisements. If the amount x_i is spent on medium i, then the total sales S is given by

$$S = \sum_{i=1}^{n} \frac{a_i x_i}{b_i + x_i}$$

The gross profit is g% of the sales. There is a limit of K dollars on the sum of the advertisement costs. Show how to find x_i so as to maximize the total net profit P.

15. The total number of products is N; the average inventory is constrained to have a value B. For the ith product the usage rate is R_i; the inventory cost C_{1i} is the product of a constant V and a factor b_i, dependent on the product type i. Also, the setup cost on an item is C_{3i}. Show that q_i, the optimal amount produced of product i, is given by

$$q_i = \frac{2B \sqrt{\dfrac{C_{3i}R_i}{b_i}}}{\displaystyle\sum_{i=1}^{n} \sqrt{C_{3i}R_ib_i}}$$

(*Note:* $B = \displaystyle\sum_{i=1}^{n} \frac{b_iq_i}{2}$ and $C_{1i} = Vb_i$).

16. The cost of running a train of n cars from A to B is $K + n\alpha$. However, it takes nt hours to assemble n cars at A, so that on the average each car waits a time $nt/2$. If the cost of a car waiting is k per hour, show that the average cost per car is

$$\frac{K}{n} + \alpha + \frac{ntk}{2}$$

Hence find the most economical length of train.

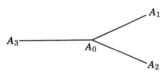

Figure 7.12

17. Suppose a railroad is as shown in Figure 7.12 with a switch yard at A_0. Cars arrive at A_i bound for A_j at a rate r_{ij} per day, $i \neq j = 0$, 1, 2, 3. [By "arrive at A_i" we mean "start their journey over the system at A_i." By "bound for A_j" we mean "end their journey at A_j."] Thus if we assemble a train of n cars at A_1 for movement to A_0, and with switching at A_0 if necessary, it will take a time $\dfrac{n}{r_{10} + r_{12} + r_{13}}$; the average delay per car will be $\dfrac{n}{2(r_{10} + r_{12} + r_{13})}$. On the other hand, if we run a through train from A_1 to A_2, the average delay will be $n/2r_{12}$. The costs of running a train of n cars from A_i to A_j is $K_{ij} + n\alpha_{ij}$, and the waiting costs are k per car per day at any point.

(a) Find an expression for the minimum cost of the system if we ignore the switch yard at A_0 and run all trains nonstop to their destinations.
(b) Find an expression for the minimum total cost if all cars not originating or terminating at A_0 are switched there. (Make a suitable assumption about delays at A_0.)
(c) Are any other policies possible?

18. The costs of building a single-story warehouse of floor area A and wall area W are $C_1A + C_2W$. The annual operating costs are

(a) depreciation and maintenance, equal to 10% of the building cost.
(b) handling materials that increases with the height of the stacks and may be taken as C_3Ah^2, where h is the height of the warehouse.

What are the most economical dimensions (length l, width w, and height h) for a warehouse capacity of 16,000 cubic feet? ($C_1 = \$16.00$ per square foot, $C_2 = \$12.00$ per square foot, and $C_3 = \$0.01$.)

19. With the formulas of exercise 18, find the rate of change of annual cost with capacity, assuming optimal dimensions are used. Hence show that if we wish to build two warehouses of combined capacity V, they should each be the same size, $V/2$. Show also that it would be cheaper to build a single warehouse of capacity V. Why might we wish to build two warehouses if they are more expensive than a single warehouse?

20. A company has a single plant, located at the origin O of coordinates. It has n markets located at points $P_i(x_i, y_i)$ $(i = 1, 2, \ldots, n)$. Sales at P_i are expected to average w_i. The cost of shipping to a market a distance d from the plant is $a + bd^2$ per unit. If a warehouse is built at the point $(u, 0)$ the cost of shipping to the warehouse is cu^2 per unit $(c < b)$. The subsequent cost of shipping to a market at a distance d' from the warehouse is then $a + bd'^2$. Customers will be supplied from the factory or warehouse, whichever source is cheaper in total costs.

(a) Show that the warehouse will supply all customers on the warehouse side of the line $x = [(c + b)/2b]u$.

(b) Show that the total costs of shipping are given by

$$\sum_{\text{all}} w_i[a + b(x_i^2 + y_i^2)] + \sum_{\text{warehouse}} w_i[(b + c)u^2 - 2bx_iu]$$

where the first sum is over all markets and the second is over those markets supplied by the warehouse.

(c) Assume that the markets are numbered $P_1, P_2, \ldots, P_n$ such that $x_1 < x_2 < \ldots < x_n$.

Show that the warehouse will either supply markets $P_1, P_2, \ldots, P_k$ for some k or $P_{i+1}, P_{i+2}, \ldots, P_n$ for some i. In the former case u is chosen to minimize

$$K_n = \sum_{j=1}^{k} w_j[(b + c)u^2 - 2bx_ju]$$

in the latter to minimize

$$H_i = \sum_{j=i+1}^{n} w_j[(b + c)u^2 - 2bx_ju].$$

(d) Show that for a given i the minimum value of

$$H_i = \frac{-b^2}{(b + c)} \left(\sum_{j=i+1}^{n} w_jx_j \right)^2 \Big/ \sum_{j=i+1}^{n} w_j$$

(e) Find the best value of u for the following data:

i	x_i	y_i	w_i	
1	-3	2	20	
2	-1	4	25	
3	2	-3	15	$a = 10,\ b = 2,\ c = 1$
4	3	-1	20	
5	5	2	30	

(f) Consider the complications that arise if we locate the warehouse at (u, v), where v is not necessarily equal to zero.

8

Taylor's Theorem and Some Applications

■ 8.1   Introduction

In many management system problems, the values of the constants are not known accurately. For example, in applying the economic lot-size formula (Section 7.2) to production systems we saw that the optimal order quantity depends on holding and setup costs. If these costs are subject to forecasting error, then the calculated order quantity must be adjusted. Analytic methods for determining the best adjustments and estimating the resulting cost savings rely on the general theory of expansion in power series, which will be developed in this chapter.

We have already seen (Section 4.10) that a power series $y = \sum_{n=0}^{\infty} a_n x^n$ defines y as a function of x, for those values of x that lie in its interval of convergence. That is, if we can find ρ such that $\sum_{n=0}^{\infty} a_n x^n$ converges for all $|x| < \rho$, the power series defines a function of x such that to each $|x| < \rho$ there corresponds a unique y. In this chapter we reverse the situation and pose the questions. When is it possible to express a function of x as a power series? If this can be done, what do we need to know about the function in order to compute the coefficients a_n and the interval of convergence ρ? The utility of being able to find the coefficients is obvious; as soon as they are known we can tabulate the function for all $|x| < \rho$.

Thus power series can be used to tabulate a wide variety of functions such as sines, cosines and logarithms to any desired degree of accuracy. By truncating the series at any convenient term, they may also be used to compute approximate values of relatively simple functions. The reader is already familiar with the algebraic expansion

$$(1 + x)^3 = 1 + 3x + 3x^2 + x^3$$

We consider a small value of x and investigate the effect of using the first two terms as an approximation. If $x = 0.01$, we have

$$(1 + x)^3 = (1.01)^3 = 1.030301$$

and $$(1 + x)^3 \simeq 1 + 3x = 1.03$$

Thus the error in approximating $(1 + x)^3$ by $1 + 3x$ is only 0.000301, which is less than 0.03% of the true value.

Power series expansions have a number of other important uses in advanced mathematics. As we shall see in Sections 8.5 and 8.8, they permit a rigorous discussion of the criteria for distinguishing between maxima and minima.

■ **8.2   Binomial Theorem (Positive Integral Values)**

Consider $f(x) = (1 + x)^k$, where k is a positive integer. By direct multiplication it is easy enough to see that $f(x) = (1 + x)^k$ has the form $a_0 + a_1 x + a_2 x^2 + \cdots + a_k x^k$. To determine the coefficients we note that by definition $f(0) = 1 = a_0$.

Now the derivatives of $f(x)$ with respect to x are *

$$f'(x) = k(1 + x)^{k-1}, \quad f''(x) = k(k - 1)(1 + x)^{k-2}, \ \ldots$$

$$f^{(r)}(x) = \frac{k!}{(k - r)!} (1 + x)^{k-r}, \ \ldots$$

$$f^{(k)}(x) = k!, \quad f^{(k+t)}(x) = 0 \qquad \text{for } t > 0$$

Thus

$$f'(0) = k, \quad f''(0) = k(k - 1), \ \ldots, f^{(r)}(0) = \frac{k!}{(k - r)!}, \ \ldots, f^{(k)}(0) = k!$$

and $$f^{(k+t)}(0) = 0, \qquad t > 0$$

But from the series expansion

$$f^{(r)}(x) = r!a_r + (r + 1)r(r - 1) \ldots 2a_{r+1}x$$

$$+ \cdots + k(k - 1) \ldots (k - r + 1)a_k x^{k-r}$$

and $$f^{(r)}(0) = r!a_r$$

$* f^{(r)}(x) = (d/dx) f^{(r-1)}(x)$ where $f^{(0)}(x) = f(x)$. $f^{(r)}(x)$ is called *the rth derivative*. If $y = f(x)$, we write $f^{(r)}(x) = d^r y/dx^r$.

Equating the two forms for $f^{(r)}(0)$, we obtain

$$r!a_r = \frac{k!}{(k-r)!}$$

or

$$a_r = \frac{k!}{r!(k-r)!}$$

and

$$(1+x)^k = \sum_{r=0}^{k} \frac{k!}{r!(k-r)!} x^r, \qquad 0! = 1$$

This result, which should be remembered, is the *Binomial Theorem* for positive integers. Note that there is no problem of convergence, for we are dealing with only a finite number of terms.

Example. If the interest rate is i, how long does it take for money to double?

With compound interest, a dollar becomes $(1+i)$ dollars at the end of one year, $(1+i)^2$ dollars at the end of two years, and $(1+i)^k$ at the end of k years. Thus we wish to find k such that

$$(1+i)^k = 2$$

Now, i is normally small, say less than 0.1, so that in expanding $(1+i)^k$ by the Binomial Theorem we can neglect the larger powers of i. We have as a first approximate equation

$$1 + ki = 2$$

or

$$k = \frac{1}{i}$$

This is equivalent to assuming *simple* rather than *compound* interest. A better approximation is obtained from the equation

$$1 + ki + \frac{k(k-1)}{2} i^2 = 2$$

or

$$k^2 i^2 + k(2i - i^2) - 2 = 0$$

Thus

$$k = \frac{-(2i - i^2) \pm \sqrt{4i^2 - 4i^3 + i^4 + 8i^2}}{2i^2}$$

Since we are neglecting powers of i greater than the second, we have

$$k = \frac{-(2i - i^2) \pm \sqrt{12i^2}}{2i^2}$$

and since k is not negative,

$$k = \frac{-2i + i^2 + 3.46i}{2i^2}$$

$$= \frac{1}{2} + \frac{0.73}{i}$$

The reader should satisfy himself that the effect of neglecting the term in i^3 in the expansion of $(1 + i)^k$ is to obtain an equation that overestimates k. Since k is to be an integer, a good working approximation is to ignore the half and to take k as the nearest integer to the result of dividing 73 by the rate of interest expressed as a percentage. Thus at 6%, money doubles in 12 years and at 3% in 25 years. More detailed calculations show that these results are both correct.

Exercise. In the above example for $i = 0.05$ find the value of k for the amount to double and triple.

■ **8.3   Taylor's Theorem**

We now turn to more general answers to our original questions and state them as *Taylor's Theorem*.

If a function $f(x)$ can be differentiated as often as we please, then, provided the power series converges,

$$f(x) = \sum_{n=0}^{\infty} a_n(x - a)^n$$

where $$a_n = \frac{f^{(n)}(a)}{n!}, \qquad n = 1, 2, \ldots$$

and $$a_0 = f(a)$$

A rigorous proof is not simple and will be deferred to Section 8.4. However, the result can be made plausible by the same argument we used for the Binomial Theorem.

Let us assume that the function has a power series expansion and that the power series can be differentiated term by term.

Note that by setting $x = a$ we have $f(a) = a_0$. Now, differentiate $f(x)$ r times and obtain

$$f^{(r)}(x) = \sum_{n=r}^{\infty} n(n - 1) \ldots (n - r + 1)a_n(x - a)^{n-r}$$

so that $f^{(r)}(a) = r!a_r$ (the only term not involving x)

Therefore $$a_r = \frac{f^{(r)}(a)}{r!}$$

It frequently happens that we desire to calculate $f(x)$, using $a = 0$ in Taylor's Theorem. The resulting series, known as *Maclaurin's Series*, is given by

$$f(x) = \sum_{n=0}^{\infty} a_n x^n$$

where $$a_n = \frac{f^{(n)}(0)}{n!}, \qquad n = 1, 2, \ldots$$

$$a_0 = f(0)$$

Example 1. As an application, let us extend the Binomial Theorem to coefficients that are not positive integers. We show that, provided $|x| < 1$,

$$f(x) = (1 + x)^k = \sum_{n=0}^{\infty} \frac{k(k-1) \ldots (k-n+1)x^n}{n!}$$

If $$f(x) = (1 + x)^k$$

then $f'(x) = k(1 + x)^{k-1}, \quad f''(x) = k(k-1)(1+x)^{k-2}$

and, generally,

$$f^{(n)}(x) = k(k-1) \ldots (k-n+1)(1+x)^{k-n}$$

Thus $$f^{(n)}(0) = k(k-1) \ldots (k-n+1)$$

and using Maclaurin's Series, if

$$f(x) = \sum_{n=0}^{\infty} a_n x^n$$

we have $$a_n = \frac{k(k-1) \ldots (k-n+1)}{n!}, \qquad a_0 = 1$$

What about convergence? We can use the ratio test, which says that the series $\sum_{n=0}^{\infty} u_n$ converges provided (see Section 4.10)

$$\lim_{n \to \infty} \left| \frac{u_{n+1}}{u_n} \right| < 1$$

Here

$$\frac{u_{n+1}}{u_n} = \frac{k(k-1)\ldots(k-n)x^{n+1}}{(n+1)!} \cdot \frac{n!}{k(k-1)\ldots(k-n+1)x^n}$$

$$= \frac{k-n}{n+1}x$$

and

$$\lim_{n\to\infty}\left|\frac{u_{n+1}}{u_n}\right| = |x|$$

Thus the series will converge, provided $|x| < 1$. At $x = -1$ the series converges provided $k > 0$. The series diverges for all values of k when $x = 1$.

Example 2. Find $\sqrt{1.02}$.

$$\sqrt{1.02} = [1 + 0.02]^{\frac{1}{2}}$$

$$= 1 + (\tfrac{1}{2})(0.02) + \frac{(\tfrac{1}{2})(-\tfrac{1}{2})(0.02)^2}{2!}$$

$$+ \frac{(\tfrac{1}{2})(-\tfrac{1}{2})(-\tfrac{3}{2})(0.02)^3}{3!} + \cdots$$

$$= 1 + 0.01 - 0.00005 + 0.0000005 + \cdots$$

$$= 1.0099505$$

Example 3. We have seen in the economic lot-size formula (Section 7.2) that the optimal run length q_0 is given by

$$\sqrt{2c_3 R/c_1}$$

If $c_1 = 0.01$, $c_3 = 50$, and $R = 1000$, compute the approximate error in q_0 if c_3 is overestimated by 10%. How much extra cost is incurred because of the error in c_3?

We have that

$$q = \sqrt{2c_3 R/c_1} = \sqrt{10^7} = 3160$$

and the total average cost

$$= \sqrt{2c_1 c_3 R} = \sqrt{10^3} = 31.6 \text{ dollars per month}$$

Now c_3 is overestimated by 10%, $c_3 = 50 + 5 = 55$, and

$$q = \sqrt{[2(c_3 + h)R]/c_1}$$

where h is the amount of error in c_3.

The total average cost $f(c_3 + h)$ is

$$f(c_3 + h) = \tfrac{1}{2}c_1\sqrt{[2(c_3 + h)R]/c_1} + c_3R\sqrt{c_1/[2R(c_3 + h)]}$$

$$= \sqrt{c_1c_3R/2}\,[(1 + h/c_3)^{1/2} + (1 + h/c_3)^{-1/2}]$$

Now $\quad f(c_3 + h) = f(c_3) + hf'(c_3) + \dfrac{h^2}{2!}f''(c_3) + \dfrac{h^3}{3!}f'''(c_3) + \cdots$

$$f'(c_3 + h) = \sqrt{c_1c_3R/2}\left[\frac{1}{2c_3}\left(1 + \frac{h}{c_3}\right)^{-1/2}\right.$$

$$\left. - \frac{1}{2c_3}\left(1 + \frac{h}{c_3}\right)^{-3/2}\right]$$

$$f''(c_3 + h) = \sqrt{c_1c_3R/2}\left[-\frac{1}{4c_3{}^2}\left(1 + \frac{h}{c_3}\right)^{-3/2}\right.$$

$$\left. + \frac{3}{4c_3{}^2}\left(1 + \frac{h}{c_3}\right)^{-5/2}\right]$$

$$f'''(c_3 + h) = \sqrt{c_1c_3R/2}\left[\frac{3}{8c_3{}^3}\left(1 + \frac{h}{c_3}\right)^{-5/2}\right.$$

$$\left. - \frac{15}{8c_3{}^3}\left(1 + \frac{h}{c_3}\right)^{-7/2}\right]$$

$$f'(c_3) = 0$$

$$f''(c_3) = \frac{1}{4c_3{}^2}\sqrt{2c_1c_3R}$$

$$f'''(c_3) = -\frac{3}{4c_3{}^3}\sqrt{2c_1c_3R}$$

$$f(c_3 + h) - f(c_3) = \sqrt{2c_1c_3R}\left[\frac{1}{8}\frac{h^2}{c_3{}^2} - \frac{1}{8}\frac{h^3}{c_3{}^3}\cdots\right]$$

$$= \frac{31.6}{8}\frac{h^2}{c_3{}^2}\left[1 - \frac{h}{c_3}\right]$$

$$= \frac{(31.6)(0.01)(0.9)}{8}\qquad\left(\text{since }\frac{h}{c_3} = 0.1\right)$$

$$= 0.035 \text{ dollars per month}$$

If $h/c_3 = 0.2$, $f(c_3 + h) - f(c_3) = 0.13$ dollars per month. In general, for h/c_3 small, the cost of error is approximately proportional to the square of the relative error.

Exercises

1. Expand the following series to four terms:

(a) $(1 + x)^5$ (d) $(1 - x)^{-\frac{1}{2}}$
(b) $(1 - x)^{-2}$ (e) $\log (1 + x)$
(c) $(1 + x)^{\frac{3}{2}}$ (f) $\sin (x + 10°)$

2. Find the approximate value of the following, using Taylor's Series, to three decimal places:

(a) $\sqrt{170}$ (d) $\log 1.1$

(b) $\sqrt{48}$ (e) $\sin 100°$

(c) $\sqrt[5]{0.90}$ (f) $\cos 35°$

3. In Example 3, compute the percentage error in q_0 if c_1 is overestimated by 10%.

4. If the error in estimating b in exercise 6 on page 168 is $+10\%$, find the cost of error.

5. In a population forecast the following model is used. The male and female birthrates are fixed proportions of the number of potential parents. The number of potential parents can be approximated by the smaller of the male and female populations. Thus if there are $X(t)$ males and $Y(t)$ females at the end of year t, then the male birthrate is $mX(t)$ and the female birthrate is $fX(t)$ when $X(t) < Y(t)$. When $X(t) > Y(t)$, they are $mY(t)$ and $fY(t)$. In addition, a fraction d of those alive at the beginning or born during the year die by the end of the year. If, initially, $X(0) < Y(0)$, show that

$$X(t) = (1 - d)^t (1 + m)^t X(0)$$

$$Y(t) = (1 - d)^t \left\{ Y(0) + \frac{f}{m} X(0)[(1 + m)^t - 1] \right\}$$

Show also that if d, m, and f are so small that all powers above the first and all products can be neglected, then if $m > f$, there will be equal numbers of males and females after a time t where

$$t = \frac{Y(0) - X(0)}{X(0)(m - f)}$$

What happens when $Y(0) = X(0)$?

6. The gross national product of the United States is 160% of that of the Soviet Union. If the growth rate in America is 3% per annum while that of Russia is 5%, how long will it be before the two countries achieve equality? Suppose we assume that the Russian growth rate will slow down so that in t years time it has diminished by $kt\%$, until it reaches the current American rate. If the American rate remains constant, estimate the largest value of k that will enable the two economies to achieve equality. When will this happen?

■ **8.4 A More Rigorous Treatment of the Proof of Taylor's Theorem and the Remainder Term**

So far our discussion of this celebrated theorem has been aimed at plausibility rather than at rigor. We now turn to a more precise formulation and proof, but first we require some preliminary lemmas.

Lemma 1. If $f(x)$ is continuous for $a \leq x \leq b$, then $f(x)$ is bounded in the interval $a \leq x \leq b$, i.e., there exist $m \leq M$ such that $m \leq f(x) \leq M$ for all $a \leq x \leq b$. Although this result is intuitively obvious, a proof involves concepts beyond the scope of this book; see, for example, Hardy, *Pure Mathematics*. The reader should draw graphs until he is satisfied of its truth.

Lemma 2. If $f(x)$ is continuous for $a \leq x \leq b$, there exists x_1 and x_2 such that $a \leq x_1 \leq b$, $a \leq x_2 \leq b$, and $f(x_2) \geq f(x) \geq f(x_1)$ for all $a \leq x \leq b$, i.e., $f(x)$ has a maximum and minimum in the interval $a \leq x \leq b$.

By Lemma 1, $f(x)$ is bounded from above. Let us choose M to be the least upper bound. The existence of a least upper bound is not obvious. However, suppose someone asserts that there is no least upper bound (L.U.B.), i.e., if we produce a number and claim it is the least upper bound, he can always find an upper bound that is smaller. Imagine we accept his challenge and offer M_1 as a L.U.B. He now offers $M_2 < M_1$, and we offer $M_3 < M_2$ and so on. In this way we produce a decreasing sequence of numbers, none of which is less than the values of $f(x)$ in the interval $a \leq x \leq b$. Moreover, none of these numbers can be less than the lower bound m. Using law 5 on limits in Chapter 4, Section 4.4, the sequence $M_1, M_2, \ldots$ has a limit M. Clearly no number smaller than M can be an upper bound. That is, $f(x) \leq M$ for all $a \leq x \leq b$; and for every $\epsilon > 0$ there exists x' such that $a \leq x' \leq b$ and $f(x') > M - \epsilon$.

If we can find x_2 such that $f(x_2) = M$, then the lemma is proved. Suppose, if possible, no such x_2 exists, and consider the function

$$g(x) = \frac{1}{M - f(x)}$$

By assumption, $M - f(x)$ is always greater than zero so that $g(x)$ is continuous and, by Lemma 1, is bounded; thus there exists $A > 0$ and such that $g(x) \leq A$ for all $a \leq x \leq b$.

Therefore
$$\frac{1}{M - f(x)} \leq A$$

or
$$f(x) \leq M - \frac{1}{A}$$

This contradicts the assumption that M is the least upper bound, and we conclude that x_2 must exist.

In a similar fashion we can show that there exists x_1 such that $f(x) \geq f(x_1)$ for all $a \leq x \leq b$.

Lemma 3. Rolle's Theorem. If (i) $f(x)$ is differentiable for every x such that $a \leq x \leq b$,* (ii) $f'(x)$ is continuous for $a < x < b$, and (iii) $f(a) = f(b)$, then there exists x_0 such that $a \leq x_0 \leq b$ and $f'(x_0) = 0$.

The lemma is trivial if $f(x)$ is constant. If it is not, then $f(x)$ must have either a maximum and/or a minimum in the interior of the interval, i.e., at least one of the following occur:

1. There exists x_1 such that $a < x_1 < b$ and $f(x_1) < f(x_1 + h)$ for all h sufficiently small.
2. There exists x_2 such that $a < x_2 < b$ and $f(x_2) > f(x_2 + h)$ for all h sufficiently small.

We have seen (Section 7.1) † that at points such as x_1 and x_2, $f'(x) = 0$. Thus we can always find at least one point x_0. Frequently there may be several.

---

* If $f(x)$ is not defined for $x < a$, or $x > b$, we need to modify our definitions of continuity and differentiability at $x = a$ and $x = b$. Thus we will consider $f(x)$ to be continuous at $x = a$ provided $\lim_{h \to +0} f(a + h) = f(a)$ with other definitions in a similar fashion.

† In Chapter 7 we pointed out that if $f(x)$ has a maximum at $x = x_0$, then for all sufficiently small $h > 0$ we must have $f'(x_0 - h) > 0$ and $f'(x_0 + h) < 0$. It follows that as long as $f'(x)$ is continuous, we must have $f'(x_0) = 0$.

Lemma 4.   The Mean Value Theorem.   If $f(x)$ is differentiable for $a \le x \le b$, then there exists x_0 such that $a \le x_0 \le b$ and

$$f'(x_0) = \frac{f(b) - f(a)}{b - a}$$

In words the theorem says that there is always a tangent parallel to the chord joining two points on a graph of a differentiable function (Figure 8.1).

To prove this result we apply Lemma 3 to a suitably chosen function. Let

$$g(x) = f(x) + \frac{b - x}{b - a}[f(b) - f(a)]$$

Clearly $g(a) = g(b) = f(b)$ and we see that

$$g'(x) = f'(x) - \frac{f(b) - f(a)}{b - a}$$

By Lemma 3 we can find x_0 such that $g'(x_0) = 0$, and it follows that

$$f'(x_0) = \frac{f(b) - f(a)}{b - a}$$

Thus $f(b) = f(a) + (b - a)f'(x_0)$ where $a \le x_0 \le b$

If we write $b = a + h$, we have

$$f(a + h) = f(a) + hf'(a + \theta h)   \text{where } 0 \le \theta \le 1$$

The theorem is frequently stated in this way.

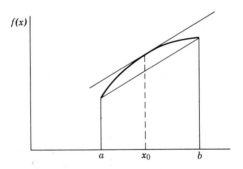

Figure 8.1   The Mean Value Theorem.

Lemma 5.   Generalization of the Mean Value Theorem (Taylor's Theorem).   The mean value theorem is a particular case of the following result, which will be recognized as a more precise statement of Taylor's Theorem.

Let $f(x)$ be a function such that $f'(x)$, $f''(x)$, $\ldots, f^{(n)}(x)$ exist for $a \leq x \leq b$, then

$$f(b) = f(a) + (b-a)f'(a) + \frac{(b-a)^2}{2!} f''(a)$$

$$+ \cdots + \frac{(b-a)^{n-1}}{(n-1)!} f^{(n-1)}(a) + R_n$$

where R_n is a remainder term which we will define later.

The proof is similar to that of the mean value theorem.   Let

$$F_n(x) = f(b) - f(x) - (b-x)f'(x) - \frac{(b-x)^2}{2!} f''(x)$$

$$- \cdots - \frac{(b-x)^{n-1}}{(n-1)!} f^{(n-1)}(x)$$

so that

$$F_n(a) = f(b) - f(a) - (b-a)f'(a) - \frac{(b-a)^2}{2!} f''(a)$$

$$- \cdots - \frac{(b-a)^{n-1}}{(n-1)!} f^{(n-1)}(a)$$

Let $$G_n(x) = F_n(x) - \left(\frac{b-x}{b-a}\right)^n F_n(a)$$

$$\left.\begin{matrix} G_n(a) = 0 \\ G_n(b) = 0 \end{matrix}\right\} \text{so that } G_n(a) = G_n(b)$$

We now apply Lemma 3 to $G_n(x)$.

$$G_n'(x) = F_n'(x) + \frac{n}{b-a}\left(\frac{b-x}{b-a}\right)^{n-1} F_n(a) \quad \text{by differentiation of } G_n(x)$$

and

$$F_n'(x) = - \left[f'(x) + (b-x)f''(x) + \frac{(b-x)^2}{2!} f'''(x) \right.$$

$$\left. + \cdots + \frac{(b-x)^{n-1}}{(n-1)!} f^{(n)}(x) \right]$$

$$+ \left[f'(x) + (b-x)f''(x) + \frac{(b-x)^2}{2!} f'''(x) \right.$$

$$\left. + \cdots + \frac{(b-x)^{n-2}}{(n-2)!} f^{(n-1)}(x) \right]$$

Thus
$$F'_n(x) = -\frac{(b-x)^{n-1}}{(n-1)!}f^{(n)}(x)$$

But there exists x_0 such that $a \le x_0 \le b$ and $G'_n(x_0) = 0$, by Lemma 3. That is,

$$-\frac{(b-x_0)^{n-1}}{(n-1)!}f^{(n)}(x_0) + \frac{n}{(b-a)^n}(b-x_0)^{n-1}F_n(a) = 0$$

or
$$F_n(a) = \frac{(b-a)^n}{n!}f^{(n)}(x_0)$$

Replacing $F_n(a)$ by its expression in terms of f, f', etc., yields

$$f(b) = f(a) + (b-a)f'(a) + \frac{(b-a)^2}{2!}f''(a)$$
$$+\cdots+ \frac{(b-a)^{n-1}}{(n-1)!}f^{(n)}(a) + F_n(a)$$

Thus the remainder term R_n in our statement of the theorem is simply

$$R_n = \frac{(b-a)^n}{n!}f^{(n)}(x_0), \qquad \text{where } a \le x_0 \le b$$

The utility of the theorem lies in the fact that if we can show
$$\lim_{n\to\infty} R_n = 0$$
and the series
$$\sum_{n=0}^{\infty} \frac{(b-a)^n}{n!}f^{(n)}(a)$$

converges, we can compute $f(b)$ to any desired accuracy merely by summing the series numerically.

Example. As an illustration of the use of the remainder term R_n, let us estimate the error in computing 1.02 by taking the first four terms in the expansion of $(1 + 0.02)^{1/2}$, using Taylor's Theorem.

We have

$$f(x) = (1+x)^{1/2} = 1 + \frac{1}{2}x - \frac{1}{2}\cdot\frac{1}{2}\cdot\frac{1}{2!}x^2 + \frac{1}{2}\cdot\frac{1}{2}\cdot\frac{3}{2}\cdot\frac{1}{3!}x^3 + R_n$$

where
$$R_n = \frac{x^4}{4!}f^{(4)}(x_0), \quad \text{and} \quad 0 \le x_0 \le x$$

Now
$$f^{(4)}(x_0) = \tfrac{1}{2}(-\tfrac{1}{2})(-\tfrac{3}{2})(-\tfrac{5}{2})(1 + x_0)^{-7/2}$$
$$= -\tfrac{15}{16}(1 + x_0)^{-7/2}$$

$$R_n = -\frac{15}{16} \cdot \frac{1}{4!} x^4(1 + x_0)^{-7/2} = -\frac{15}{384} x^4(1 + x_0)^{-7/2}$$

In order to estimate the error in neglecting R_n, we require an upper bound to the numerical value of R_n. Now $(1 + x_0)^{-7/2} < 1$, $x = 0.02$, and $R_n < \frac{15}{384}(0.02)^4 = 0.000,000,006$. In other words, the error is less than one part in a hundred million. Probably the most important use of Taylor's Theorem is to tabulate various mathematical functions. In fact, sine, cosine, tangent, and logarithm functions may be computed in this way.

Exercises

1. Find the error in estimating $(1.05)^{1/3}$, using four terms in Taylor's Theorem.
2. Determine $(1.04)^{1/2}$ to within 0.01%.
3. How many terms must be used to assure that $(1.02)^{1/2}$ is determined to an error of less than 0.01%?
4. Expand $\sin 35°$ about $a = 30°$, using four terms in Taylor's Theorem, and find the error.

■ 8.5 Criteria for Maxima and Minima: One Variable Case

Taylor's Theorem also enables us to make our discussion of maxima and minima more precise. We now state necessary and sufficient conditions for the existence of extreme points.

Theorem. If $f(x)$ is twice differentiable in the neighborhood of x_0, then a necessary condition for $f(x)$ to have a maximum or minimum at x_0 is that $f'(x_0) = 0$. A sufficient condition for a maximum is that, in addition, $f''(x_0) < 0$, and a sufficient condition for a minimum is $f''(x_0) > 0$.

It should be noted that $f'(x_0) = 0$ is not sufficient in itself (for example, $f(x) = x^3$ and $x_0 = 0$) while $f''(x_0) > 0$ is not necessary (for example, $f(x) = x^4$, $x_0 = 0$ so $f''(x_0) = 0$; in fact, x^4 has a minimum when $x = 0$).

Proof. We have seen (Sections 7.1 and 8.4) that if $f'(x)$ is continuous, $f'(x_0) = 0$ is necessary for a minimum or maximum. The reader may prove that the existence of $f''(x_0)$ implies the continuity of $f'(x)$ in the neighborhood of x_0.

By Taylor's Theorem, if $f'(x_0) = 0$, then for small h we have $f(x_0 + h)$ $= f(x_0) + (h^2/2!) f''(x_0 + \theta h)$ where $0 \leq \theta \leq 1$. For a maximum we must have $f(x_0 + h) \leq f(x_0)$ for all sufficiently small h. Hence if $f''(x_0 + \theta h) \leq 0$ for all sufficiently small h, we will have a maximum. A sufficient condition for this is that $f''(x_0) < 0$; the proof that $f'(x_0) = 0$ and $f''(x_0) > 0$ are sufficient conditions for a minimum follows similar lines.

Exercise. Suppose $f'(x_0) = f''(x_0) = 0$. What are the conditions for (a) a maximum, (b) a minimum, (c) neither.

■ 8.6   l'Hospital's Rule

This rule, stated as a theorem below, enables us to find limits of ratios that are not expressible as the ratio of the limits of numerator and denominator because these limits are either both zero or both infinity.

Theorem

(i) If $\qquad \lim\limits_{x \to a} f(x) = 0 \qquad$ and $\qquad \lim\limits_{x \to a} g(x) = 0$

then $\qquad\qquad \lim\limits_{x \to a} \dfrac{f(x)}{g(x)} = \lim\limits_{x \to a} \dfrac{f'(x)}{g'(x)}$

(ii) If $\qquad\qquad \lim\limits_{x \to a} f(x) = \infty, \quad \lim\limits_{x \to a} g(x) = \infty$

and $\qquad\qquad \lim\limits_{x \to a} \dfrac{f'(x)}{g'(x)} = L$

then $\qquad\qquad \lim\limits_{x \to a} \dfrac{f(x)}{g(x)} = L$

We will only prove the first of these results for the case where a is finite, but before doing so we draw the reader's attention to the additional condition required in the second statement. Where both functions tend to zero it is possible that $f'(x) \to F \neq 0$ and $g'(x) \to G \neq 0$, so that we obtain

$$\lim_{x \to a} \frac{f(x)}{g(x)} = \frac{F}{G}$$

If F and G are both zero, we can apply the theorem to f'/g' and consider the separate limits of f'' and g'' and so on until we finally obtain a determinate form. However, if f and g tend to infinity, and a is finite, then as often as we differentiate we will obtain an indeterminate form (i.e., $f'(x) \to \infty$, $f''(x) \to \infty$, $g'(x) \to \infty$, $g''(x) \to \infty$ etc.). Thus we must specify the existence of $\lim [f'(x)/g'(x)]$ in order to have a valid result in (ii).

Proof. By Taylor's Theorem:

$$f(x) = f(a) + (x - a)f'[a + \theta_1(x - a)]$$

$$g(x) = g(a) + (x - a)g'[a + \theta_2(x - a)]$$

where $$0 \le \theta_1 \le 1, \quad 0 \le \theta_2 \le 1$$

But $$f(a) = g(a) = 0$$

Therefore $$\frac{f(x)}{g(x)} = \frac{f'[a + \theta_1(x - a)]}{g'[a + \theta_2(x - a)]}$$

Now, as $x \to a$, the numerator on the right tends to $f'(a)$ and the denominator to $g'(a)$. Thus if these are not both zero or infinite, we have a determinate form on the right, and the result follows. If the right-hand side is indeterminate, we can apply the theorem again to $f'(x)/g'(x)$ and so on until we have a determinate form. For a proof when a is infinite see exercise 6, following this section.

The second part of the theorem, which applies when $f \to \infty$ and $g \to \infty$, cannot be rigorously proved by elementary reasoning, and we will omit a proof here.

Example 1. Find the limit, as $x \to \infty$, of $\dfrac{3x^4 + 2x^3 + x + 5}{4x^4 + 3x^2 + 7}$.

Let
$$f(x) = 3x^4 + 2x^3 + x + 5, \quad g(x) = 4x^4 + 3x^2 + 7$$
then
$$f'(x) = 12x^3 + 6x^2 + 1, \quad g'(x) = 16x^3 + 6x$$

$$f''(x) = 36x^2 + 12x \qquad g''(x) = 48x^2 + 6$$

$$f'''(x) = 72x + 12 \qquad g'''(x) = 96x$$

$$f^{(4)}(x) = 72 \qquad g^{(4)}(x) = 96$$

We see that f'/g', f''/g'', and f'''/g''' are all indeterminate as x goes to infinity. However, $f^{(4)}/g^{(4)} = \frac{72}{96} = \frac{3}{4}$, so we conclude all four ratios tend to $\frac{3}{4}$ as x tends to infinity.

Example 2. Let us define a function $t(x)$ such that $t(0) = 0$ and $t'(x) = 1/(1 + x^2)$. Find $\lim\limits_{x \to 0} t(x)/x$.

We observe that as $\lim\limits_{x \to 0} t(x) = 0 = \lim\limits_{x \to 0} x$ we can apply l'Hospital's Rule. We take $f(x) = t(x)$ and $g(x) = x$. Then

$$\lim_{x \to 0} \frac{t(x)}{x} = \lim_{x \to 0} \frac{t'(x)}{1} = \lim_{x \to 0} \frac{1/(1 + x^2)}{1} = 1$$

Note that if we wish to tabulate $t(x)$, we can use Taylor's Theorem. We have

$$t'(x) = \frac{1}{1 + x^2} \qquad \text{or} \qquad (1 + x^2)t'(x) = 1$$

Differentiate both sides:

$$(1 + x^2)t''(x) + 2xt'(x) = 0$$

For $x = 0$ we have $t''(0) = 0$.
Differentiate again:

$$(1 + x^2)t'''(x) + 4xt''(x) + 2t'(x) = 0$$

For $x = 0$ we have $t'''(0) = -2$.
With the use of Newton's formula for differentiating products,* we find

$$(1 + x^2)t^{(n+1)}(x) + 2nxt^{(n)}(x) + n(n - 1)t^{(n-1)}(x) = 0$$

and setting $x = 0$,

$$t^{(n+1)}(0) = -n(n - 1)t^{(n-1)}(0)$$

Since $t'(0) = 1$, $t''(0) = 0$, we have

(i) for n even, $t^{(n)}(0) = 0$
(ii) for n odd, $t^{(n)}(0) = (-1)^{\frac{n-1}{2}} (n - 1)!$

But by Taylor's Theorem,

$$t(x) = t(0) + xt'(0) + \frac{x^2}{2!}t''(0) + \frac{x^3}{3!}t'''(0) + \cdots$$

$$= x - \frac{x^3}{3} + \frac{x^5}{5} - \frac{x^7}{7} \cdots$$

---

* If $y = u(x)v(x)$, then $\dfrac{d^n y}{d\,x^n} = \sum\limits_{r=0}^{n} \dfrac{n!}{r!\,(n-r)!} u^{(r)}v^{(n-r)}$ where $u^{(n)} = d^n u/d\,x^n$, $v^{(n-r)}$
$= d^{n-r} u/d\,x^{n-r}$ and $u^{(0)} = u$, $v^{(0)} = v$. See exercise 3 at the end of this chapter.

The ratio test shows that the series converges when $|x| < 1$. In fact, it also converges when $x = 1$, and it may be shown that $t(1) = \pi/4$, where π is the ratio of the circumference to the diameter of a circle.

Exercises

1. Define a function $L(x)$ such that $L(0) = 0$ and $L'(x) = 1/(1 + x)$. Find $\lim_{x \to 0} L(x)/x$. Express $L(x)$ in terms of powers of x.

2. With the same definition of $L(x)$ as in exercise 1, find the $\lim_{x \to \infty} \dfrac{L(x)}{x}$.

3. If $\lim_{x \to a} f(x) = 0$ and $\lim_{x \to a} g(x) = 0$, show how to find

$$\lim_{x \to a} \left[\frac{1}{f(x)} - \frac{1}{g(x)} \right]$$

Hint: $\dfrac{1}{f} - \dfrac{1}{g} = \dfrac{g - f}{fg}$

4. Find out why the second part of l'Hospital's Rule cannot be proved by applying the first part to the functions $h(x) = 1/f(x)$ and $k(x) = 1/g(x)$ and the ratio $k(x)/h(x)$.

5. Find the following limits:

(a) $\lim_{x \to 0} \dfrac{(1 + x)^n - (1 + nx)}{x^2}$

(b) $\lim_{x \to \infty} \dfrac{x^2 + x}{3x^2 - 5}$

(c) $\lim_{x \to 1} \dfrac{x^n - 1}{x - 1}$

(d) $\lim_{x \to 1} \dfrac{x^2 - 3x + 2}{x - 1}$

6. Extend the proof of the first part of l'Hospital's Rule to the case where a is infinite.

[Write $\lim_{x \to \infty} \dfrac{f(x)}{g(x)} = \lim_{y \to 0} \dfrac{f(1/y)}{g(1/y)}$ and apply the result already proved.]

■ **8.7   Taylor's Theorem for Several Variables** *

Taylor's Theorem can be generalized for functions of several variables. We will consider only the case of two variables, for further extensions are similar but more tedious. We wish to express $f(x + h, y + k)$ in terms of h, k and the partial derivatives of $f(x, y)$. We can do so by defining a function $\phi(t)$ by the equation

$$\phi(t) = f(x + ht, y + kt)$$

and finding a formula for $\phi(t)$. Once we have this, the desired result follows on setting $t = 1$. Now

$$\phi(t) = \phi(0) + t\phi'(0) + \frac{t^2}{2!}\phi''(0) + \cdots \frac{t^{n-1}}{(n-1)!}\phi^{(n-1)}(0) + \frac{t^n}{n!}\phi^{(n)}(\theta t)$$

where $0 \le \theta \le 1$. It remains to find the derivatives of ϕ at $t = 0$ and to set $t = 1$ in the expansion of $\phi(t)$.

Write

$$x + ht = X, \quad y + kt = Y$$

so that we can regard ϕ as a function of X and Y. Then

$$\frac{\partial \phi}{\partial X} = \frac{\partial f}{\partial x}, \quad \frac{\partial \phi}{\partial Y} = \frac{\partial f}{\partial y}$$

But

$$\phi'(t) = \frac{\partial \phi}{\partial X} \cdot \frac{dX}{dt} + \frac{\partial \phi}{\partial Y}\frac{dY}{dt}$$

$$= h\frac{\partial f}{\partial x} + k\frac{\partial f}{\partial y}$$

We can write this symbolically in terms of the operators $\dfrac{d}{dt}, \dfrac{\partial}{\partial x}, \dfrac{\partial}{\partial y}$ as

$$\frac{d}{dt} = h\frac{\partial}{\partial x} + k\frac{\partial}{\partial y}$$

Now $\phi''(t)$ is found by using the operator d/dt twice, i.e.,

$$\frac{d^2}{dt^2} = \left(\frac{d}{dt}\right)\left(\frac{d}{dt}\right) = \left(h\frac{\partial}{\partial x} + k\frac{\partial}{\partial y}\right)\left(h\frac{\partial}{\partial x} + k\frac{\partial}{\partial y}\right)$$

$$= h^2\left(\frac{\partial}{\partial x}\right)^2 + k^2\left(\frac{\partial}{\partial y}\right)^2 + hk\left(\frac{\partial}{\partial x}\right)\left(\frac{\partial}{\partial y}\right) + hk\left(\frac{\partial}{\partial y}\right)\left(\frac{\partial}{\partial x}\right)$$

* This section may be omitted on a first reading.

We now interpret the right-hand side in an obvious fashion. The first term means differentiate twice partially with respect to x. The second term means differentiate twice with respect to y. The third term means differentiate with respect to x, the result of differentiating with respect to y, while in the last term x and y are interchanged. It usually happens that the order is immaterial when we differentiate once each with respect to different variables, and the last two terms can be combined. We write

$$\frac{d^2}{dt^2} = h^2 \frac{\partial^2}{\partial x^2} + k^2 \frac{\partial^2}{\partial y^2} + 2hk \frac{\partial^2}{\partial x \partial y}$$

Thus

$$\phi(0) = f(x, y), \quad \phi'(0) = h \frac{\partial f}{\partial x} + k \frac{\partial f}{\partial y}$$

$$\phi''(0) = h^2 \frac{\partial^2 f}{\partial x^2} + k^2 \frac{\partial^2 f}{\partial y^2} + 2hk \frac{\partial^2 f}{\partial x \partial y}$$

and the theorem for two variables is

$$f(x + h, y + k) = \phi(1) = f(x, y) + h \frac{\partial f}{\partial x} + k \frac{\partial f}{\partial y}$$

$$+ \frac{1}{2!} \left(h^2 \frac{\partial^2 f}{\partial x^2} + k^2 \frac{\partial^2 f}{\partial y^2} + 2hk \frac{\partial^2 f}{\partial x \partial y} \right)$$

$$+ \cdots$$

Additional terms can be obtained by writing symbolically:

$$\frac{d^n \phi}{dt^n} = \left(h \frac{\partial}{\partial x} + k \frac{\partial}{\partial y} \right)^n f(x, y)$$

Example. A formula that can be used for estimating sales response S to advertising is

$$S = \frac{xE}{y + E}$$

where x and y are constants and E is the number of exposures. (When one person sees the advertising once we count it as one exposure.)

The constants x and y are estimated from past experience as $x = 20{,}000$, $y = 100{,}000$, but they may each be in error by up to 10%. If we "buy" 150,000 exposures, what range of sales can be expected?

Now

$$S = S(x, y) = \frac{xE}{y + E}$$

Therefore

$$S(20{,}000 + h, \quad 100{,}000 + k) - S(20{,}000, \quad 100{,}000) \simeq h\,\frac{\partial S}{\partial x} + k\,\frac{\partial S}{\partial y}$$

and

$$\frac{\partial S}{\partial x} = \frac{E}{y + E} = \frac{150{,}000}{250{,}000} = 0.6$$

$$\frac{\partial S}{\partial y} = -\frac{xE}{(y + E)^2} = -\frac{20{,}000 \times 150{,}000}{(250{,}000)^2} = -0.048$$

Now $h = \pm 2000, \quad k = \pm 10{,}000$

The error could range from

$$+(0.6 \times 2000 + 0.048 \times 10{,}000)$$

to

$$-(0.6 \times 2000 + 0.048 \times 10{,}000)$$

that is, ± 1680.   The expected sales would be

$$S(20{,}000, \quad 100{,}000) = \frac{20{,}000 \times 150{,}000}{100{,}000 \times 150{,}000}$$

$$= 12{,}000$$

so the possible range is 10,320 to 13,680.   Note that if we are optimistic and assume the errors in x and y are both in the same direction, they will tend to cancel, and the range will be

$$\pm(0.6 \times 2000 - 0.048 \times 10{,}000) = \pm 720.$$

■ 8.8   Criteria for Optimization: Two Variable Case *

We have seen that if h and k are small, then

$$f(x + h, y + k) - f(x, y) \simeq h\,\frac{\partial f}{\partial x} + k\,\frac{\partial f}{\partial y}$$

$$+ \frac{1}{2!}\left(h^2\,\frac{\partial^2 f}{\partial x^2} + 2hk\,\frac{\partial^2 f}{\partial x \partial y} + k^2\,\frac{\partial^2 f}{\partial y^2}\right)$$

Clearly if $f(x + h, y + k) \geq f(x, y)$ for all small h, k we must have $\partial f/\partial x = 0$ and $\partial f/\partial y = 0$ at (x, y).   The same condition is also necessary for a minimum.

* This section may be omitted on a first reading.

It should also be clear that the critical term that distinguishes between a maximum and a minimum is

$$h^2 \frac{\partial^2 f}{\partial x^2} + 2hk \frac{\partial^2 f}{\partial x \partial y} + k^2 \frac{\partial^2 f}{\partial y^2}$$

To avoid unnecessary writing we denote this term by

$$F(h, k) = ah^2 + bk^2 + 2chk$$

Then for a maximum we must have $F(h, k) < 0$ and for a minimum $F(h, k) > 0$ for all h and k. We now investigate the conditions on h and k for these inequalities to hold. We have

$$F(h, k) = a\left(h^2 + 2hk\frac{c}{a} + k^2\frac{b}{a}\right) = a\left[\left(h + \frac{c}{a}k\right)^2 + \left(\frac{b}{a} - \frac{c^2}{a^2}\right)k^2\right]$$

Since squares are always positive we see that sufficient conditions for $F(h, k)$ to be positive are

$$a > 0 \quad \text{and} \quad \frac{b}{a} - \frac{c^2}{a^2} > 0$$

or $\qquad\qquad a > 0 \quad \text{and} \quad ab - c^2 > 0$

Sufficient conditions for $F(h, k)$ to be negative are that

$$-F(h, k) > 0$$

$$-a > 0 \quad \text{and} \quad \frac{-b}{-a} - \frac{(-c)^2}{(-a)^2} > 0$$

or $\qquad\qquad a < 0 \quad \text{and} \quad ab - c^2 > 0$

The reader should show that

(i) If $a > 0$ and $ab - c^2 > 0$, then $b > 0$.
(ii) If $a < 0$ and $ab - c^2 < 0$, then $b < 0$.

Thus the conditions are symmetrical with respect to a and b and this is as we would expect. In terms of the derivatives we see sufficient conditions for a maximum are

$$\frac{\partial f}{\partial x} = \frac{\partial f}{\partial y} = 0 \quad \text{and} \quad \frac{\partial^2 f}{\partial x^2} < 0, \qquad \frac{\partial^2 f}{\partial x^2} \cdot \frac{\partial^2 f}{\partial y^2} - \left(\frac{\partial^2 f}{\partial x \partial y}\right)^2 > 0$$

and for a minimum

$$\frac{\partial f}{\partial x} = \frac{\partial f}{\partial y} = 0 \quad \text{and} \quad \frac{\partial^2 f}{\partial x^2} > 0, \qquad \frac{\partial^2 f}{\partial x^2} \cdot \frac{\partial^2 f}{\partial y^2} - \left(\frac{\partial^2 f}{\partial x \partial y}\right)^2 > 0$$

Exercises for Chapter 8

1. Find the following limits:

(a) $\lim\limits_{x \to a} \dfrac{x^3 - ax^2 - a^2 x + a^3}{x^2 - a^2}$

(e) $\lim\limits_{x \to 0} \dfrac{e^x - e^{-x}}{\sin x}$

(b) $\lim\limits_{x \to 3} \dfrac{\sqrt{3x} - \sqrt{12 - x}}{2x - 3\sqrt{19 - 5x}}$

(f) $\lim\limits_{x \to 0} \left[\dfrac{1}{\log (1 + x)} - \dfrac{1}{x} \right]$

(c) $\lim\limits_{x \to 1} \left(\dfrac{2}{x^2 - 1} - \dfrac{1}{x - 1} \right)$

(g) $\lim\limits_{x \to \infty} \dfrac{x + \log x}{x \log x}$

(d) $\lim\limits_{x \to \infty} \dfrac{3x^2 - 5x + 6}{8x^2 + 2}$

(h) $\lim\limits_{x \to 0} \dfrac{\sin nx}{x}$

2. Prove the Binomial Theorem, for positive integers, by mathematical induction.

3. Use the Binomial Theorem to prove Newton's general formula for differentiating a product n times. The formula states that if $f(x) = u(x)v(x)$, then

$$f^{(n)}(x) = uv^{(n)} + nu^{(1)}v^{(n-1)} + \frac{n(n - 1)}{2!} u^{(2)}v^{(n-2)} + \cdots + u^{(n)}v$$

Hint: Let $D \equiv d/dx$. Then $D(uv) = u\,Dv + v\,Du = (D_1 + D_2)uv$, where D_1 is an operator which differentiates u and not v; D_2 differentiates v and not u.

4. (a) For values of x numerically less than 1, show that

$$\frac{1}{1 - x} = 1 + x + x^2 + x^3 + x^4 + \cdots$$

(b) Differentiating with respect to x we get

$$\frac{1}{(1 - x)^2} = 1 + 2x + 3x^2 + 4x^3 + \cdots.$$

Check this result by using Taylor's Theorem.

5. (a) Find the nth term, u_n, of the following series, using the Binomial Theorem,

$$(1 + x)^{1/x}$$

(b) Apply the ratio test to (a); show that

$$\lim\limits_{n \to \infty} \left| \frac{u_{n+1}}{u_n} \right| = |x|$$

and the series converges for $|x| < 1$.

(c) Using (a), show that

$$\lim\limits_{x \to 0} u_n = \frac{1}{n!}$$

that is,

$$\lim\limits_{x \to 0} (1 + x)^{1/x} = \sum_{n=0}^{\infty} \frac{1}{n!}$$

The numerical value of this sum is denoted by e.

(d) Find e to four decimal places.

6. Using the procedure of exercise 5, show that

$$\lim_{x \to 0} (1 + x)^{2/x} = e^2$$

and, in general, derive the result that

$$\lim_{x \to 0} (1 + x)^{r/x} = e^r$$

7. If interest at a per cent compounded yearly is equivalent to interest at b per cent compounded r times a year, show that a is greater than b by approximately (neglecting terms in b^3 and higher)

$$\frac{r - 1}{2r} \frac{b^2}{100}$$

8. It has been found that a company's sales increases at a constant annual rate of 5% less a constant amount C. Show that the sales during the nth year is given by

$$S_n = (1 + 0.05)^{n-1}(S_1 - 20C) + 20C$$

Find the number of years in which the sales would be doubled, where $S_1 = 1$ million units, $C = 10{,}000$ units.

9. Two variables, x and y, are related by an equation $f(x, y) = 0$. Subject to certain conditions which usually apply in practice this implies that y is a function of x. Show that

(a) $\dfrac{dy}{dx} = -\dfrac{f_x}{f_y}$

(b) $f_{xx} + f_{yy}\left(\dfrac{dy}{dx}\right)^2 + 2f_{xy}\dfrac{dy}{dx} + f_y\dfrac{d^2y}{dx^2} = 0$

10. A loan of amount P is to be repaid by n equal instalments of I each, the first due $1/k$ years hence and the others at intervals of $1/k$ years. (Usually $k = 12$ and the payments are monthly or $k = 52$ and they are weekly.) We wish to find a formula for the true rate of annual interest. The total interest paid is $nI - P$. Let $(nI - P)/P = x$ and let y be the annual rate of interest. Then we may use Taylor's Theorem to express y in powers of x.

Show the following:

(a) $P = I[(1 + y)^{-1/k} + (1 + y)^{-2/k} + \cdots + (1 + y)^{-n/k}]$

(b) $(1 + y)^{-1/k} + (1 + y)^{-2/k} + \cdots + (1 + y)^{-n/k} - n/(1 + x) = 0$

(c) When $x = 0$, then $y = 0$

(d) If we ignore x^2 and higher powers of x, then $y = 2kx/(n + 1)$. (Use exercise 9 to find dy/dx and then apply Taylor's Theorem.)

11. (a) Use mathematical induction to show that $1^2 + 2^2 + 3^2 + \cdots + n^2 = n(n + 1)(2n + 1)/6$.

(b) Apply the result of exercise 9(b) to differentiate y in exercise 10(b) a second time.

(c) Thus show that y is approximately equal to

$$\frac{2kx}{n+1} + \frac{2k(3k - n - 2)x^2}{3(n+1)^2}$$

(d) Compute y when a loan of $1000 is repaid by 12 equal monthly instalments totalling $1070.

12. In the compound interest formula, if i is the annual interest rate, and interest is compounded k times yearly, the total amount for an investment of $1 after n years is

$$\left(1 + \frac{i}{k}\right)^{nk}$$

(a) Show that

$$\lim_{k \to \infty} \left(1 + \frac{i}{k}\right)^{nk} = e^{ni}$$

(see exercise 5)

(b) For $n = 20$ and $i = 0.05$ find the total amount of $1 by the discrete and continuous method.

13. The costs of manufacturing x items is

$$ax^2 + bx + c, \text{ in dollars}$$

and the price p at which each item can be sold is

$$p = \alpha - \beta x^2$$

Find the value of x that makes the derivative of net profit equal to zero, and show that this value maximizes profit.

14. A chemical firm produces two salt products at a constant average cost of 5¢ and 6¢ per pound, respectively. The selling price of each product is x¢ and y¢ per pound, respectively, where the number of tons sold per week is given by N_1 and N_2 and

$$N_1 = 25(y - x)$$

$$N_2 = 320 + 25(x - 2y)$$

Find the values of x and y that yield a maximum or minimum profit, and verify that the result is optimal.

Answer: $x = 8.9$¢, $y = 9.4$¢

9

Deterministic Models

■ 9.1 Introduction

In Chapter 1 we pointed out that the basic mathematical problem in analyzing management systems is that of *optimization*. We assume that we have a measure of effectiveness which can be expressed as a function of certain control variables. The problem is to choose those values of the control variables that maximize the effectiveness function. Frequently the existence of restrictions or constraints makes the task far from simple. In Chapters 2 through 5 we introduced the mathematical concepts necessary for analysis, and in Chapters 6 through 8 we developed techniques of optimization. In this chapter we shall discuss some applications to particular systems, which will serve as a review of the methods developed so far. As we shall be mainly concerned with development of mathematical models of management systems, much of the details of analysis has been left as exercises for the reader.

It is seldom possible to study all the facets of a management system at the same time. The models presented in this chapter illustrate some major areas where decisions are required. In an elementary text it is not possible to develop and solve a general theory of the firm. In all cases it will be assumed that the functional relationships are known and constant or, equivalently, the systems are *deterministic*. In other words, one and only one value of the effectiveness function will occur for any given set of values for the control variables. Moreover, given the values of the control variables, we know how to compute the effectiveness value that will result. Such systems may be contrasted with those in which some of the relevant factors cannot be known until after a decision is taken. Systems of this type require a knowledge of probability theory and are discussed in Chapter 12.

■ 9.2 Marketing Models

Pricing

Consider a firm that competes with other firms for a fixed known market where prices charged are the most important factor. All other factors are considered equivalent for all competing firms. The demand for the firm's product may be a complex function of the price charged. We will assume, at first, that over the range of possible prices there is a linear relationship between unit sales price p and quantity sold annually q, given by

$$(1) \qquad\qquad q = a - bp$$

where a and b are known, fixed, positive constants. The first curve in Figure 9.1 illustrates the linear demand function over a range of values; extrapolation beyond the range shown is not valid.

The linear *cost function* illustrated in Figure 9.1 is given by

$$(2) \qquad\qquad C(q) = u + vq, \qquad u > 0, v > 0$$

where C is the total cost of production, u is the fixed cost, and v is the unit cost of production.

Suppose that the manager wishes to find a unit price so that the net annual profit is a maximum. The annual net profit P is given by

$$P = \text{revenue} - \text{cost}$$
$$= qp - C(q)$$
$$= qp - u - vq$$
$$= q(p - v) - u$$

and using equation (1),

$$P = (a - bp)(p - v) - u$$
$$= (a + bv)p - bp^2 - u - av$$

The net profit function is a parabola and is illustrated in Figure 9.1. Because the coefficient of p^2 is negative, the parabola reaches a maximum.

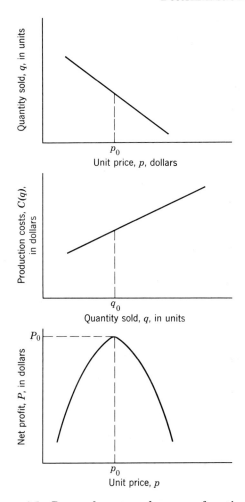

Figure 9.1   Demand, cost, and revenue functions.

To find the optimum price, we take the derivative of P with respect to p, and set it equal to zero.

$$\frac{dP}{dp} = a + bv - 2bp = 0$$

or

$$p_0 = \frac{a + bv}{2b}$$

where p_0 is the optimal price, since $d^2P/dp^2 < 0$.

Substitute the value of p_0 into the demand function; the corresponding demand q_0 is given by

$$q_0 = \frac{(a - bv)}{2}$$

The maximum net profit is thus

$$P_0 = \frac{(a^2 + b^2v^2 - 2abv - 4bu)}{4b}$$

Notice that the net profit function is symmetric about the line $p = p_0 = (a + bv)/2b$.

Suppose that the total cost of production is not linear but is a quadratic function of the quantity produced,

$$C(q) = u + vq + wq^2, \qquad u, v, w > 0$$

The total profit P is given by

$$\begin{aligned}
P &= pq - (u + vq + wq^2) \\
&= p(a - bp) - [u + v(a - bp) + w(a - bp)^2] \\
&= -(u + av + a^2w) + (a + bv + 2abw)p - (b + b^2w)p^2
\end{aligned}$$

$$\frac{dP}{dp} = a + bv + 2abw - (2b + 2b^2w)p = 0$$

The optimal sales price is thus

$$p_0 = \frac{a + bv + 2abw}{2b + 2b^2w}$$

and the optimal production quantity is

$$q_0 = \frac{a - bv}{2 + 2bw}$$

Now consider the general case where the quantity sold varies with the unit sales price, $q = q(p)$, so that the profit function becomes

$$P = p \times q(p) - C(q)$$

Taking the derivative of P with respect to p, we have

$$\frac{dP}{dp} = q(p) + pq' - q'\frac{dC}{dq} = 0$$

where

$$q' = \frac{dq}{dp}$$

and the optimal sales price p_0 is given by

$$\frac{dC}{dq}\bigg|_{q=q(p_0)} = p_0 + \frac{q(p_0)}{q'(p_0)}$$

Exercise.   Show that if

$$q = ae^{-bp}, \qquad a, b > 0$$

and

$$C(q) = u + vq, \qquad u, v > 0$$

then the optimal price is given by

$$p_0 = v + \frac{1}{b}$$

Pricing and Advertising

We now consider the case of two decision variables, the unit sales price and the magnitude of advertising effort. Suppose that the quantity sold q is a function of the unit sales price p and the advertising effort x, given by

$$(3) \qquad q = [a + b(1 - e^{-cx})]e^{-dp}$$

where a, b, c, and d are positive constants. If the annual production costs are given by

$$(4) \qquad\qquad C = vq, \qquad v > 0$$

then the total annual profits are

$$(5) \qquad\qquad P = q(p - v) - x$$

where q is given by equation (3).

To find the optimal price and advertising effort, we differentiate (5) with respect to p and x and equate both derivatives to zero.

$$(6) \qquad\qquad \frac{\partial P}{\partial p} = q + (p - v)\frac{\partial q}{\partial p} = 0$$

$$(7) \qquad\qquad \frac{\partial P}{\partial x} = (p - v)\frac{\partial q}{\partial x} - 1 = 0$$

where from equation (3)

$$\frac{\partial q}{\partial p} = -dq \qquad \text{and} \qquad \frac{\partial q}{\partial x} = bce^{-(cx+dp)}$$

Hence from (6),

(8)
$$q - (p - v)\, dq = 0$$

and from (7),

(9)
$$(p - v)bce^{-(cx+dp)} = 1$$

From (8) we see that either $q = 0$ or $p = (vd + 1)/d$. Obviously $q = 0$ will not yield a maximum profit (why?), so we take

(10)
$$p = \frac{vd + 1}{d}$$

to be the optimal price.

Substituting for p in (9) yields

$$\left(\frac{bc}{d}\right) e^{-cx-dv-1} = 1$$

$$cx + dv + 1 = \log \frac{bc}{d}$$

or

(11)
$$x = \left(\log \frac{bc}{d} - dv - 1\right)\frac{1}{c}$$

Expressions (10) and (11) yield the optimal sales price and advertising effort. The optimal production quantity may be found by substitution in (3). The reader should obtain the second derivatives and verify that equations (10) and (11) do lead to maximum profit.

In the *general* case, if

$$P = p \times q(p, x) - C(q) - x$$

then
$$\frac{\partial P}{\partial p} = q + p\frac{\partial q}{\partial p} - \frac{dC}{dq}\frac{\partial q}{\partial p} = 0$$

(12)
$$q + \frac{\partial q}{\partial p}\left(p - \frac{dC}{dq}\right) = 0$$

$$\frac{\partial P}{\partial x} = p\frac{\partial q}{\partial x} - \frac{dC}{dq}\frac{\partial q}{\partial x} - 1 = 0$$

(13)
$$\frac{\partial q}{\partial x}\left(p - \frac{dC}{dq}\right) = 1$$

Equations (12) and (13) may be solved for p and x.

Exercises

1. A firm manufactures two similar products, and the costs of production are $c_i q_i$, $i = 1, 2$, $c_i =$ constant, $q_i =$ sales quantity of product i. Suppose that the q_i depend on the *relative* prices of the two products,

$$q_1 = a_1 p_2 - b_1 p_1$$

$$q_2 = a_2 p_1 - b_2 p_2$$

where the a_i and b_i are positive constants ($i = 1, 2$). We wish to find the product unit prices and the sales quantities that maximize the total net profit. The total net profit P is given by

$$P = p_1 q_1 + p_2 q_2 - c_1 q_1 - c_2 q_2$$

(a) Find the partial derivatives of P with respect to p_1 and p_2.
(b) Solve the equations

$$\frac{\partial P}{\partial p_1} = 0 \quad \text{and} \quad \frac{\partial P}{\partial p_2} = 0$$

(c) Show that if the solutions are positive and if $4b_1 b_2 > (a_1 + a_2)^2$, then the equations yield optimal prices.
(d) Discuss the optimal policy when these conditions are violated.

2. Suppose that two firms compete in a market where a total of D units are sold annually. The annual sales of each firm's product are

$$q_1 = D[\tfrac{1}{2} + k(p_2 - p_1)]$$

$$q_2 = D[\tfrac{1}{2} + k(p_1 - p_2)]$$

where p_i is the unit sales prices of product i ($i = 1, 2$), k is a positive constant, and $|p_1 - p_2| < 1/2k$. The costs of production are $c_i q_i$ for each firm.

(a) Show that if firm i attempts to maximize its net profit, it will choose a price $p_i{}^*$, given by

$$\tfrac{1}{2} + k(p_j - p_i{}^*) = (p_i{}^* - c_i)k$$

where p_j is the competitor's price.

(b) Show that if both firms use this policy, the optimal prices will be

$$p_i{}^* = \frac{2}{3}c_i + \frac{1}{3}c_j + \frac{1}{2k}$$

Thus $|p_1{}^* - p_2{}^*| = \frac{1}{3}|c_1 - c_2|$.
(c) What happens if $|c_1 - c_2| > 3/2k$?
(d) Find the maximum profit for each firm on the assumption that $|c_1 - c_2| < 3/2k$.

3. We can generalize the model of the previous exercise to the case of n firms as follows. Let

$$Q_i = D\left[\frac{1}{n} + \frac{k}{n-1}\sum_{j=1}^{n}(p_j - p_i)\right]$$

then

$$q_i = \begin{cases} 0, & Q_i \le 0 \\ Q_i, & 0 < Q_i < D \\ D, & Q_i \ge D \end{cases}$$

(a) Show that if all n firms follow optimal policies and the condition below is met, then the optimal price for firm i is given by

$$p_i{}^* = \frac{1}{nk} + \frac{1}{2n-1}\sum_{j=1}^{n}c_j + \frac{n-1}{2n-1}c_i$$

Condition:

$$0 \le \frac{1}{n} + \frac{k}{n-1}\sum_{j=1}^{n}(p_j{}^* - p_i{}^*) \le 1, \qquad i = 1, 2, \ldots, n$$

(b) Show that the condition is equivalent to

$$0 \le \frac{1}{n} + \frac{k}{2n-1}\left[\sum_{j=1}^{n}c_j - nc_i\right] \le 1, \qquad i = 1, 2, \ldots, n$$

(c) What happens to a firm for which this quantity is

(i) negative?
(ii) greater than one?

4. A firm has performed an analysis of its warehouse distribution system in order to determine the optimal size of territory to be served. The marketing cost was found to be dependent on

V, the dollar volume sold through the territory
A, the area, in square miles, served by the warehouse.

The warehousing costs per dollar's worth of item handled, C, decrease with the volume and increase with the square root of the area.

Thus
$$C = a + \frac{b}{V} + c\sqrt{A}$$

where a, b, and c are positive constants.

Assuming that $V = kA$ where k is a constant, find the optimal value of A.

■ 9.3   Production Models

In this section we consider deterministic production models. The problem is to determine production schedules so as to minimize total costs. We will use the following notation:

c_1 = cost of holding one unit of inventory for one time period

c_2 = cost of a shortage of one unit, lasting one time period

c_3 = setup cost which is incurred whenever a new production run is started

k = production rate, in units per time period

r = rate of demand in units per time period

q = quantity produced at each setup

We observed in Section 7.2 and Section 7.9 that it is possible to produce in economic lot sizes that minimize the total cost of holding stock, shortages, and production setups. We discussed two cases:

Case 1.   (Section 7.2)   Shortages not permitted and production instantaneous $(c_2 = \infty; k = \infty)$.

Case 2.   (Section 7.9)   Shortages permitted and production instantaneous $(c_2 < \infty; k = \infty)$.

We will now develop some generalizations.

Case 3.   Suppose that shortages are not permitted and the production rate k is finite $(k > r)$.

A typical inventory cycle will look like Figure 9.2.

Suppose each run produces an amount q. The production part of the cycle lasts a time $t_1 = q/k$ and the peak inventory is $q - rt_1$. The length of the cycle is $t = q/r$ and the cost of holding inventory is c_1 times the area of triangle ABC, that is,

$$\frac{1}{2} c_1 \frac{(q - rt_1)q}{r}$$

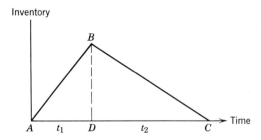

Figure 9.2   Production cycle—no shortages.

The setup cost per cycle is c_3, so that the average cost per unit time is

$$K = \frac{1}{t}\left[\frac{c_1 q}{2r}(q - rt_1) + c_3\right]$$

The reader should now find the optimal value of q. See exercise 1 following this section.

Case 4. Suppose that shortages are permitted at a cost c_2 per unit, per time period. Suppose also that k is finite. A cycle will now look like Figure 9.3.

 If we permit shortages, the peak shortage occurs when production commences at the beginning of a cycle. Let t_1 be the time until all shortages have been filled (OA in Figure 9.3); t_2 is the balance of the production phase (AB); t_3 is the time from peak inventory (BQ) until inventory is again zero (BC); and t_4 is the time until the next cycle starts with a new production run (CD). Clearly the peak shortage is represented by

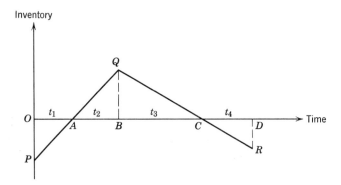

Figure 9.3   Production cycle with shortages.

OP and DR, which must be equal. The holding cost is the area of triangle AQC times c_1 and the shortage cost is the sum of the areas of triangles OPA and CDR times c_2.

The reader should now find the optimal production schedule. See exercise 2 following this section.

Utilization of Man Power and Equipment

It often happens that production facilities can be used in various combinations to manufacture a given product. The basic resources in any manufacturing system are manhours of labor L and hours of machine usage U. In general, the same results can be achieved with a large amount of labor and little mechanization or vice versa. As a concrete example, suppose the quantity produced q is given by

$$q = aL + bU + cLU$$

where a, b, c are positive constants.

Suppose further that labor costs c_1 per manhour and the costs of machinery are c_2 per hour. Thus the total production cost, K, is given by

$$K = c_1L + c_2U$$

We wish to determine the values of L and U which minimize K for a given amount of production q. This can be done with the aid of a La-

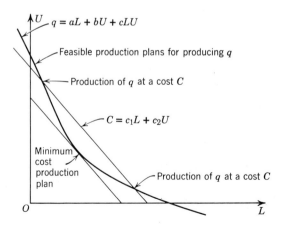

Figure 9.4   Optimum production costs.

grange multiplier and the reader should do so as an exercise. The following graphical method is of interest.

For a fixed value of q, plot the curve $q = aL + bU + cLU$. The possible production plans are represented by points on the curve between $L = 0$, $U = q/b$ and $L = q/a$, $U = 0$ (see Figure 9.4). Now draw in the line $C = c_1 L + c_2 U$. The cost for any plan (L, U) which is represented by this line, is C. If the line cuts the curve, there is a plan that produces q at a cost C. However $C/\sqrt{c_1{}^2 + c_2{}^2}$ is the distance of the line from the origin so the minimum cost will occur for the line nearest the origin which still has a point on the curve. The minimum cost line is the tangent to the curve parallel to $C = c_1 L + c_2 U$.

Service Facilities

A service facility, such as a machine center, desires to process n jobs so that the total waiting and processing time for all n jobs is a minimum. If $T_i = $ the processing time for the ith job, $i = 1, 2, \ldots, n$, then the total processing and waiting time for a given sequence of jobs, $S = (1, 2, \ldots, n)$, is

$$T = T_1 + (T_1 + T_2) + (T_1 + T_2 + T_3) + \cdots + (T_1 + T_2 + \cdots + T_n)$$

This is a sum of n terms where the ith term is the elapsed time until job i is completed. Now, rewriting, we have

$$T = nT_1 + (n - 1)T_2 + (n - 2)T_3 + \cdots + 2T_{n-1} + T_n$$

Since T_1 has the largest weight, we can only minimize T by choosing first the job with the shortest processing time. It is easy enough to see that the optimum sequence is such that

$$T_1 \le T_2 \le \cdots \le T_n$$

Exercises

1. This exercise refers to Case 3.

   (a) Verify that the optimal production quantity, q_0, is given by:

   $$q_0 = \sqrt{\frac{2c_3 r}{c_1(1 - r/k)}}$$

   (b) Find the corresponding cycle time and the corresponding costs.
   (c) Show that if $k = \infty$, the results reduce to Case 1.

2. This exercise refers to Case 4. Let q be the quantity produced per cycle.

(a) Verify the following relationships:

(i) $q = r(t_1 + t_2 + t_3 + t_4) = k(t_1 + t_2)$
(ii) peak inventory $= t_2(k - r) = t_3 r$
(iii) peak shortage $= t_1(k - r) = t_4 r$

(b) Hence show that the total cost per unit time is given by:

$$K = \frac{\frac{1}{2}c_1 t_3 r(t_2 + t_3) + \frac{1}{2}c_2 t_4 r(t_1 + t_4) + c_3}{t_1 + t_2 + t_3 + t_4}$$

$$= \frac{\frac{1}{2}(c_1 t_2{}^2 + c_2 t_1{}^2)(k - r) + c_3 r/k}{t_1 + t_2}$$

(c) By taking partial derivatives, show that the optimal values of t_1 and t_2 are given by:

$$t_1 = \sqrt{\frac{2c_1 c_3 r}{c_2 k(k - r)(c_1 + c_2)}} \qquad t_2 = \sqrt{\frac{2c_2 c_3 r}{c_1 k(k - r)(c_1 + c_2)}}$$

(d) Show further that the optimal value of

$$t = t_1 + t_2 + t_3 + t_4$$

is

$$t = \sqrt{\left(\frac{2c_3}{c_1 r}\right)\left(\frac{1}{1 - r/k}\right)\left(\frac{c_1 + c_2}{c_2}\right)}$$

and the optimal value of q is

$$q = \sqrt{\left(\frac{2c_3 r}{c_1}\right)\left(\frac{1}{1 - r/k}\right)\left(\frac{c_1 + c_2}{c_2}\right)}$$

(e) Verify that the results agree with Cases 1, 2, and 3 when we give k and c_2 appropriate values.

3. The economic lot-size formula of Section 7.2 can be generalized to the case of cycles in which several products are made in sequence in each cycle. Suppose there are N products, and the following data are given:

c_{1i} = holding cost for item i
c_{3i} = setup cost for item i
r_i = demand per time period for item i
k_i = production rate of item i $i = 1, 2, \ldots, N$
q_i = production quantity of item i
t_i = duration of production of item i

During each cycle, which lasts a total time t for all items, we make items 1, 2, ..., N, in sequence, starting a new cycle when the stock of item 1 runs out (no shortages are permitted).

Show that

(a) $\dfrac{r_1}{q_1} = \dfrac{r_2}{q_2} = \cdots = \dfrac{r_N}{q_N} = \dfrac{1}{t}$

(b) $(k_i - r_i)t_i = S_i = $ maximum stock

(c) $k_i t_i = q_i = r_i t$

(d) The total cost of holding inventory per cycle is

$$\sum_{i=1}^{N} \frac{1}{2} c_{1i} S_i t$$

(e) The total cost of setup is $\displaystyle\sum_{i=1}^{N} c_{3i}$

(f) Show that the cost per unit time is

$$K = \sum_{i=1}^{N} \frac{1}{2} c_{1i} \left(1 - \frac{r_i}{k_i}\right) q_i + \sum_{i=1}^{N} c_{3i} \frac{r_i}{q_i}$$

(g) Find the optimal value of q_i.

4. Let us generalize the problem of sequencing n jobs, to the case where the processing time on job i is T_i and the cost while job i awaits completion is c_i per unit time. Let S be a given sequence; the corresponding cost K is given by

$$K = c_1 T_1 + c_2(T_1 + T_2) + \cdots + c_n(T_1 + T_2 + \cdots + T_n)$$

Let S' be the sequence obtained by interchanging jobs i and $i + 1$.

(a) Find an expression for the cost K' of S'.

(b) By considering the difference $K - K'$, show that the optimal sequence is (1, 2, ..., n) such that

$$\frac{T_1}{c_1} \leq \frac{T_2}{c_2} \leq \cdots \leq \frac{T_n}{c_n}$$

(If $\mu_i = 1/T_i$, then μ_i is the *rate* at which jobs of type i are performed. The condition for optimality is equivalent to the $c\mu$ rule, which states that we must have

$$c_1\mu_1 \geq c_2\mu_2 \geq \cdots \geq c_n\mu_n)$$

■ 9.4 Equipment Replacement and Maintenance

We now consider two examples of optimal replacement and maintenance policies.

Replacement Policy

An item has an acquisition cost A and cumulative operating costs $F(t)$ up to time t since installation. The operating cost *rate* at time t is $f(t) = dF/dt$. We wish to find the economic life, under the assumption that at time t the item can be sold for a price $S(t)$.

Let $K(t)$ be the average cost per unit time, if the item is sold at time t. Then

$$K(t) = \frac{[A + F(t) - S(t)]}{t}$$

To find t_0, the optimal value of t, which minimizes K we differentiate with respect to t. The reader should show that t_0 will minimize K provided

(i) $f(t_0) - S(t_0) = K(t_0)$

and

(ii) $f'(t_0) > S''(t_0)$

What happens if $f'(t_0) < S''(t_0)$?

Preventative Maintenance

Scheduled maintenance, such as major overhaul, is performed on equipment like truck engines and machine tools in order to achieve minimal costs of operation and maintenance. Routine maintenance or repair is performed as required in order to continue operations.

Consider the scheduled maintenance interval of a truck engine. Too frequent performance of engine overhaul will increase this component of the total costs, whereas too infrequent performance of overhaul will result in excessive operating costs, including repair costs. The relation-

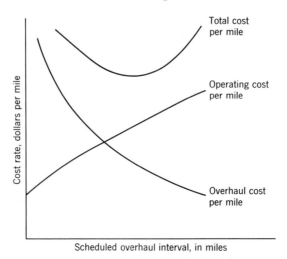

Figure 9.5   Truck engine overhaul and operating costs.

ships between costs and the interval are presented in Figure 9.5. The optimal maintenance interval is that which balances overhaul and operating costs.

Exercise

Suppose that the cost of truck engine overhaul is A and the operating costs are at the rate $a + bm$ per mile when the engine has run m miles since the last overhaul. If the engine is overhauled at M miles, the total costs are

$$K = A + aM + \frac{b}{2} M^2$$

and the average cost per mile is K/M. This is the curve plotted in Figure 9.5.

(a) Find the value of M that minimizes total cost per mile.
(b) Find the optimal engine overhaul interval and the corresponding minimal cost for an overhaul cost of $1000, when $a = 0.03$ and $b = 0.00002$.

■ **9.5   Research and Development**

A problem in the management of R and D programs is the *general budgeting* problem. Suppose a firm has an amount B to invest in n

independent development programs, where the payoff for an investment of x_i, in program i, is estimated to be $y_i(x_i)$, $i = 1, 2, \ldots, n$.

We will show that the optimal allocation of the budget B divides the programs into two groups—one of which may be empty.

(a) those programs which receive funds
(b) those programs which receive no funds.

We will also show that the marginal return for any program in group (a) is the same as for any other program in group (a). Our problem is to maximize:

$$\sum_{i=1}^{n} y_i(x_i)$$

subject to

$$\sum_{i=1}^{n} x_i = B$$

Letting

$$F = \sum_{i=1}^{n} y_i(x_i) + \lambda \left(B - \sum_{i=1}^{n} x_i \right)$$

we have

(14)
$$\frac{\partial F}{\partial x_i} = y_i'(x_i) - \lambda = 0$$

The marginal return on the last dollar invested in program i is $y_i'(x_i)$. Our results show that a necessary condition for a maximum return is that the marginal returns for all programs should be the same. This is almost obvious because if $y_i'(x_i) > y_j'(x_j)$, we could increase the total return by $y_i'(x_i) - y_j'(x_j)$ by spending a dollar more on program i and a dollar less on program j, unless either $x_i = B$ or $x_j = 0$. Thus we see that for all programs that receive investments between 0 and B, the marginal returns must be equal.

To solve the equations (14) numerically we could take a trial value of λ and then solve n equations

$$y_i'(x_i) = \lambda$$

Let us denote the results by $x_i = x_i(\lambda)$.

Now compute

$$B(\lambda) = \sum_{i=1}^{n} x_i(\lambda)$$

If $B(\lambda) \neq B$, we then use trial-and-error methods to find a value of λ^* for which $B(\lambda^*)$ is equal to B. If the $x_i(\lambda^*) \geq 0$ for all i, we have the optimal program. If any $x_i(\lambda^*) < 0$, we decide that there will be no investment in program i. It is then necessary to start the calculation again, omitting those programs for which $x_i(\lambda^*) \leq 0$. It is clear that the maximum return is at least as great as the largest value of $x_i(B)$, so that eventually the above procedure will arrive at a set of nonnegative x_i.

Exercise. Suppose $y_i(x_i) = a_i x_i[1 - e^{-b_i x_i}]$, where $i = 1, 2,$ and we have the following data:

i	a_i	b_i^{-1}	
1	1000	6000	$B = 15{,}000$
2	700	4000	

Find λ, x_1, and x_2 for a maximum return.

Dynamic Programming

If we wish to spend all the budget B, we have a procedure for maximizing the return, but it will often happen that B is an upper limit on the budget and the optimal return may be obtained by spending less than B. We may state the problem as follows:

Maximize $Z = \sum_{i=1}^{n} y_i(x_i)$ with respect to all x_i that satisfy

$$\sum_{i=1}^{n} x_i \leq B \quad \text{and} \quad x_i \geq 0, \qquad i = 1, 2, \ldots, n$$

We can solve this problem by the procedure already described if we also examine what happens when

$$\frac{\partial Z}{\partial x_i} = 0, \qquad i = 1, 2, \ldots, n.$$

If the solutions to these equations satisfy the restrictions, they may yield the maximum. Strictly speaking we must also examine all the possible cases where some or all of the x_i are zero. There are $2^n - 1$ such cases. In practice it may be "obvious" that the only x_i that are zero are those discovered by the Lagrange multiplier technique.

The following approach is instructive. We can regard the maximum value of Z as a function of B, which we will denote by $f_n(B)$. Now

$$f_1(X) = \max_{0 \leq x \leq X} y_1(x)$$

This is a relatively easy problem to solve even if $y_1(x)$ is given numerically. If $y_1(x)$ can be differentiated twice, the maximum either occurs when $x = 0$, when $x = B$, or at one of the points where $y_1'(x) = 0$ and $y_1''(x) < 0$.

Let us suppose we have found $f_1(X)$ for all values of X, such that $0 \leq X \leq B$. Then $f_2(X)$ must satisfy

$$f_2(X) = \max_{0 \leq x \leq X} \{y_2(x) + f_1(X - x)\}$$

and, in general,

$$f_r(X) = \max_{0 \leq x \leq X} \{y_r(x) + f_{r-1}(X - x)\}, r = 2, 3, \ldots, n$$

This equation is almost obvious when viewed in the correct light. Whatever allocation x we make to program r, we must make the optimal use of the remaining funds. These amount to $X - x$, and the optimal return from programs $1, 2, \ldots, r - 1$ is $f_{r-1}(X - x)$. We can now compute $f_1(X), f_2(X), \ldots, f_n(X)$ successively for values of X such that $0 \leq X \leq B$. The optimal return for the original problem is $f_n(B)$, and the optimal allocation will have been obtained incidentally. This system of calculation is called *dynamic programming*.

As an illustration of the computational procedure we will use the following data.

x	0	1000	2000	3000	4000	5000	6000	7000	8000	9000	10000
$y_1(x)$	0	1200	2500	3800	5000	7000	9000	12000	11000	10000	9000
$y_2(x)$	0	−600	−1200	200	1000	2000	3000	4000	5000	6000	6500
$y_3(x)$	0	−100	1500	3000	6000	7000	7000	6500	6500	6000	6000

Note that the following argument will not work:

Allocate the first $1000 to the program that yields the largest return (program 1). Now allocate the next $1000 to the project that yields the largest *marginal* return: a return of ($2500 − 1200) = $1300 for program 1. Continue in this way until we reach an allocation of $7000 to program 1. At this stage a $1000 for any of the programs gives a negative marginal return and we stop.

Clearly we can do better than this by allocating $5000 to program 1 and $4000 to program 3.

If we solve the problem by finding $f_1(x)$, $f_2(x)$, and $f_3(x)$, the computations for f_1 and f_2 are shown below. The reader should compute f_3 and the optimal allocations for all budgets up to $10,000.

(In Table 9.1, x_1 and x_2 are the optimal allocations to programs 1 and 2.)

TABLE 9.1   CALCULATION FOR $f_1(X)$ AND $f_2(X)$

x or X	0	1000	2000	3000	4000	5000	6000	7000	8000	9000	10000
$y_1(x)$	0	1200	2500	3800	5000	7000	9000	12000	11000	10000	9000
x_1	0	1000	2000	3000	4000	5000	6000	7000	7000	7000	7000
$f_1(X)$	0	1200	2500	3800	5000	7000	9000	12000	12000	12000	12000
$y_2(X)$	0	-600	-1200	200	1000	2000	3000	4000	5000	6000	6500
$y_2(0) + f_1(X)$	—	1200	2500	3800	5000	7000	9000	12000	12000	12000	12000
$y_2(1) + f_1(X - 1)$	—	-600	600	1900	3200	4400	6400	8400	11400	11400	11400
$y_2(2) + f_1(X - 2)$	—	—	-1200	0	1300	2600	3800	5800	7800	10800	10800
$y_2(3) + f_1(X - 3)$	—	—	—	200	1400	2700	4000	5200	7200	9200	12200
$y_2(4) + f_1(X - 4)$	—	—	—	—	1000	2200	3500	4800	6000	8000	10000
$y_2(5) + f_1(X - 5)$	—	—	—	—	—	2000	3200	4500	5800	7000	9000
$y_2(6) + f_1(X - 6)$	—	—	—	—	—	—	3000	4200	5500	6800	8000
$y_2(7) + f_1(X - 7)$	—	—	—	—	—	—	—	4000	5200	6500	7800
$y_2(8) + f_1(X - 8)$	—	—	—	—	—	—	—	—	5000	6200	7500
$y_2(9) + f_1(X - 9)$	—	—	—	—	—	—	—	—	—	6000	7200
$y_2(10) + f_1(X - 10)$	—	—	—	—	—	—	—	—	—	—	6500
x_2	0	0	0	0	0	0	0	0	0	0	3000
$f_2(X)$	0	1200	2500	3800	5000	7000	9000	12000	12000	12000	12200

It will be seen that this system involves the calculation of 66 values of $f_{n-1}(X - x) + y_n(x)$ at each stage after $f_1(X)$ is known. For three programs there are 132 such calculations in all. If we examine all possible allocations of \$10,000 to the three programs, we would have to examine a total of 286 allocations. With n programs, dynamic programming requires examination of 66 $(n - 1)$ allocations out of a possible $\left\{ \dfrac{1}{\lfloor n} (10 + n)(9 + n) \ldots 12.11 \right\}$ allocations. (For $n = 4, 5, 6, 7$ the figures are 198, 264, 330 and 396, compared with 1001, 3003, 8008 and 19, 448.)

Exercises for Chapter 9

1. A firm has production cost and sales demand relationships given by

$$\text{costs:} \begin{cases} C = 1000 + 5q, & 0 \le q \le 500 \\ C = 2000 + 4q, & 500 < q \le 2000 \end{cases}$$
$$\text{sales:} \quad q = 3000 - 250p$$

where C = total annual costs, q = quantity sold annually, and p = unit sales price. Find the optimal price that maximizes the total annual profit.

2. The firm in exercise 1 can also use its facilities to manufacture a second product whose cost function is

$$C' = 1500 + 4q'$$

and whose demand function is

$$q' = 2400 - 200p'$$

Find optimal prices if (i) $q + q' \le 2000$; (ii) $q + q' \le 1500$.

3. Suppose that the cost and demand functions are given by $C = u + 3q$ and $q = a - bp^2$, using the notation in the pricing models of Section 9.2. Show that the unit price which yields a maximum value for the net profits is

$$p_0 = 1 + \sqrt{1 + (a/3b)}$$

4. A manufacturer purchases bearings to order. The cost of the shipment depends on a fixed cost F and a variable cost a, so that the cost of shipment is $F + aq$, where the quantity ordered is q. The total cost C of shipping, inventory, and ordering is given by

$$C = \frac{c_1}{2} q + c_3 \frac{R}{q} + \frac{R}{q}(F + aq)$$

where c_1 is the unit cost of holding
c_3 is the unit cost of ordering
R is the annual requirement

Find the economic order quantity and compare the result with the economic lot-size formula of Section 7.2.

5. Show that the production quantity that minimizes the total average cost of all units produced is such that the marginal cost of producing one additional unit equals the average cost.

6. A firm manufactures two products in quantities x and y, respectively. Manufacturing costs depend on the quantities produced of each product as follows:

$$C(x) = \begin{cases} 0, & x = 0 \\ 1000 + 5x, & 0 < x \le 500 \\ 2000 + 4x, & 500 < x \le 2000 \end{cases}$$

$$C(y) = \begin{cases} 0, & y = 0 \\ 1500 + 4y, & 0 < y \le 500 \\ 2500 + 3y, & 500 < y \le 2000 \end{cases}$$

Find the optimal values of x and y that minimize the total manufacturing cost, $C = C(x) + C(y)$, if $x + y = 500, 1000, 1500, 2000,$ and 2500.

7. Suppose a firm has a capacity b_i and a manufacturing cost

$$C(x_i) = a_i x_i, \qquad 0 \le x_i \le b_i, \qquad i = 1, 2, \ldots, n$$

for each of its n possible products. Show that the optimal production quantities that minimize the total production cost for a limited total production capacity, B, where

$$\sum_{i=1}^{n} x_i = B \le \sum_{i=1}^{n} b_i$$

is given by the following procedure:

(i) Rank products such that

$$a_1 \leq a_2 \leq a_3 \leq \cdots \leq a_{n-1} \leq a_n$$

(ii) With this ordering, let k be defined such that

$$\sum_{j=1}^{k} b_j \leq B < \sum_{j=1}^{k+1} b_j$$

(iii) Allocate the total production capacity such that

$$x_1 = b_1, \ x_2 = b_2, \ \ldots, \ x_k = b_k$$

$$x_{k+1} = B - \sum_{j=1}^{k} b_j$$

$$x_{k+2} = x_{k+3} = \cdots = x_n = 0$$

8. (a) Show that if $x_i \geq 0 \ (i = 1, 2, \ldots, n)$ and $\sum_{i=1}^{n} x_i = B$, then we can minimize $\sum_{i=1}^{n} a_i x_i$ by choosing $x_k = B$, where k is defined such that $a_k = \min_{i} \{a_i\}$.

   (b) We might attempt to make a model of a manufacturing process as follows:

   A firm has manufacturing costs $c_i(x_i) = a_i x_i$ when it produces an amount x_i of product i $(i = 1, 2, \ldots, n)$. The total production capacity for all products is B. The optimal production policy is given by (a) above.

   Criticize the lack of reality of this model.

9. Suppose a firm manufactures two similar products $(i = 1, 2)$ unit cost, a_i, and quantity sold, q_i, dependent on the *relative* prices, p_i,

$$q_1 = c_1 + c_2 p_2 - c_3 p_1$$

$$q_2 = b_1 + b_2 p_1 - b_3 p_2$$

   (a) Show that the optimal pricing policy for each product that maximizes the *total* net profits is given by

$$p_1 = \frac{2b_3(a_2 b_2 - a_1 c_3 - c_1) + (b_2 + c_2)(a_1 c_2 - a_2 b_3 - b_1)}{(b_2 + c_2)^2 - 4b_3 c_3}$$

$$p_2 = \frac{2c_3(a_1 c_2 - a_2 b_3 - b_1) + (b_2 + c_2)(a_2 b_2 - a_1 c_3 - c_1)}{(b_2 + c_2)^2 - 4b_3 c_3}$$

   (b) Find the restrictions on the constants to assure that the solution in (a) yields maximum profits.

Part Three

Stochastic Systems

10

Integration

■ 10.1 Introduction

We have seen (Chapter 6) that in order to determine the maximum value of a function, we need to consider the way in which it changes over a range of values. Thus if we have a relationship between net profit and advertising expenditure, say $P = f(x)$, where P is the profit and x the advertising effort, we set $dP/dx = f'(x)$ equal to zero in order to find the optimal value of x. It sometimes happens that we are able to conduct marketing experiments that give us an empirical form for the rate of change, and we wish to use it to determine the original relationship. For example, if we are introducing a new product and wish to find the total sales over the first year, we might keep records of monthly sales and add them up. If we continue observations for a second year, we might find total sales over 2 years in two steps:

1. sum monthly sales for second year;
2. add to the total the sales during first year.

Now, imagine we kept records in terms of the annual sales rate. We might have had sales of 327 units in January, and on multiplying by 12 we could say that the annual sales rate in January was $12 \times 327 = 3908$. Instead of keeping records of annual sales rate for each separate month, we might have subdivided the data and found annual rates as 52 times weekly totals or even 300 times daily totals on the basis of 300 working days per year. If we continue the subdivision we are, in effect, estimating the annual sales rate at each instant of the year. Let $S(t)$ be the total sales up to time t; then our data yields an estimate of the derivative $S'(t)$. Once we have done this we are faced with the problem of finding $S(t)$. The mathematical process of finding a function whose derivative is equal to a given function is called *integration*.

Example 1. A firm conducts pricing experiments and finds that an increase of \$1 in the unit sales price results in a constant decrease of b units in sales volume. What is the relationship between sales and price?

Suppose that there is a relationship between sales volume s and price p. Then the rate of change of sales, with respect to price, is ds/dp, and we are told that

$$(1) \qquad \frac{ds}{dp} = -b$$

We know (Chapter 6) that if a is any constant and

$$(2) \qquad s = a - bp$$

then (1) is satisfied. The determination of values for a and b is made by means of data collected from pricing experiments. Thus we see that there are many functions with derivatives equal to $-b$. In order to find the value of a that yields the specific function we need some further information. If we are also told that the sales volume is V when the price is \$50, then

$$V = a - 50b$$

and so

$$a = V + 50b, \quad s = V + b(50 - p)$$

Of course sales volume cannot be negative, so the relationship could not hold if $p > 50 + V/b$. In fact, it is unlikely to be true for prices close to this value. Most probably it would only be used for prices close to \$50.

Example 2. Suppose that we know the rate of change of a function y is given by $x + 2$. What is the original function?

We wish to find y, where

$$(3) \qquad \frac{dy}{dx} = x + 2$$

We know that if c is any constant and $y = x^2/2 + 2x + c$, then dy/dx satisfies equation (3). We see that just as in the first example, there

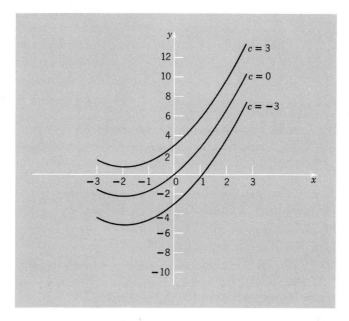

Figure 10.1 $y = x^2/2 + 2x + c$ $(c = -3, 0, 3)$.

are infinitely many functions with the required derivative. In Figure 10.1 the function y is plotted for $c = -3, 0, 3$. Each curve of the set has a derivative equal to $x + 2$, and this may be interpreted geometrically by saying that the curves are all parallel. We may specify the particular curve by assigning a value to y for a given value of x; for example, if at $x = 2$, $y = 7$, we have $7 = 2^2/2 + 4 + c$, and $c = 1$.

We call the inverse of a derivative of a function the (*indefinite*) *integral*.

Definition. If $f(x)$ is a given function, an *integral of* $f(x)$ is any function, $y = F(x)$, whose derivative is $f(x)$, and we write

$$y = F(x) = \int f(x)\, dx \qquad \text{(Read "}y \text{ is the integral of } f(x)\, dx.\text{")}$$

where
$$\frac{dy}{dx} = f(x) = F'(x)$$

Note that the symbol for integration consists of two parts separated by the function to be integrated, namely, $\int \ldots dx$. The first part indicates the operation and the second the variable. Thus $\int x^2 z \, dx$ is different from $\int x^2 z \, dz$. The former is $x^3 z / 3 + c$ and the latter $x^2 z^2 / 2 + c'$. It is easy to see that if c is any constant and $F(x)$ is an integral of $f(x)$, then $F(x) + c$ is also an integral. This is because

$$\frac{d(y + c)}{dx} = \frac{dy}{dx} = f(x)$$

We will not include the constant in all cases.

We have defined integration as the inverse process of differentiation, that is, integration is the process of obtaining from a given function a second function whose derivative is the original function.

We will demonstrate that other interpretations of integration are (1) the limit of a sequence of finite sums and (2) the area enclosed by curves in a plane.

Example 3.   Find $\int (x^3 + x + 2) \, dx$.

We ask ourselves which functions, when differentiated, yield x^3, x, and 2; these are $x^4/4$, $x^2/2$, and $2x$, respectively. Since we can always add an arbitrary constant to the integral, we have

$$\int (x^3 + x + 2) \, dx = \frac{x^4}{4} + \frac{x^2}{2} + 2x + c$$

and

$$\frac{d(x^4/4 + x^2/2 + 2x + c)}{dx} = x^3 + x + 2$$

Example 4.   A manufacturer observes that adding one employee to an assembly operation increases the production rate by 10 units per hour. What is the production rate in terms of the number of employees?

We approximate the discrete case with a continuous variable. Let $y = $ production rate and $x = $ number of employees. We have $dy/dx = 10$ or $y = 10x + c$. If the current labor force of 100 employees produces items at the rate of 500 units per hour, we have $500 = 10(100) + c$ or $c = -500$, and thus $y = 10x - 500$. This equation cannot be valid for values of x less than 50.

Exercises

1. An airline hires 100 stewardesses, and a constant number quit each month. If 82 stewardesses are still employed at the end of 1 year, how many will be employed after 2 years? After x months? What is the maximum length of service of the stewardesses? (*Hint:* Let $y = $ the number of stewardesses and $x = $ the number of months since employed; then $dy/dx = -a$.)

2. If airline stewardesses quit at rates proportional to the number of months of service and if 82 out of 100 stewardesses are still employed at the end of 1 year, what is the expected number remaining after 2 years? What is the maximum length of service of the stewardesses? (*Hint:* In this case, $dy/dx = -ax$.)

■ 10.2   Finite Sums

In Chapter 6 we started by defining *differences* $\Delta f(x)$ over an interval h, by the equation,

$$\Delta f(x) = f(x + h) - f(x)$$

We went on to define *rates of change* by dividing the difference by the interval h, that is, $\Delta f(x)/h$. Finally, we obtained the derivative $f'(x)$ by letting h tend to zero, that is,

$$f'(x) = \lim_{h \to 0} \frac{f(x + h) - f(x)}{h}$$

Now, differences have an interesting property with respect to sums. Suppose we wish to perform the sum

$$S = \Delta f(x) + \Delta f(x + h) + \Delta f(x + 2h) + \cdots + \Delta f(x + nh)$$

Then $S = f(x + h) - f(x)$

$$+ f(x + 2h) - f(x + h)$$

$$+ f(x + 3h) - f(x + 2h)$$

$$\vdots$$

$$+ f(x + \overline{n - 1}h) - f(x + \overline{n - 2}h)$$

$$+ f(x + nh) - f(x + \overline{n - 1}h)$$

$$+ f(x + \overline{n + 1}h) - f(x + nh)$$

$$= f(x + \overline{n + 1}h) - f(x)$$

since all other terms cancel out.
Therefore

$$\sum_{r=0}^{n} \Delta f(x + rh) = [f(x + rh)]_{r=0}^{r=n+1} = f(x + \overline{n + 1}h) - f(x)$$

Now, suppose we wish to find the sum of a function $\phi(x)$ between the limits $x = a$ and $x = b$, that is,

$$S = \phi(a) + \phi(a + h) + \cdots + \phi(b - h) + \phi(b)$$

and suppose we know a function $\Phi(x)$ such that

$$\Delta\Phi(x) = \Phi(x + h) - \Phi(x) = \phi(x)$$

Then we see that

$$S = [\Phi(x)]_{x=a}^{x=b+h} = \Phi(b + h) - \Phi(a)$$

Rule.   To sum the function $\phi(x)$ between $x = a$ and $x = b$, find a function $\Phi(x)$ whose difference is $\phi(x)$.   The required sum is the difference between $\Phi(b + h)$ and $\Phi(a)$.

The function $\Phi(x)$ is called an *indefinite sum* of $\phi(x)$.   We say indefinite sum because it is easy to see that if $\Delta\Phi(x) = \phi(x)$, then $\Delta[\Phi(x) + k]$, where k is any constant, also yields $\phi(x)$.   Thus there is an infinity of suitable functions Φ.

Note that if we regard S as a function $S(b)$ of the upper limit, we can difference $S(b)$ with respect to b.   We have

$$\Delta S(b) = \sum_{x=a}^{b+h} \phi(x) - \sum_{x=a}^{b} \phi(x) = \phi(b + h)$$

that is, the difference of a sum yields the original function.

Example.   Find $S = \sum\limits_{x=1}^{n} x^2$.   (The interval $h = 1$.)

We have

$$\sum_{x=1}^{n} x^2 = \sum_{x=1}^{n} [x(x - 1) + x] = \left[\frac{x(x - 1)(x - 2)}{3} + \frac{x(x - 1)}{2}\right]_{x=1}^{x=n+1}$$

[For $\Delta x(x - 1)(x - 2) \ldots (x - r + 1) = rx(x - 1) \ldots (x - r + 2)$ (See Chapter 6.)]

Therefore $S = \dfrac{(n + 1)n(n - 1)}{3} + \dfrac{n(n + 1)}{2}$

$$= \tfrac{1}{6}(2n^3 + 3n^2 + n)$$

$$= \tfrac{1}{6}n(n + 1)(2n + 1)$$

Exercises

1. Show that if $x_{(r)} = x(x - 1) \ldots (x - r + 1)/r!$, then

$$\Delta x_{(r)} = (x + 1)_{(r)} - x_{(r)} = x_{(r-1)}$$

Hence verify that

  (a) The sum of the arithmetic progression $a, a + d, a + 2d, \ldots, l$,
       where there are n terms, is $\dfrac{n(a + l)}{2}$.

  (b) $\displaystyle\sum_{x=1}^{n} x^3 = \dfrac{n^2(n + 1)^2}{4}$

2. Show that if $u_x = a^x$, then $\Delta u_x = (a - 1)u_x$. Hence verify that

$$\sum_{x=0}^{n-1} a^x = \frac{1 - a^n}{1 - a}$$

■ **10.3   Areas under Curves**

We now turn to a graphical interpretation of the summation process. Suppose we plot the graph $y = \phi(x)$ (Figure 10.2a) and ask what is the area under the curve between the lines $x = a$ and $x = b$. In attempting to solve the problem graphically we might divide the area into small rectangles, as in Figure 10.2b, and add up the areas of the rectangles. It is true we would be ignoring the shaded part above the top of the rectangles, but if the widths were small enough, the error might be negligible. Suppose the width of each rectangle is h; then we can compute the total area S from the sum

$$S = h[\phi(a) + \phi(a + h) + \phi(a + 2h) + \cdots + \phi(b - h)]$$

$$= h[\Phi(x)]_{x=a}^{x=b}$$

What happens if we let $h \to 0$?

  To see what occurs, let us move the right-hand boundary $x = b$ by the width of one rectangle to $x = b + h$. If the previous sum was $S(b)$, the new sum is $S(b + h)$, and the difference is

$$S(b + h) - S(b) = h[\Phi(x)]_{x=a}^{x=b+h} - h[\Phi(x)]_{x=a}^{x=b}$$

$$\doteq h\{\Phi(b + h) - \Phi(b)\}$$

$$= h\phi(b)$$

  Similarly, $S(b - h) - S(b) = -h\phi(b - h)$. Now divide by h and $-h$:

$$\frac{S(b + h) - S(b)}{h} = \phi(b) \qquad \text{and} \qquad \frac{S(b - h) - S(b)}{-h} = \phi(b - h)$$

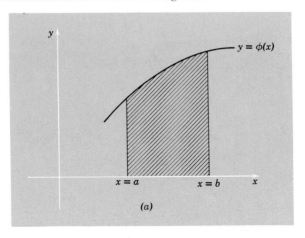

(a)

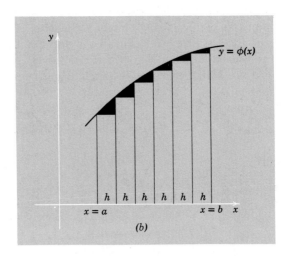

(b)

Figure 10.2   Areas under curves.

These results are true for all values of h; when we let h tend to zero we have (assuming $\phi(b - h)$ tends to $\phi(b)$ as h tends to zero)

$$S'(b) = \phi(b)$$

This, of course, is what we might have expected from the behavior of sums and differences.

Now, when $h \to 0$, the sum S tends to the area under the curve between $x = a$ and $x = b$. (The ignored pieces tend to zero as $h \to 0$.) We thus obtain the *important* results:

1. If $S(b)$ denotes the area under the curve $y = \phi(x)$, from $x = a$ to $x = b$, then as we vary b, $S'(b) = \phi(b)$.

2. If we wish to find the area we must first find a function whose derivative is $\phi(x)$, say $\Phi(x)$, and then compute

$$[\Phi(x)]_{x=a}^{x=b} = \Phi(b) - \Phi(a)$$

The last result follows as soon as we recognize that there are many functions whose derivative is $\phi(x)$. Suppose $\Phi(x)$ is such a function; then $\Phi(x) + k$ is another function with the same property. We know that $S(b) = \Phi(b) + k$ for some constant k. Now $S(a) = 0$ (i.e., when $a = b$, there is no area under the curve). Thus $S(a) = \Phi(a) + k = 0$, and so $k = -\Phi(a)$. As we saw in Section 10.1, any function $\Phi(x)$, such that $\Phi'(x) = \phi(x)$, is called an *indefinite* integral of $\phi(x)$; the process of finding $\Phi(x)$ is called *integration*, and when we insert the limits a and b, we have a *definite integral*. Definite integrals are written

$$\int_a^b \phi(x) \, dx$$

The limits are shown at either end of the integral sign. The *upper* and *lower* limits of the integral are b and a respectively. Note also that

$$\int_b^a \phi(x) \, dx = -\int_a^b \phi(x) \, dx$$

Note that the range, a to b, of integration may be split into pieces if convenient; if $a < c < b$, then

$$\int_a^c \phi(x) \, dx + \int_c^b \phi(x) \, dx = [\Phi(x)]_a^c + [\Phi(x)]_c^b$$

$$= [\Phi(c) - \Phi(a)] + [\Phi(b) - \Phi(c)]$$

$$= \Phi(b) - \Phi(a)$$

$$= \int_a^b \phi(x) \, dx$$

Example 1. Find the area under the curve $y = x^2$ between $x = 0$ and $x = X$.

As an approximation let us divide the interval into segments of width X/k each. Then the total area of the rectangles standing on these segments is

$$S = \frac{X}{k}\left\{0 + \left(\frac{X}{k}\right)^2 + \left(\frac{2X}{k}\right)^2 + \left(\frac{3X}{k}\right)^2 + \cdots + \left(\frac{(k-1)X}{k}\right)^2\right\}$$

$$= \frac{X^3}{k^3}\{1^2 + 2^2 + 3^2 + \cdots + (k-1)^2\}$$

$$= \frac{X^3}{k^3}\frac{k(k-1)(2k-1)}{6} \qquad \text{(from the example in 10.2)}$$

Now, we let $k \to \infty$, which has the effect of decreasing the width of the intervals to zero.

Therefore $$\lim_{k\to\infty} S = \lim_{k\to\infty} \frac{X^3}{6}\left(1 - \frac{1}{k}\right)\left(2 - \frac{1}{k}\right)$$

$$= \frac{X^3}{3}$$

We conclude:

(i) the area under the curve is $X^3/3$.
(ii) an indefinite integral of x^2 is $x^3/3$.
(iii) all indefinite integrals of x^2 are given by $x^3/3 + C$, where C is any constant.

In practice we never find an integral in this way. Instead the simpler techniques discussed in Sections 10.4 and 10.5 are used.

Example 2. In a certain industry, the rate at which revenue is produced is $\phi(t)$ at time t. The present value of income produced at time t is $e^{-rt}\phi(t)$ (see Chapter 16). What is the present value of all income produced during the first x years? Evaluate the result when $\phi(t) = a + bt$.

We have to interpret the phrase "rate at which revenue is produced is $\phi(t)$ at time t." It can only mean that if $R(t)$ is the total revenue up to time t, then

$$R'(t) = \phi(t)$$

or $$R(x) = \int_0^x \phi(t)\, dt$$

We say that the amount of revenue produced in the small interval t to $t + dt$ is $\phi(t)\, dt$, which means that the total revenue is found by integrating $\phi(t)$ with respect to dt. By similar reasoning, the present value of the revenue produced in this interval is $\phi(t)e^{-rt}\, dt$, and the total present value is $K(x)$, where

$$K(x) = \int_0^x \phi(t)e^{-rt}\, dt$$

When $\phi(t) = a + bt$,

$$K(x) = \int_0^x (a + bt)e^{-rt}\, dt$$

The evaluation of this integral requires "integration by parts," which will be discussed in Section 10.4, but the reader should check, by differentiating, that an indefinite integral is

$$e^{-rt}\left(-\frac{b}{r^2} - \frac{bt}{r} - \frac{a}{r}\right)$$

and that

$$K(x) = \frac{ar + b}{r^2}(1 - e^{-rx}) - \frac{b}{r^2}e^{-rx}$$

Note that when $x \to \infty$, $K(x)$ approaches the limit $(ar + b)/r^2$. This means that although the revenue function $\phi(t)$ increases indefinitely with time, revenue in the far distant future is of such little worth today that no matter how long the process continues, the present value of the income remains finite.

Exercises

1. Find the area under the curves $y = x^3$ and $y^2 = 4x$ between $x = 0$ and $x = h$.

2. Let
$$\phi(x) = \begin{cases} x^3 - 2x^{5/2} + 3x + 1, & x \leq 1 \\ x^5 + 2x^2, & x \geq 1 \end{cases}$$

Find
$$\int_0^2 \phi(x)\, dx$$

3. In Example 2, find $K(x)$ for the function $\phi(t) = 100 + 5t$.

■ 10.4 Methods of Integration

In the previous sections we introduced the integral of a function and demonstrated that the integral could be found by determining a function whose derivative is the given function. We try to recognize a function, which, when differentiated, will give the function being integrated. Almost all methods of integration ultimately involve this recognition, and it is necessary to learn the integrals of more common functions in order to find solutions. An extended list of integrals may be found in any set of standard mathematical tables.

We have already integrated various functions involving powers and sums of powers. For completeness we will start with statements of the almost obvious results that were implicitly used.

From exercise 4, Section 6.4, we have the following

$$\frac{d}{dx} ku(x) = k \frac{du}{dx}$$

and

$$\frac{d}{dx} [u(x) \pm v(x)] = \frac{du}{dx} \pm \frac{dv}{dx}$$

It follows that

$$\int kf(x)\, dx = k \int f(x)\, dx$$

and

$$\int [f(x) \pm g(x)]\, dx = \int f(x)\, dx \pm \int g(x)\, dx$$

In addition, from Section 6.6, as long as $n \neq -1$,

$$\frac{d}{dx} \left(\frac{x^{n+1}}{n+1} \right) = x^n$$

Combining these results enables us to integrate all functions that involve only sums of powers.

Example 1. $\displaystyle\int (x^5 + 3x^3 + 2x + 1)\, dx = \frac{x^6}{6} + \frac{3}{4}x^4 + x^2 + x + c$

Example 2. $\displaystyle\int (x^3 + 2x^{3/2} + x^{-2})\, dx = \frac{x^4}{4} + \frac{4}{5}x^{5/2} - x^{-1} + c$

Example 3. The rate of change of sales of a product is proportional to the sales price, $ds/dp = -bp$. Show that the product sales s is given in terms of the price p as $s = a - (b/2)p^2$.

The Integration of Special Functions

Using the definition of integrals, and Section 6.8, we have

$$\frac{d \log x}{dx} = \frac{1}{x}, \qquad \int \frac{dx}{x} = \log x + c$$

$$\frac{da^x}{dx} = a^x \log a, \qquad \int a^x \, dx = \frac{a^x}{\log a} + c$$

$$\frac{de^x}{dx} = e^x, \qquad \int e^x \, dx = e^x + c$$

$$\frac{d \sin x}{dx} = \cos x, \qquad \int \cos x \, dx = \sin x + c$$

$$\frac{d \cos x}{dx} = - \sin x, \qquad \int \sin x \, dx = - \cos x + c$$

$$\frac{d \tan x}{dx} = \sec^2 x, \qquad \int \sec^2 x \, dx = \tan x + c$$

These results can be used together with the following methods to integrate many expressions containing trigonometrical, logarithmic, and exponential functions.

The Method of Substitution

In differentiating a function such as $y = (x + 2)^5$ we substitute $z = x + 2$ and use the formula

$$\frac{dy}{dx} = \frac{dy}{dz} \cdot \frac{dz}{dx}$$

We can use a very similar process in integration. Suppose we know

$$\int f(z) \, dz = F(z)$$

and we wish to integrate a function $f\{z(x)\}z'(x)$ with respect to x, that is, we require

$$\int f\{z(x)\}z'(x) \, dx$$

The result is $F\{z(x)\}$. We can verify this by differentiation;

$$\frac{dF\{z(x)\}}{dx} = \frac{dF}{dz} \cdot \frac{dz}{dx} = f(z)z'(x) = f\{z(x)\}z'(x)$$

In practice we often write: "Let $dz = z'(x)\,dx$," instead of "$dz/dx = z'(x)$." Strictly speaking, this has no meaning, but we interpret it to mean that the result of integrating $f\{z(x)\}$ with respect to $z'(x)\,dx$ is the same as integrating $f(z)$ with respect to dz. The trick in utilizing this method lies in recognizing a suitable function $z(x)$ that will result in a function $f(z)$ whose integral we know.

Example 4.   Find $I = \int(x+2)^5\,dx$.   Let $z = x+2$, so $dz = dx$. Then

$$I = \int z^5\,dz = \frac{z^6}{6} = \frac{(x+2)^6}{6}$$

Example 5.   Find $I = \int(x^2+3x+7)^4(2x+3)\,dx$.   Let $z = x^2 + 3x + 7$, so $dz = (2x+3)\,dx$, and consequently

$$I = \int z^4\,dz = \frac{z^5}{5} = \frac{(x^2+3x+7)^5}{5}$$

Example 6.   Find $I = \int \dfrac{dx}{ax+b}$.   Let $z = ax + b$, so $dz = a\,dx$.

Therefore

$$I = \int \frac{1}{a} \cdot \frac{1}{z} \cdot dz = \frac{1}{a}\int \frac{dz}{z} = \frac{1}{a}\log z = \frac{1}{a}\log\,(ax+b)$$

This result is frequently useful and should be remembered. It is only correct as long as x takes values that make $ax + b > 0$. If $ax + b < 0$, we can write

$$I = \int \frac{dx}{ax+b} = -\int \frac{dx}{-ax-b} = -\frac{1}{a}\log\,[-(ax+b)]$$

If the range of integration includes $x = -b/a$, so $ax + b = 0$, the integral does not exist. We will discuss this question further in Section 10.7.

Example 7.   Find $I = \int \sin^3 x\,dx = \int(1 - \cos^2 x)\sin x\,dx$.   Let $\cos x = z$, so $dz = -\sin x\,dx$.   Therefore

$$I = -\int(1 - z^2)\,dz = -\left[z - \frac{z^3}{3}\right] = \frac{\cos^3 x}{3} - \cos x$$

Example 8. Find $I = \int e^{ax+b}\, dx$. Let $z = ax + b$, $dz = a\, dx$.

Therefore $\qquad I = \dfrac{1}{a}\int e^z\, dz = \dfrac{1}{a} e^z = \dfrac{e^{ax+b}}{a}$

Example 9. Find $I = \displaystyle\int \dfrac{dx}{ax^2 + bx + c}$. Before we can see a suitable substitution, some preliminary manipulation is necessary.

$$ax^2 + bx + c = a\left(x^2 + \frac{b}{a}x + \frac{c}{a}\right)$$

$$= a\left[x^2 + \frac{b}{a}x + \left(\frac{b}{2a}\right)^2 + \frac{c}{a} - \left(\frac{b}{2a}\right)^2\right]$$

$$= a\left[\left(x + \frac{b}{2a}\right)^2 + (\sqrt{c/a - b^2/4a^2})^2\right]$$

(We assume $c/a > b^2/4a^2$ so that the square root is real; if $c/a < b^2/4a^2$, a different approach is necessary and it will be described in the next section.)

To avoid unnecessary writing let us put

$$\frac{b}{2a} = \beta$$

and $\sqrt{c/a - b^2/4a^2} = \gamma$.

Thus $\qquad I = \dfrac{1}{a}\displaystyle\int \dfrac{dx}{(x + \beta)^2 + \gamma^2}$

Now let $\qquad \tan z = \dfrac{x + \beta}{\gamma}$

$$\sec^2 z \,\frac{dz}{dx} = \frac{1}{\gamma}$$

(This can be seen by solving for x and finding dx/dz.) Therefore

$$[1 + \tan^2 z]\frac{dz}{dx} = \frac{1}{\gamma}$$

or $\qquad \dfrac{dz}{dx} = \dfrac{1}{\gamma[1 + \tan^2 z]} = \dfrac{1}{\gamma\left[1 + \left(\dfrac{x + \beta}{\gamma}\right)^2\right]}$

Therefore $dz = \dfrac{\gamma\, dz}{\gamma^2 + (x + \beta)^2}$

Therefore $I = \dfrac{1}{a\gamma} \displaystyle\int dz = \dfrac{z}{a\gamma} = \dfrac{1}{a\gamma} \tan^{-1}\left(\dfrac{x + \beta}{\gamma}\right)$

($\tan^{-1} y$ is defined as the angle θ such that $y = \tan \theta$; $0 \leq \theta \leq 2\pi$).
    The result need not be remembered, but the method of substitution involving a tangent should be.

Exercises

1. Find the following integrals:

   (a) $\int x^{4/5}\, dx$
   (b) $\int (ax^3 + bx^2 + cx + d)\, dx$
   (c) $\int (cx + b)^5\, dx$
   (d) $\int xe^{-x^2}\, dx$

   (e) $\displaystyle\int \dfrac{\log x}{x}\, dx$

   (f) $\displaystyle\int \left(\dfrac{1}{\sqrt{x}} - \sqrt{x}\right) dx$

2. Find the following integrals:

   (a) $\displaystyle\int \dfrac{x\, dx}{1 - x^2}$

   (b) $\int x(1 + x^2)^4\, dx$

   (c) $\displaystyle\int \dfrac{dx}{x^2 + 9}$

   (d) $\int \tan (1 + 2x)\, dx$

   (e) $\displaystyle\int \dfrac{\sin x\, dx}{1 + \cos x}$

3. Find the following integrals:

   (a) $\int e^{5x}\, dx$

   (b) $\displaystyle\int \dfrac{e^x\, dx}{1 + e^x}$

   (c) $\displaystyle\int \dfrac{(x + 5)\, dx}{4 + x^2}$

   (d) $\displaystyle\int \left(\dfrac{2}{x} - \dfrac{3}{x^2} - \dfrac{1}{3 - x}\right) dx$

4. Find the following integrals:

   (a) $\displaystyle\int_0^{\pi} \sin x\, dx$

   (b) $\displaystyle\int_0^{2\pi} \sin x\, dx$

   (c) $\displaystyle\int_0^{\pi/2} \sin^2 x\, dx$ (Recall $\cos 2x = 1 - 2\sin^2 x$.)

(d) $\displaystyle\int_0^{\pi/4} \tan x \, dx \left(\text{Recall } \tan x = \dfrac{\sin x}{\cos x}.\right)$

(e) $\displaystyle\int_0^1 \dfrac{1}{x^2 + 16} \, dx$

(f) $\displaystyle\int \dfrac{\sec^2 x}{\tan^2 x + 4} \, dx$

(g) $\displaystyle\int \dfrac{dx}{\sqrt{1 - x^2}}$ (Let $x = \sin t$.)

(h) $\displaystyle\int \dfrac{dx}{\sqrt{1 - x^2}}$ (Let $x = \cos t$.)

[What is the connection between (g) and (h)?]

5. A firm has determined that sales volume s varies with advertising effort x as follows:

$$\frac{ds}{dx} = \frac{a}{(b + x)^2} \qquad (a, b \text{ are constants})$$

Show that

$$s = c - \frac{a}{b + x} \qquad (c \text{ is a constant of integration})$$

The Method of Partial Fractions

We know from Example 6 that we can integrate $1/(ax + b)$ in terms of the logarithm function. It can be shown that any rational function can be split into the sum of terms of three types:

    1. a polynomial
    2. fractions with constant numerators and linear denominators
    3. fractions with linear numerators and quadratic denominators of the form *

$$\frac{Ax + B}{ax^2 + bx + c}$$

Each term can then be integrated separately and the results added to give the integral of the original.

* If $ax^2 + bx + c$ has real factors, such ratios can be split into the sum of two fractions of type (2). The condition for real factors is $b^2 \geq 4ac$. If $b^2 < 4ac$, there are no real factors and the ratio must be integrated as it is.

Example 10.

$$I = \int \frac{dx}{x^2 + 5x + 6}$$

$$\frac{1}{x^2 + 5x + 6} = \frac{1}{(x + 3)(x + 2)} = \frac{A}{x + 3} + \frac{B}{x + 2}$$

$$= \frac{x(A + B) + 2A + 3B}{(x + 3)(x + 2)}$$

Thus we must have $x(A + B) + 2A + 3B = 1$.

If this is always true, we can equate coefficients on both sides:

$$A + B = 0$$

$$2A + 3B = 1$$

Hence $A = -1$, $B = 1$.

Therefore

$$I = \int \left(\frac{1}{x + 2} - \frac{1}{x + 3} \right) dx$$

$$= \log (x + 2) - \log (x + 3)$$

$$= \log \frac{x + 2}{x + 3}$$

Example 11. $I = \int \frac{x^6 - 3x^5 + 10x^4 - 23x^3 + 11x^2 + 36x + 8}{x^4 + 8x^2 - 9}$

The first step is to notice that the degree of the numerator exceeds that of the denominator, and so we may divide out and obtain a polynomial and a *proper* fraction.

The result is

$$x^2 - 3x + 2 + \frac{x^3 + 4x^2 + 9x + 26}{x^4 + 8x^2 - 9}$$

The first part can now be integrated. The fraction, which we shall call F, must be split up. To do so we find the factors * of the denominator, which are $x^2 + 9$, $x - 1$, and $x + 1$.

$$F = \frac{Ax + B}{x^2 + 9} + \frac{C}{x - 1} + \frac{D}{x + 1}$$

* Notice we require linear factors if possible; the only quadratic factor has no *real* linear factors.

where A, B, C, D are to be determined. Notice that the quadratic denominator has a linear numerator. Adding the partial fractions yields

$$F = \frac{\left\{\begin{array}{l}(Ax + B)(x - 1)(x + 1) + C(x^2 + 9)(x + 1) \\ + D(x^2 + 9)(x - 1)\end{array}\right\}}{(x^2 + 9)(x - 1)(x + 1)}$$

$$= \frac{x^3 + 4x^2 + 9x + 26}{x^4 + 8x^2 - 9}$$

We can either equate coefficients in the numerators or give x specific values and substitute in both expressions for the numerators of F.

Set $x = 1$: $40 = 20C$ or $C = 2$.
Set $x = -1$: $20 = -20D$ or $D = -1$.
Set $x = 0$: $26 = -B + 9C - 9D = -B + 27$ or $B = 1$.

Lastly we equate the coefficients of x^3 on both sides: $A + C + D = 1$, $A + 1 = 1$ or $A = 0$.
Thus

$$I = \int \left(\frac{1}{x^2 + 9} + \frac{2}{x - 1} - \frac{1}{x + 1} + x^2 - 3x + 2\right) dx$$

$$= \frac{1}{3} \tan^{-1} \frac{x}{3} + 2 \log (x - 1) - \log (x + 1) + \frac{x^3}{3} - \frac{3}{2} x^2 + 2x$$

Example 11 illustrates most of the possibilities that arise in integrating rational functions. The only remaining case is where the quadratic factor has a numerator with a nonzero coefficient of x.

Example 12.

$$I = \int \frac{2x + 6}{x^2 + 2x + 17} dx$$

$$= \int \frac{2x + 6}{(x + 1)^2 + 16} dx = \int \left(\frac{2x + 2}{(x + 1)^2 + 16} + \frac{4}{(x + 1)^2 + 16}\right) dx$$

The second term can be integrated by an inverse tangent form. To integrate the first term we observe that the derivative of $(x + 1)^2 + 16$ is $2(x + 1) = 2x + 2$, and this suggests the substitution $z = (x + 1)^2 + 16$.

Let $z = (x + 1)^2 + 16$ so that $dz/dx = 2x + 2$, and the first term is

$$\int \frac{dz}{z} = \log z = \log [(x + 1)^2 + 16].$$

For the second term, set $\tan z = \dfrac{x + 1}{4}$ and use the reasoning of Example 6. The final result is

$$I = \log (x^2 + 2x + 17) + \tan^{-1} \left(\frac{x + 1}{4}\right)$$

Exercises

1. Integrate the following:

(a) $\dfrac{x - 1}{x^2 - x - 12}$

(b) $\dfrac{3x^2 - x + 5}{x^3 - 2x^2 + x - 2}$

(c) $\dfrac{x^2 + 1}{x^4 + 1}$

Hint:

$$\left(\frac{x^2 + 1}{x^4 + 1} = \frac{1 + 1/x^2}{x^2 + 1/x^2} = \frac{1 + 1/x^2}{(x - 1/x)^2 + 2}; \text{substitute } x - \frac{1}{x} = t\right)$$

2. Integrate the following:

(a) $\displaystyle\int \frac{dx}{x^2 - 16}$ (d) $\displaystyle\int \frac{dx}{x^2(1 + x)}$

(b) $\displaystyle\int \frac{x \, dx}{(x + 2)^2}$ (e) $\displaystyle\int \frac{dx}{x^2(1 + x^2)}$

(c) $\displaystyle\int \frac{x \, dx}{(x + 2)^3}$ (f) $\displaystyle\int \frac{x^5 \, dx}{(1 + x)(2 - x)}$

3. The rate of change of sales volume s with respect to advertising effort is found to be

$$\frac{ds}{dx} = \frac{10 + x}{1 + 2x + x^2} \qquad (x \text{ in dollars, } s \text{ in units of } \$10^4)$$

Show that s is given by

$$s = \log (x + 1) - \frac{9}{x + 1} + c$$

The Method of Integration by Parts

We now develop a useful technique for integrating products, such as xe^{-x} or $e^x \sin x$. We start with the formula for differentiating a product. If $y = uv$, where u and v are functions of x, we have seen (Section 6.5) that

$$\frac{dy}{dx} = \frac{d(uv)}{dx} = u \frac{dv}{dx} + v \frac{du}{dx}$$

We now write this as

$$u \frac{dv}{dx} = \frac{d(uv)}{dx} - v \frac{du}{dx}$$

and integrate both sides

$$\int u \left(\frac{dv}{dx} \right) dx = uv - \int v \left(\frac{du}{dx} \right) dx$$

The utility of this formula lies in the fact that the integral on the right may be simpler than that on the left. Of course it is necessary to be able to choose u and v in an appropriate fashion.

Example 13. $I = \int xe^{-x} \, dx$

Let $u = x$ and $dv/dx = e^{-x}$. Therefore

$$\frac{du}{dx} = 1 \qquad \text{and} \qquad v = \int e^{-x} \, dx = -e^{-x}$$

$$I = -xe^{-x} + \int e^{-x} \, dx$$

$$= -xe^{-x} - e^{-x} = -(x+1)e^{-x}$$

Example 14. $I = \int e^x \sin x \, dx$

Let $u = \sin x$ and $dv/dx = e^x$. Therefore

$$\frac{du}{dx} = \cos x \qquad \text{and} \qquad v = \int e^x \, dx = e^x$$

$$I = e^x \sin x - \int e^x \cos x \, dx$$

To perform the remaining integral let $u = \cos x$ and $dv/dx = e^x$.

Therefore

$$\frac{du}{dx} = -\sin x \quad \text{and} \quad v = e^x$$

$$I = e^x \sin x - e^x \cos x - \int e^x \sin x \, dx = e^x \sin x - e^x \cos x - I$$

$$I = \tfrac{1}{2}e^x (\sin x - \cos x)$$

Exercises

1. Integrate the following:

   (a) $\int x^2 e^{-x} \, dx$

   (b) $\int \log x \, dx$ (*Hint:* $\log x = 1 \times \log x$)

   (c) $\int x \log x \, dx$

   (d) $\int axe^{-x^2} \, dx$

2. If $y = f(x)$ implies that $x = g(y)$, we say that g is the *inverse* function of f, and we often write $g(y) = f^{-1}(y)$. Show that if $F(x) = \int f(x) \, dx$, then

$$\int f^{-1}(y) \, dy = yf^{-1}(y) - F\{f^{-1}(y)\}$$

[Let $x = f^{-1}(y)$ or $y = f(x)$, $dy = f'(x) \, dx$; use integration by parts.]

3. Find the following integrals, stating in each case the range of validity [e.g., $\displaystyle\int \frac{dx}{2 + 3x} = \frac{1}{3}\log (2 + 3x)$ or $-\frac{1}{3}\log - (2 + 3x)$ according to whether $x > -\frac{2}{3}$ or $x < -\frac{2}{3}$. The integral does not exist if $x = \frac{2}{3}$].

   (a) $\displaystyle\int \frac{dx}{x^2 - 9}$

   (b) $\displaystyle\int \frac{dx}{(x - 2)(x - 1)}$

   (c) $\displaystyle\int \frac{x \, dx}{(x - 2)(x - 1)}$

   (d) $\displaystyle\int \frac{2x^2 \, dx}{(x^2 + 1)(x - 1)}$

   (e) $\displaystyle\int \frac{dx}{x^4 - 1}$

   (f) $\displaystyle\int \frac{dx}{x^4 + 1} = \int \frac{dx}{\left\{ \begin{array}{l}(x^2 + \sqrt{2}x + 1) \times \\ (x^2 - \sqrt{2}x + 1)\end{array}\right\}}$

4. The rate of increase in profits per dollar increase in sales price dP/dp is given by

$$\frac{dP}{dp} = (a - 1) + \frac{c}{p} - \log p \quad \text{(where } a \text{ and } c \text{ are constants)}$$

Show that profits are given by

$$P = (a - 1)p + c \log p - (\log p - 1)p + \text{constant}$$

This result can be simplified as

$$P = (p - c)(a - \log p) \qquad \text{(where the constant equals } -ac)$$

For $c = $ unit cost, the first expression is the net profit per unit sold. The second expression might be the number of units sold as a function of the sales price p.

■ 10.5 Numerical Integration

In many practical problems the integral of a function cannot be determined by the methods of Section 10.4. In such cases we are forced to fall back on numerical approximation. In this section we present three elementary methods: Trapezium Rule, Simpson's Rule, and Taylor's Series Expansion. All three replace the function to be integrated by an approximation whose integral is known. In the first two we use linear and quadratic approximations. In the third method we use Taylor's Theorem and integrate the series term by term.

The Trapezium Rule

This rule uses a series of straight-line segments to approximate the given function $f(x)$.

Suppose we require $\displaystyle\int_{a}^{b} f(x)\,dx$ and we do not know an indefinite integral for $f(x)$. In Figure 10.3 let A_0P_0 be the line $x = a$ and A_nP_n the

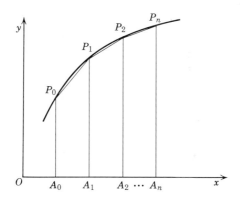

Figure 10.3   Trapezium rule.

line $x = b$; divide the area under the curve into strips of equal width $h = (b - a)/n$ as shown in the figure.

Let us denote the ordinates $A_0P_0, A_1P_1 \ldots A_nP_n$ by $y_0, y_1, y_2, \ldots y_n$ [i.e., $y_0 = f(a)$; $y_r = f(a + rh)$; $y_n = f(b)$]. Then the area of the trapezium $A_{r-1}P_{r-1}P_rA_r$ is

$$\frac{h}{2}(y_{r-1} + y_r), \qquad r = 1, 2, \ldots, n$$

The total area of all the trapezia is

$$\frac{h}{2}[(y_0 + y_1) + (y_1 + y_2) + (y_2 + y_3) + \cdots + (y_{n-1} + y_n)]$$

$$= h\left[\tfrac{1}{2}y_0 + \sum_{r=1}^{n-1} y_r + \tfrac{1}{2}y_n\right]$$

Thus the Trapezium Rule states

$$\int_a^b f(x)\, dx \simeq h\left[\tfrac{1}{2}(y_0 + y_n) + \sum_{r=1}^{n-1} y_r\right]$$

This should be compared with the two summation formulas

$$\int_a^b f(x)\, dx \simeq h\sum_{r=0}^{n-1} y_r \qquad \text{and} \qquad \int_a^b f(x)\, dx \simeq h\sum_{r=1}^{n} y_r$$

Examination of Figures 10.2a and 10.3 shows that the Trapezium Rule will give a closer approximation to the area under a curve than will simple summation.

The difference between the two is $h/2(y_n - y_0)$, and if h is small, it may be negligible. When we are using an electronic computer it is feasible to make h very small (and n very large), in which case the summation formula is often good enough.

Note we can bound the integral by $h\sum_{r=0}^{n-1} y_r$ and $h\sum_{r=1}^{n} y_r$, where

$$h\sum_{r=0}^{n-1} y_r \leq \text{integral} \leq h\sum_{r=1}^{n} y_r$$

or

$$h\sum_{r=1}^{n} y_r \leq \text{integral} \leq h\sum_{r=0}^{n-1} y_r$$

depending on which sum is smaller. The Trapezium Rule averages the two bounds.

Simpson's Rule

This rule uses a series of quadratic curves to approximate the given function $f(x)$. Suppose we require $\int_{-h}^{h} f(x)\,dx$ in terms of $y_{-1} = f(-h)$, $y_0 = f(0)$, and $y_1 = f(h)$.

Let us start by fitting a quadratic curve to pass through the points $(-h, y_{-1})$, $(0, y_0)$, and (h, y_1) in Figure 10.4. Such a curve will be very close to $f(x)$ provided h is small. The required curve is

$$g(x) = \frac{1}{2h^2}[x(x-h)y_{-1} - 2(x-h)(x+h)y_0 + x(x+h)y_1]$$

This can easily be verified by finding $g(-h)$, $g(0)$, and $g(h)$.

Now $g(x) = \dfrac{1}{2h^2}[2h^2 y_0 + hx(y_1 - y_{-1}) + x^2(y_{-1} - 2y_0 + y_1)]$

Therefore

$$\int_{-h}^{h} g(x)\,dx = \frac{1}{2h^2}\int_{-h}^{h}[2h^2 y_0 + hx(y_1 - y_{-1}) + x^2(y_{-1} - 2y_0 + y_1)]\,dx$$

$$= \frac{1}{2h^2}\left[2h^2 y_0 x + \frac{h}{2}x^2(y_1 - y_{-1})\right.$$

$$\left. + \frac{x^3}{3}(y_{-1} - 2y_0 + y_1)\right]_{x=-h}^{h}$$

$$= \frac{1}{2h^2}\left[+ 4h^3 y_0 + \frac{2h^3}{3}(y_{-1} - 2y_0 + y_1)\right]$$

$$= \frac{h}{3}(y_{-1} + 4y_0 + y_1)$$

Suppose we require $\int_{a}^{b} f(x)\,dx$ and we wish to divide the range into more than two parts. Let us divide it into $2n$ parts and set $h = (b-a)/2n$. We can now apply the above result to each pair of intervals separately. To do so we label the ordinates $y_0, y_1, y_2, \ldots, y_{2n}$ [i.e., $y_r = f(a + rh)$].

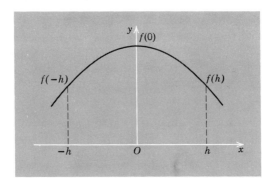

Figure 10.4   Simpson's rule.

We have

$$\int_a^b f(x)\,dx = \int_a^{a+2h} f(x)\,dx + \int_a^{a+4h} f(x)\,dx + \cdots + \int_{a+2h}^{a+2h} f(x)\,dx$$

$$\simeq \frac{h}{3}(y_0 + 4y_1 + y_2) + \frac{h}{3}(y_2 + 4y_3 + y_4)$$

$$+ \frac{h}{3}(y_4 + 4y_5 + y_6) + \cdots$$

$$+ \frac{h}{3}(y_{2n-2} + 4y_{2n-1} + y_{2n})$$

Therefore

$$\int_a^b f(x)\,dx \simeq \frac{h}{3}\{y_0 + y_{2n} + 4(y_1 + y_3 + \cdots + y_{2n-1})$$

$$+ 2(y_2 + y_4 + \cdots + y_{2n-2})\}$$

This result is known as *Simpson's Rule*.

Example. Find $I = \int_0^1 x^3\,dx$ by using the three approximations:

1. Summation
2. Trapezium Rule
3. Simpson's Rule

Find the exact answer with the aid of the indefinite integral.
We will divide the range into 10 parts and use the following table.

r	0	1	2	3	4	5	6	7	8	9	10
x	0	0.1	0.2	0.3	0.4	0.5	0.6	0.7	0.8	0.9	1.0
$f(x) = y_r$	0	0.001	0.008	0.027	0.064	0.125	0.216	0.343	0.512	0.729	1.0

$$h = 0.1$$

(1) Summation: $\sum_{r=0}^{9} y_r = 2.025$ so $I \simeq 0.2025$

(2) Trapezium Rule: $\frac{1}{2}(y_0 + y_{10}) = 0.5$ and $\sum_{r=1}^{9} y_r = 2.025$.

Therefore $I \simeq 0.1(2.025 + 0.5) = 0.2525$.

(3) Simpson's Rule: $y_0 + y_{10} = 1.0$, $y_1 + y_3 + y_5 + y_7 + y_9 = 1.225$,

and $y_2 + y_4 + y_6 + y_8 = 0.8$. Therefore $I \simeq \dfrac{0.1}{3} (1.0 + 4 \times 1.225$

$+ 2 \times 0.8) = 0.25$.

The exact result is

$$\int_0^1 x^3 \, dx = \left[\frac{x^4}{4} \right]_0^1 = 0.25$$

Thus, as we might have guessed, Simpson's Rule is most accurate. Although we have only proved it exact for quadratic curves, it is, as the reader should show, exact for cubics. In fact, it can never be less accurate than the others.

Exercises

1. Evaluate $I = \displaystyle\int_1^2 x^3 \, dx$ by the three approximation methods.

2. Evaluate $I = \displaystyle\int_0^2 \frac{x^2}{x + 1} \, dx$ by any of the three approximation methods.

3. Evaluate $I = \displaystyle\int_{-1}^1 \frac{x^2}{x + 2} \, dx$ by taking $n = 5$ and 10 and by any approximation method.

4. Evaluate the integral $\displaystyle\int_0^1 x^3 \, dx$ by using the three approximation methods with $n = 10$, $n = 20$ and compare the results.

5. Evaluate $\displaystyle\int_0^1 e^{-x^2} \, dx$ by taking $n = 5$ and $n = 10$.

6. Evaluate $\displaystyle\int_0^{\pi} \frac{\sin x}{x} \, dx$ for $n = 18$ or $h = 10°$.

Taylor's Series

Example 1. Consider the integral $\displaystyle\int_0^{\frac{1}{4}} \frac{dx}{1-x}$. We have

$$\frac{1}{1-x} = 1 + x + x^2 + x^3 + \cdots$$

$$\int \frac{dx}{1-x} = x + \frac{x^2}{2} + \frac{x^3}{3} + \frac{x^4}{4} + \cdots$$

$$\int_0^{\frac{1}{4}} \frac{dx}{1-x} = \frac{1}{4} + \frac{1}{2}\left(\frac{1}{4}\right)^2 + \frac{1}{3}\left(\frac{1}{4}\right)^3 + \frac{1}{4}\left(\frac{1}{4}\right)^4 + \cdots$$

$$= 0.25 + 0.03125 + 0.00521 + 0.00099$$

$$+ 0.00020 + 0.00004$$

$$= 0.28769$$

Of course the result may be stated as $-\log\left(\frac{3}{4}\right)$. Tables computed to 5 decimal places give $-\log\left(\frac{3}{4}\right) = 0.28769$.

In general a function $f(x)$ can be expanded in Taylor's Series about the point a as follows:

$$f(x) = f(a) + (x-a)f'(a) + \frac{(x-a)^2}{2!}f''(a) + \cdots$$

Therefore

$$\int_{x_1}^{x_2} f(x)\, dx = \left[f(a)x + \frac{(x-a)^2}{2!}f'(a) + \frac{(x-a)^3}{3!}f''(a) + \cdots \right]_{x_1}^{x_2}$$

We must select a such that the series converges for all values of x in the interval (x_1, x_2); usually, by choosing a so that $x_1 \leq a \leq x_2$, we can obtain the desired accuracy with fewer terms.

Example 2. Find $\displaystyle\int_0^1 x^3\, dx$; let $a = \frac{1}{2}$.

$$f(x) = \left(\frac{1}{2}\right)^3 + \left(x - \frac{1}{2}\right)3\left(\frac{1}{2}\right)^2 + \frac{(x - 1/2)^2}{2!}6\left(\frac{1}{2}\right) + \frac{(x - 1/2)^3}{3!}6$$

Therefore

$$\int_0^1 f(x)\, dx = \left[\left(\frac{1}{2}\right)^3 x + \frac{3}{8}\left(x - \frac{1}{2}\right)^2 + \frac{1}{2}\left(x - \frac{1}{2}\right)^3 + \frac{1}{4}\left(x - \frac{1}{2}\right)^4\right]_0^1$$

$$= 0.125 + 0.125 = 0.25$$

Exercises

Use Taylor's Series to evaluate the following integrals:

1. $\displaystyle\int_0^{1/2} \frac{x^2}{x+1}\, dx$

2. $\displaystyle\int_0^1 e^{-x^2}\, dx$

3. $\displaystyle\int_1^2 \log x\, dx$ (*Hint:* let $a = 1$.)

■ 10.6 Differentiation under the Integral Sign

In many problems of maximization, where probabilities are involved (e.g., problems concerned with future sales demand), we find that total expected profit $F(x)$ is given by an expression of the form

$$F(x) = \int_{a(x)}^{b(x)} f(x, z)\, dz$$

Here the integration is with respect to z, but the variable x appears in the limits of integration and in the function to be integrated. We wish to choose x so as to maximize $F(x)$, and to do so we must differentiate the integral *with respect to* x. We proceed in the usual way:

$$F(x + h) - F(x) = \int_{a(x+h)}^{b(x+h)} f(x + h, z)\, dz - \int_{a(x)}^{b(x)} f(x, z)\, dz$$

Now use Taylor's Theorem:

$$f(x + h, z) = f(x, z) + h\,\frac{\partial}{\partial x} f(x + \theta_1 h, z)$$

$$a(x + h) = a(x) + ha'(x + \theta_2 h)$$

$$b(x + h) = b(x) + hb'(x + \theta_3 h)$$

where $\quad 0 \le \theta_1 \le 1, \quad 0 \le \theta_2 \le 1, \quad 0 \le \theta_3 \le 1$

Therefore

$$F(x + h) - F(x) = \int_{a(x)+ha'(x+\theta_2 h)}^{b(x)+hb'(x+\theta_3 h)} \left[f(x, z) + h\frac{\partial}{\partial x} f(x + \theta_1 h, z) \right] dz$$

$$- \int_{a(x)}^{b(x)} f(x, z)\, dz$$

$$= \int_{a(x)}^{b(x)} \left[f(x, z) + h\frac{\partial}{\partial x} f(x + \theta_1 h, z) \right] dz$$

$$+ \int_{b(x)}^{b(x)+hb'(x+\theta_3 h)} \left[f(x, z) + h\frac{\partial}{\partial x} f(x + \theta_1 h, z) \right] dz$$

$$- \int_{a(x)}^{a(x)+ha'(x+\theta_2 h)} \left[f(x, z) + h\frac{\partial}{\partial x} f(x + \theta_1 h, z) \right] dz$$

$$- \int_{a(x)}^{b(x)} f(x, z)\, dz$$

Now, if the range of integration is small, the integral is approximately equal to the range multiplied by the function to be integrated.* (This is obvious from examination of the area under a curve.) Thus for small h,

$$F(x + h) - F(x) = hb'(x + \theta_3 h) \left[f(x, b(x)) + h\frac{\partial}{\partial x} f(x + \theta_1 h, b(x)) \right]$$

$$- ha'(x + \theta_2 h) \left[f(x, a(x)) + h\frac{\partial}{\partial x} f(x + \theta_1 h, a(x)) \right]$$

$$+ h\int_{a(x)}^{b(x)} \frac{\partial}{\partial x} f(x + \theta_1 h, z)\, dz$$

Now divide by h and let h tend to zero, so that $b'(x + \theta_3 h) \to b'(x)$ and $a'(x + \theta_2 h) \to a'(x)$.

Therefore

$$F'(x) = b'(x)f(x, b(x)) - a'(x)f(x, a(x)) + \int_{a(x)}^{b(x)} \frac{\partial}{\partial x} f(x, z)\, dz$$

This is the formula for the *differential of an integral*.

Example. Suppose an item has an operating cost rate $f(t)$ at time t, that is, the cost of operating the item in the time interval $(t, t + dt)$ is

* The function can be evaluated at any point of the range.

given by $f(t)\,dt$. The cost of overhaul is a, and the item is returned to its original condition. Find the optimal overhaul interval.

The total operating cost after a period T is given by $\displaystyle\int_0^T f(t)\,dt$, and the average cost per unit time is $\dfrac{1}{T}\displaystyle\int_0^T f(t)\,dt$. The cost of overhaul, amortized over the period T, is given by a/T. The total cost, K per unit time, is given by

$$K(T) \;=\; \frac{a}{T} + \frac{1}{T}\int_0^T f(t)\,dt$$

The optimal period is that value of T that minimizes $K(T)$—or that T for which $dK/dT = 0$.

$$T^2\frac{dK}{dT} = T\frac{d}{dT}\left[\int_0^T f(t)\,dt\right] - \left[a + \int_0^T f(t)\,dt\right] = 0$$

The optimal value T_0 is such that

$$f(T_0) \;=\; \frac{a}{T_0} + \frac{1}{T_0}\int_0^{T_0} f(t)\,dt = K(T_0)$$

or the operating cost rate equals the total average cost to date. (See exercise 5 following this section.)

Exercises

1. Evaluate $\displaystyle\frac{d}{dx}\int_0^{x^2}(x^3 + 2z^2x - zx^2 + z^4)\,dz$ by using the above method. Check the result by first integrating with respect to z and then differentiating with respect to x.

2. Find the derivatives with respect to x of the following integrals:

(a) $\displaystyle\int_0^x \sin(3 + 4xz)e^{3x}\,dz$

(b) $\displaystyle\int_0^{x^2} (x + z)\log z\,dz$

3. Let the demand of a certain product be x units and $f(x)$ its probability density function; then $f(x)\,dx$ is the probability that the demand is between x and $x + dx$. Let c_1 and c_2 be the costs per unit of overestimation and underestimation respectively. Then the total expected cost,

if S units are produced (see Section 7.2 for a known demand) is given by

$$c_1 \int_{x=0}^{S} (S - x)f(x)\, dx + c_2 \int_{S}^{\infty} (x - S)f(x)\, dx$$

Show that if we wish to minimize the expected cost we must choose S to satisfy the equation

$$\int_{0}^{S} f(x)\, dx = \frac{c_2}{c_1 + c_2}$$

(Note $\qquad \int_{0}^{S} f(x)\, dx = 1 - \int_{S}^{\infty} f(x)\, dx$)

4. In exercise 3, find the optimal value of S if

(a) $f(x) = 0.1,\ 5 \le x \le 15,\ \dfrac{c_1}{c_2} = 0.12$

(b) $f(x) = 0.1 - 0.005x,\ 0 \le x \le 20,\ \dfrac{c_1}{c_2} = 0.12$

5. Refer to the example on overhaul cost in the text.

(a) What happens when $f(t) = b = $ constant?
(b) Construct an example to show that even if $f(t)$ is an increasing function of t there may be no finite value of T_0 that minimizes average costs, that is, preventative overhaul cannot be justified. [Consider $f(t) = b(1 - e^{-t})$.]

■ **10.7   Improper Integrals**

There are two types of integrals that are described as *improper*. In the first type the function to be integrated (*integrand*) becomes infinite somewhere within the range or at one or other of the limits. In the second type the range itself becomes infinite. Consider the examples

$$\int_{-1}^{0} x^{-1/3}\, dx, \quad \int_{0}^{1} x^{-1/2}\, dx, \quad \int_{-1}^{1} x^{-1/3}\, dx, \quad \int_{-1}^{1} x^{-2}\, dx, \quad \int_{1}^{\infty} x^{-2}\, dx$$

The first four integrands become infinite; in the last example the range is infinite.

Improper Integrals of Type 1

First we consider the case where the integrand becomes infinite at the upper limit. We require a meaning for $I = \int_a^b f(x)\, dx$, where $\lim_{x \to b} f(x)$ is infinite and $f(x)$ is "well-behaved" elsewhere (Figure 10.5).

We define I by the equation $I = \lim_{z \to b} \int_a^z f(x)\, dx$, where $z \to b$ through values less than b only. If the limit is finite, the integral is said to exist. If not, we say the integration cannot be performed.

As an example, consider $I = \int_{-1}^0 x^{-1/3}\, dx$. Here $f(x) = x^{-1/3}$, and as $x \to 0, f(x) \to -\infty, (x < 0)$.

Therefore
$$I = \lim_{z \to 0} \int_{-1}^z x^{-1/3}\, dx,$$

where $z \to 0$ through negative values only.

Therefore
$$I = \lim_{z \to 0} \left[\tfrac{3}{2} x^{2/3} \right]_{-1}^z$$

$$= \lim_{z \to 0} \tfrac{3}{2} z^{2/3} - \left(-\tfrac{3}{2} \right)$$

$$= \tfrac{3}{2}$$

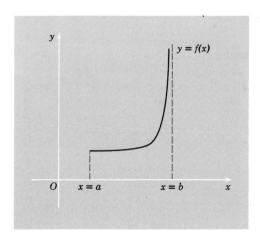

Figure 10.5   Improper integral (type 1).

Similarly, if the infinity occurs at the lower limit, we define

$$I = \int_a^b f(x)\, dx = \lim_{z \to a} \int_z^b f(x)\, dx$$

where z tends to a through values greater than a only.

Finally, if the infinity occurs in the middle of the range, we divide the range into two parts and integrate over each part separately. As an example, let us evaluate $I = \int_{-1}^1 x^{-\frac{1}{5}}\, dx$; the integrand is infinite when $x = 0$.

Here

$$I = \int_{-1}^0 x^{-\frac{1}{5}}\, dx + \int_0^1 x^{-\frac{1}{5}}\, dx$$

$$= \lim_{z \to 0^-} \int_{-1}^z x^{-\frac{1}{5}}\, dx + \lim_{y \to 0^+} \int_y^1 x^{-\frac{1}{5}}\, dx$$

($z \to 0^-$ means through negative values only; $y \to 0^+$ means through positive values only.)

Therefore

$$I = \lim_{z \to 0^-} \left[\tfrac{5}{4}x^{\frac{4}{5}}\right]_{-1}^z + \lim_{y \to 0^+} \left[\tfrac{5}{4}x^{\frac{4}{5}}\right]_y^1$$

$$= \lim_{z \to 0} \left[\tfrac{5}{4}z^{\frac{4}{5}} - \tfrac{5}{4}\right] + \lim_{y \to 0^+} \left[\tfrac{5}{4} - \tfrac{5}{4}y^{\frac{4}{5}}\right]$$

$$= -\tfrac{5}{4} + \tfrac{5}{4}$$

$$= 0$$

Note that each integral is to be evaluated separately; the two limits must exist independently of each other: otherwise the integral as a whole does not exist.

Example. Consider

$$I = \int_{-1}^1 x^{-3}\, dx = \int_{-1}^0 x^{-3}\, dx + \int_0^1 x^{-3}\, dx$$

$$= \lim_{z \to 0^-} \int_{-1}^z x^{-3}\, dx + \lim_{y \to 0^+} \int_y^1 x^{-3}\, dx$$

$$= \lim_{z \to 0^-} \left[-\tfrac{1}{2}x^{-2}\right]_{-1}^z + \lim_{y \to 0^+} \left[-\tfrac{1}{2}x^{-2}\right]_y^1$$

$$= \lim_{z \to 0^-} \left[\frac{1}{2} - \frac{1}{2z^2}\right] + \lim_{y \to 0^+} \left[\frac{1}{2y^2} - \frac{1}{2}\right]$$

$$= -\infty + \infty$$

which is indeterminate, and the integral does not exist. Now, y and z have no significance in themselves, and we might have used the same letter in both cases and written

$$I = \lim_{z \to 0^-} \left[\frac{1}{2} - \frac{1}{2z^2} \right] + \lim_{z \to 0^+} \left[\frac{1}{2z^2} - \frac{1}{2} \right]$$

At this point there is a temptation to perform the sum *first* and then the limiting process. If we did, we would obtain

$$I = \lim_{z \to 0} 0 = 0$$

Unfortunately this is incorrect. In all processes involving limits, great care must be taken to perform the operations in the correct order, for interchange of operations may lead to incorrect results.

Improper Integrals of Type 2

In this case we wish to give meaning to $I = \int_a^\infty f(x)\, dx$, where the range of integration is infinite. We define I in an obvious fashion:

$$I = \lim_{z \to \infty} \int_a^z f(x)\, dx$$

Example 1. Evaluate $I = \int_1^\infty x^{-2}\, dx$

$$I = \lim_{z \to \infty} \int_1^z x^{-2}\, dz$$

$$= \lim_{z \to \infty} \left[-x^{-1} \right]_1^z$$

$$= \lim_{z \to \infty} \left(1 - \frac{1}{z} \right)$$

$$= 1$$

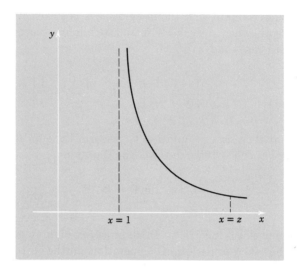

Figure 10.6   Improper integral (type 2).

The graphical interpretation is that the area under the curve between $x = 1$ and $x = z$ can be made as close to 1 as we please by increasing z sufficiently (see Figure 10.6).

Note that if both limits are infinite, we must carry out each limiting process independently of the other. If the limits do not exist separately (i.e., are not each finite), the entire integral does not exist.

Example 2. Let $f(x) = \begin{cases} x^{-2}, & x \geq 1 \quad \text{or} \quad x \leq -1 \\ 1, & -1 < x < 1 \end{cases}$

See Figure 10.7.

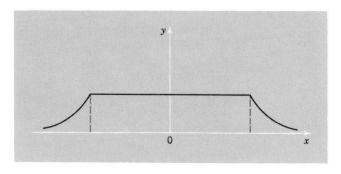

Figure 10.7   Improper integral (type 3).

Find $\quad I = \displaystyle\int_{-\infty}^{\infty} f(x)\,dx$

$$I = \int_{-\infty}^{-1} x^{-2}\,dx + \int_{-1}^{1} 1\,dx + \int_{1}^{\infty} x^{-2}\,dx$$

$$= \lim_{z \to -\infty} \int_{z}^{-1} x^{-2}\,dx + \int_{-1}^{1} (1)\,dx + \lim_{y \to \infty} \int_{1}^{y} x^{-2}\,dx$$

$$= \lim_{z \to -\infty} (1 + z^{-1}) + 2 + \lim_{y \to \infty} (1 - y^{-1})$$

$$= 1 + 2 + 1$$

$$= 4$$

On the other hand $I = \displaystyle\int_{-\infty}^{\infty} x^{-\frac{1}{3}}\,dx$ does not exist.

$$I = \lim_{w \to 0^{-}} \tfrac{3}{2} w^{\frac{2}{3}} - \lim_{z \to -\infty} \tfrac{3}{2} z^{\frac{2}{3}} + \lim_{v \to \infty} \tfrac{3}{2} v^{\frac{2}{3}} - \lim_{y \to 0^{+}} \tfrac{3}{2} v^{\frac{2}{3}}$$

Here all four limits must be taken separately. Both the first and last exist and are zero. The second and third do not exist, and we conclude that the original integral does not exist. As in a previous example we must be careful to avoid the error of cancelling the second limit with the third, by using z as the variable in both cases.

A detailed discussion of improper integrals is beyond our scope. We caution the reader to treat them with suspicion. There is always the possibility that they do not exist, in the same sense that an infinite sum may not exist (may diverge). Many tests have been devised for examining improper integrals. Interested readers are referred to other texts.

Example 3. For $n = 0, 1, 2, \ldots$ define

$$I_n = \int_{0}^{\infty} x^n e^{-ax}\,dx \qquad \text{and} \qquad I_n(t) = \int_{0}^{t} x^n e^{-ax}\,dx$$

Show that the infinite integral exists.

Integration by parts yields

$$I_n(t) = [nx^{n-1} e^{-ax}]_{0}^{t} + \frac{n}{a} \int_{0}^{t} x^{n-1} e^{-ax}\,dx$$

When $x = 0$, $nx^{n-1}e^{-ax} = 0$, and $\lim_{t \to \infty} nt^{n-1}e^{-at} = 0$ (proof by l'Hospital's Rule).

Therefore
$$I_n = \frac{n}{a} \int_0^\infty x^{n-1}e^{-ax}\, dx$$

Therefore
$$I_n = \frac{n}{a} I_{n-1} \qquad \text{if } I_{n-1} \text{ exists}$$

We can now repeat the argument and show

$$I_{n-1} = \frac{n-1}{a} I_{n-2} \qquad \text{if } I_{n-2} \text{ exists}$$

and so on, successively. If n is a positive integer, we find

$$I_n = \frac{n!}{a^n} I_0$$

and
$$I_0(t) = \int_0^t e^{-ax}\, dx = \frac{1}{a}(1 - e^{-at})$$

Hence I_0 exists and is equal to $1/a$.

Therefore
$$I_n = \frac{n!}{a^{n+1}}$$

If $a = 1$, n is a positive integer, we see I_n is merely $n!$ If n is not an integer, I_n still exists for $n > -1$ and is a function of n. It is related to the *Gamma Function* and is of frequent use in statistical work. The Gamma Function is defined by

$$\Gamma(n) = \int_0^\infty x^{n-1}e^{-x}\, dx, \qquad n > 0$$

Exercise

Show that

(a) $\Gamma(n) = \int_0^1 (-\log t)^{n-1}\, dt.$

(b) $\Gamma(n) = 2\int_0^\infty x^{2n-1}e^{-x^2}\, dx$

Exercises for Chapter 10

1. Find the following integrals:

   (a) $\displaystyle\int \frac{x\,dx}{1 + 5x^2}$ (e) $\displaystyle\int x^2 \log x\,dx$

   (b) $\displaystyle\int a^x e^x\,dx$ (f) $\displaystyle\int \frac{x^3\,dx}{x - 1}$

   (c) $\displaystyle\int \frac{dx}{1 + \sin x}$ (g) $\displaystyle\int x^2 \sin x\,dx$

   (d) $\displaystyle\int \frac{3x\,dx}{x^4 + 16}$ (h) $\displaystyle\int \cos^3 x \sin^2 x\,dx$

2. Evaluate the following integrals:

   (a) $\displaystyle\int_0^5 \frac{5x\,dx}{\sqrt{25 - x^2}}$ (d) $\displaystyle\int_0^4 \frac{dx}{1 + \sqrt{x}}$

   (b) $\displaystyle\int_0^1 \frac{dx}{\sqrt{4 - 3x}}$ (e) $\displaystyle\int_0^{\pi/2} \sin^4 x\,dx$

   (c) $\displaystyle\int_0^1 \sqrt{2x + x^2}\,dx$ (f) $\displaystyle\int_0^\infty \frac{x^2\,dx}{(1 + x)^5}$

3. Calculate the approximate values of the following integrals:

   (a) $\displaystyle\int_0^3 e^{-x^2/2}\,dx$ (d) $\displaystyle\int_0^1 x^2 e^{-x^2}\,dx$

   (b) $\displaystyle\int_0^5 \sqrt{x + x^2}\,dx$ (e) $\displaystyle\int_1^2 \frac{e^x\,dx}{x}$

   (c) $\displaystyle\int_0^1 \sqrt{x}\,e^{-3x}\,dx$ (f) $\displaystyle\int_1^2 \log x\,dx$

4. The *Gamma* distribution is given by
   $$f_n(x) = k_n x^n e^{-ax}, \qquad x \geq 0,\ a > 0,\ \text{and } n > -1$$
   where k_n is a constant such that $\displaystyle\int_0^\infty f_n(x)\,dx = 1$.
   Show that:

   (a) If n is a positive integer, $k_n = \dfrac{a^{n+1}}{n!}$

   (b) The mean m is given by
   $$m = \int_0^\infty x f(x)\,dx = \frac{n + 1}{a}$$

   (c) The variance σ^2 is given by
   $$\sigma^2 = \int_0^\infty x^2 f(x)\,dx - m^2 = \frac{n + 1}{a^2}$$

5. The *Normal* distribution is given by

$$f(x) = \frac{1}{\sqrt{2\pi}\sigma} e^{-(x-\mu)^2/2\sigma^2}, \qquad -\infty \leq x \leq +\infty$$

Assuming

$$\int_0^\infty e^{-t^2/2} \, dt = \sqrt{\pi/2}$$

show that the mean, given by $\int_{-\infty}^\infty xf(x) \, dx$, is equal to μ and that the variance, given by $\int_{-\infty}^\infty (x - \mu)^2 f(x) \, dx$, is equal to σ^2. [Note that if $g(x) = g(-x)$, then $\int_{-\infty}^\infty xg(x) \, dx = 0$. (Why?) Hence if $g(x - \mu) = g(\mu - x)$ and $\int_{-\infty}^\infty g(x) \, dx = 1$, we have $\int_{-\infty}^\infty xg(x) \, dx = \mu$. (Why?) For the variance substitute $t = (x - \mu)/\sigma$ and integrate by parts.]

6. Show that if $f_1(x, b(x)) = f_2(x, b(x))$, and

$$F = \int_0^{b(x)} f_1(x, z) \, dz + \int_{b(x)}^\infty f_2(x, z) \, dz$$

then

$$\frac{dF}{dx} = \int_0^{b(x)} \frac{\partial f_1}{\partial x} \, dz + \int_{b(x)}^\infty \frac{\partial f_2}{\partial x} \, dz$$

7. In the exercises for Section 10.6, we obtained, for the inventory example, $\int_0^S f(x) \, dx = C_2/(C_1 + C_2)$.

   (a) Find S when $f(x) = xe^{-x}$, $C_1/C_2 = \frac{1}{8}$.
   (b) Also, find S when $f(x) = \frac{1}{2}x^2 e^{-x}$, $C_1/C_2 = \frac{1}{10}$.

8. In the overhaul example of Section 10.6, find the optimal overhaul interval T_0 in miles if $f(t) = 0.05 + 0.001t$, $a = \$500$. (*Answer:* $T_0 = 1000$ miles.)

9. Show that if $0 \leq f(x) \leq g(x)$ for all x and if $\int_a^b g(x) \, dx$ is proper, then so is $\int_a^b f(x) \, dx$. (Case 1. a, b finite; $g(x) \to \infty$ as $x \to b$ and $g(x)$ is "well behaved" elsewhere. If $f(x)$ is always finite there is no problem; if not, then for small $h > 0$

$$\phi(h) = \int_a^{b-h} f(x) \, dx$$

must be an increasing function of h. But

$$\phi(h) \leq \int_a^b g(x) \, dx$$

Hence $\lim_{h \to 0^+} \phi(h)$ exists. Case 2. Suppose $b = \infty$; then the argument is similar.)

10. Show that $I_n = \int_0^\infty x^n e^{-x} \, dx$ is proper as long as $n > -1$. (First write $x^n e^{-x} = x \cdot x^{n-1} e^x$, and, integrating by parts, show that if n is positive, then

$I_n = nI_{n-1}$; as $I_0 = 1$ we see I_n is proper when $n = 1, 2, \ldots$ Now for $n > 0$ we must consider the upper limit. Let k be any integer greater than n, and compare I_k and I_n. For $-1 < n < 0$ we must compare I_n with I_0 for the upper limit and with $x^{-n}\, dx$ for the lower limit.)

11. In Example 2, Section 10.3, the present value, $K(x)$, of a revenue function $\phi(t)$ is given by $K(x) = \int_0^x \phi(t) e^{-rt}\, dt$. If $r = 0.1$ find $K(x)$ for the following cases:

     (a) $\phi(t) = 100e^{0.05t}$
     (b) $\phi(t) = 100 + 6t + 0.1t^2$
     (c) $\phi(t) = 100 - 2t$

12. Suppose that costs occur in cycles of duration T and that the cost at time t from the start of a cycle is given by $r(t)$, i.e., if θ is absolute time, and a cycle starts at time zero, the cost at time θ is given by

$$r(\theta), \qquad 0 \le \theta \le T$$

$$r(\theta - T), \qquad T < \theta \le 2T$$

$$r(\theta - 2T), \qquad 2T < \theta \le 3T, \quad \text{etc.}$$

If interest is charged continuously at a rate k per year, show that K, the present value of the costs during a cycle, as of the start of the cycle is given by

$$\int_0^T e^{-kt} r(t)\, dt = K$$

Hence, as of time zero, the costs during cycle n from time $(n-1)T$ to nT are worth $e^{-k(n-1)T}K$, and thus the present worth of all future costs is $K/(1 - e^{-kT})$.

13. The initial cost of a piece of equipment is C. The salvage value and repair costs at age t are $S(t)$ and $r(t)$ respectively. If annual interest is at rate k, and the equipment is replaced every T years, show that the present value of all future costs is

$$\frac{1}{1 - e^{-kt}} \left\{ C - S(T)e^{-kT} + \int_0^T r(t)e^{-kt}\, dt \right\}$$

Show also that the present value is minimized by choosing T to satisfy

$$r(T) - S'(T) + kS(T) = kK(T)$$

where $K(T)$ is the value of cost during a cycle as of the start of the cycle. Find the best value of T when $C = 50{,}000$; $S(t) = 50{,}000e^{-t/10}$; $r(t) = 2500e^{0.3t}$; and $k = 0.15$.

14. After an advertising campaign, a product has a sales rate $f(t) = 1000e^{-0.5t}$ where t is the number of months since the close of the campaign.

     (a) Find the total cumulative sales after 3 months.
     (b) Find the sales during the fourth month.
     (c) Find the total sales as a result of the campaign.

15. A television manufacturer is considering a 2-year warranty on guaranteed repairs to the purchaser. The repair cost rate for a typical television set is given by $f(t) = 0.05 + 0.06t$, where t is the time, in years, since purchase.

(a) Find the required additional charge for the warranty given by the cumulative repair costs at the end of 2 years.

(b) Find the time at which the cumulative repair costs equal the original purchase price.

(c) Solve (a) and (b) if $f(t) = 0.05 + 0.06(1 - e^{-0.5t})$.

16. Show that if $f(x) \geq 0$, then $\int_0^\infty f(x) \, dx$ and $\sum_0^\infty f(x)$ either both converge or both diverge. (Let $F_1(z) = \int_0^z f(x) \, dx$ and $F_2(z) = \sum_0^z f(x)$; both are increasing functions of z. It is not hard to see that if either F_1 or F_2 tends to a limit as z tends to infinity, we must have $f(x)$ tending to zero. Ultimately $f(x_1) \geq f(x_2)$ for all large x_1 and $x_2 > x_1$. Hence show that if either F_1 or F_2 tends to a limit, it can be used to find a bound on the other, and the result follows.)

17. Show that $\int_1^\infty x^{-k} \, dx$ exists as long as $k > 1$. Hence show that the k-series, $1^{-k} + 2^{-k} + 3^{-k} + \cdots$, converges only when $k > 1$.

11

Differential Equations

■ 11.1 Introduction

One basic problem in analyzing any system is to discover the functional relationships between the variables that represent the various parts. Sometimes this can be done in a more or less straightforward manner, as for example, in the relationship between costs and order quantity in the economic lot-size problem of Section 7.2. In other cases we can find relationships between some of the variables and rates of change of others. We then have the problem of discovering the functional relationships between the variables themselves. In the previous chapter we saw that if we have the equation

$$(1) \qquad \frac{dx}{dt} = f(t)$$

we can discover the relationship between x and t by integration. We have to recognize any function $F(t)$ with the property $F'(t) = f(t)$. Then x must have the form

$$x = F(t) + c$$

In order to find c we need one pair of values of x and t, say $x = x_0$ when $t = t_0$. Then the exact relationship between x and t is

$$x = F(t) - F(t_0) + x_0$$

that is, $\qquad c = x_0 - F(t_0)$

It is simpler to write equation (1) as

$$dx = f(t)\, dt$$

and then to integrate both sides

$$\int dx = \int f(t)\, dt \qquad \text{or} \qquad x + c' = F(t) + c''$$

Of course we can combine c' and c'' into one constant c, as we did in Chapter 10. In more complicated examples we have relationships between x, dx/dt, and t. Such relationships are called *differential equations*. In this chapter we examine some methods for discovering the functional relationships between x and t expressed by a differential equation.

Example 1. Suppose that the population of a region x grows at a rate proportional to its size, that is, at time t we have

(2)
$$\frac{dx}{dt} = rx$$

where r is a constant. What is the population at a time t, $x(t)$?

We know that for any constant A, the exponential function

(3)
$$x = A \exp(rt)$$

has the property that

$$\frac{dx}{dt} = rA \exp(rt) = rx$$

Thus (3) is a solution to (2). Notice that just as in the case of integration we have an arbitrary constant A which cannot be found from the

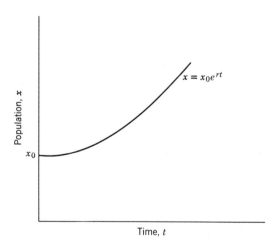

Figure 11.1   Population growth.

differential equation. To find the value of A; suppose that at a time $t = 0$, $x = x_0$, whence $A = x_0$. The solution to the original problem is $x = x_0 \exp (rt)$. The population function is plotted in Figure 11.1.

Definition.   An equation that involves the derivative of a function is called a *differential equation*. A condition of the form $x = x_0$ at $t = t_0$ is known as a *boundary condition* of the differential equation. In particular, $x = x_0$, when $t = 0$, is called an *initial* condition.

Example 2.   A firm observes that the rate of decrease of sales with respect to price is directly proportional to the sales volume and inversely proportional to the sales price plus a constant, that is,

$$(4) \qquad \frac{ds}{dp} = - \frac{bs}{a + p}$$

where s is the sales volume, p is the unit sales price, and a and b are constants. Find the relationship between sales volume and price.

In order to solve the equation

$$\frac{dy}{dx} = f(x)$$

we transform this equation into the form

$$dy = f(x)\, dx$$

integrate both sides, and obtain the solution,

$$y = \int f(x)\, dx$$

In a similar manner, we write equation (4) as

$$(5) \qquad \frac{ds}{s} = - \frac{b\, dp}{a + p}$$

integrate both sides of equation (5),

$$\int \frac{ds}{s} = - \int \frac{b\, dp}{a + p}$$

and obtain $\log s = -b \log (a + p) + \log c$, where $\log c$ is the constant of integration. Thus

$$\log s + b \log (a + p) = \log c$$

$$\log s(a + p)^b = \log c$$

$$s(a + p)^b = c$$

(6)
$$s = \frac{c}{(a + p)^b}$$

To verify that (6) is a solution to (4),

$$\frac{ds}{dp} = \frac{d[c/(a + p)^b]}{dp} = -\frac{bc}{(a + p)^{b+1}} = -\frac{s}{a + p}$$

The value of c may be obtained from (6) by substituting particular values of p and s. The sales price function is plotted in Figure 11.2.

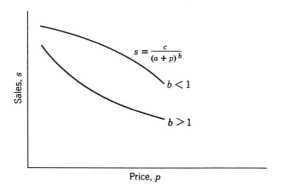

Figure 11.2   Pricing and sales volume.

Example 3.   We consider now a generalization of Example 1. Suppose that the population increases at a rate proportional to the product of two factors,

$$\frac{dx}{dt} = ax\left(1 - \frac{x}{b}\right), \qquad (a, b \text{ are constants})$$

To find x as a function of t we can proceed as in Example 2,

$$\frac{b\,dx}{x(b - x)} = a\,dt$$

$$\int \frac{b\,dx}{x(b - x)} = at + k$$

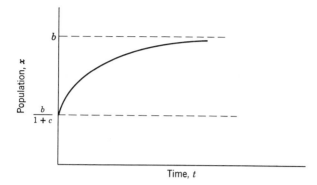

Figure 11.3   The logistic curve, $x = b/[1 + c \exp(-at)]$.

Since

$$\int \frac{b\,dx}{x(b-x)} = \int \left(\frac{1}{x} + \frac{1}{b-x}\right) dx = \log x - \log(b-x) = -\log \frac{b-x}{x}$$

$$\log \frac{b-x}{x} = -at - k$$

$$\frac{b-x}{x} = c \exp(-at) \qquad (c = \exp(-k) \text{ is a constant})$$

Thus

$$x = \frac{b}{1 + c \exp(-at)}$$

The graph, sometimes known as the *logistic curve*, is presented in Figure 11.3.

■ 11.2   Classification of Differential Equations

We will use the notation $x^{(n)} = d^n x/dt^n$ for the nth derivative of x with respect to t. The most general differential equation can be written

$$f(x, x^{(1)}, x^{(2)}, \ldots, x^{(n)}; t) = 0$$

where f is an arbitrary function of the $n + 2$ variables x, $x^{(1)}$, $x^{(2)}$, $\ldots$, $x^{(n)}$ and t. The general solution of such an equation has the form

$$x = A_1 f_1(t) + A_2 f_2(t) + \cdots + A_n f_n(t)$$

where $f_1, f_2, \ldots, f_n$ are functions that satisfy the equation and $A_1, \ldots,$ A_n are arbitrary constants. In order to determine the A's we need a sufficient number of boundary conditions, that is, we need to specify x at n different values of t or, alternatively, n equations between x and its derivatives. Methods of solution depend on classifying equations so that we can recognize the form of the solution. The simplest class is the *linear differential equation*, which has the form

$$\phi_n(t)x^{(n)} + \phi_{n-1}(t)x^{(n-1)} + \cdots + \phi_0(t)x = g(t)$$

When the functions $\phi_0 \ldots \phi_n$ are merely constants, that is,

$$(7) \qquad a_nx^{(n)} + a_{n-1}x^{(n-1)} + \cdots + a_1x^{(1)} + a_0x = g(t)$$

we have the *linear equation with constant coefficients*. The highest derivative that occurs determines the *order* of the equation—in this case the order is n. In the general equation, if m is the highest power of the highest order derivative that occurs, then the equation is of *degree m*. We will not discuss equations involving powers of derivatives higher than one because in general their solution is very difficult. In the following sections we will develop methods for solving various types of linear differential equations. Most of the discussion in this chapter will be concerned with linear equations with constant coefficients or equations that can be reduced to this form. However there are two other general equations which we will discuss first.

■ 11.3 Separable Equations

The equation $\dfrac{f(x)\,dx}{g(t)\,dt} = 1$ is called *separable*. We write

$$\int f(x)\,dx = \int g(t)\,dt$$

and the solution is obtained by integration. Let $\int f(x)\,dx = F(x)$ and $\int g(t)\,dt = G(t)$. The solution is found by solving (in the algebraic sense) $F(x) = G(t) + c$ where c is a constant of integration, found from a boundary condition. We have

$$\frac{dF}{dx} \cdot \frac{dx}{dt} = \frac{dG}{dt}$$

or

$$f(x)\,\frac{dx}{dt} = g(t)$$

and this verifies the solution.

Example 1. The relation between sales volume s and advertising effort x is given by the following differential equation,

$$\frac{ds}{dx} = a(b - s)$$

Find the functional relation, $s = s(x)$.

The above equation can be written as

$$\frac{ds}{b - s} = adx$$

and the solution is found by integrating both sides of the differential equation,

$$-\log (b - s) = ax + \log c$$

where c is a constant. We have

$$\log c + \log (b - s) = -ax$$

$$\log c(b - s) = -ax$$

$$c(b - s) = \exp (-ax)$$

$$cb - cs = \exp (-ax)$$

$$s = b - (1/c) \exp (-ax)$$

For $x = 0$, $s = s_0$, $s_0 = b - (1/c)$,

$$s = b - (b - s_0) \exp (-ax)$$

The graph of s versus x is presented in Figure 11.4. With no advertising effort, sales volume is s_0 and the maximum achievable sales is b.

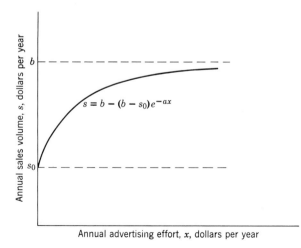

Figure 11.4 Sales volume and advertising efforts.

Example 2. Solve the differential equation,

$$(x^2 + 2) \frac{dx}{dt} = \sin t$$

Therefore $(x^2 + 2) \, dx = \sin t \, dt$

Therefore $\dfrac{x^3}{3} + 2x = c - \cos t$

If the initial condition is $x(0) = 0$, we see that $c = 1$ and $x^3 + 6x = 3 - 3 \cos t$.

Exercises

1. Find the solutions of the following separable differential equations:

(a) $\dfrac{dy}{dx} = -\dfrac{4y}{x}$ (c) $\dfrac{dy}{dx} = y \sin x$

(b) $\dfrac{dy}{dx} = \dfrac{xy}{1 + x^2}$ (d) $\dfrac{dy}{dx} = \dfrac{\log x}{y}$

2. Solve the equation

(a) $\dfrac{dy}{dx} = \dfrac{y}{x + y}$

$\left(\textit{Hint:} \text{ Substitute } y = vx, \ \dfrac{dy}{dx} = x\dfrac{dv}{dx} + v. \right)$

(b) $\dfrac{dy}{dx} = \dfrac{y^2}{xy - x^2}$

(*Note:* A differential equation of the form

$$\frac{dy}{dx} = \frac{f(x, y)}{g(x, y)} = \frac{\displaystyle\sum_{i=0}^{n} a_i x^i y^{n-i}}{\displaystyle\sum_{i=0}^{n} b_i x^i y^{n-i}}$$

may be transformed into a separable equation, if f and g are polynomials with all terms of the same degree, by the substitution $y = vx$.)

3. Solve Example 1 of Section 11.1 using the method of Section 11.3.

■ 11.4   Equations Solved with Integrating Factors

Consider the equation

$$\frac{dx}{dt} + f(t)x = g(t)$$

Multiply the equation by a function $h(t)$, determined in such a way that the left-hand side becomes the derivative of a product. We wish to find $h(t)$.

$$h(t)\frac{dx}{dt} + f(t)h(t)x = g(t)h(t)$$

Now consider $$\frac{d}{dt}[\phi(t)x] = \phi'(t)x + \phi(t)\frac{dx}{dt}$$

Comparing these two equations,

$$h(t) = \phi(t)$$

and $$f(t)h(t) = \phi'(t)$$

Therefore $$h(t)f(t) = h'(t)$$

Therefore $$f(t) = \frac{h'(t)}{h(t)} \qquad \text{or} \qquad f(t) = \frac{1}{h}\frac{dh}{dt}$$

Integrating both sides of the previous equation, yields

$$\int f(t)\, dt = \int \frac{dh}{h} = \log h$$

Therefore $$h(t) = \exp \int f(t)\, dt$$

The function $h(t)$ is called an *integrating factor*.
   Returning to the original equation we have

$$\frac{d}{dt}[h(t)x] = g(t)h(t)$$

Integrating both sides,

$$h(t)x = \int g(t)h(t)\, dt + c$$

and so x may be found as a function of t.

Example 1.

$$\frac{dx}{dt} + \frac{1}{t} x = \sin t; \qquad x = 0 \text{ when } t = \pi$$

Here $f(t) = \frac{1}{t}$ and $\int \frac{1}{t} dt = \log t$. The integrating factor is exp (log t) $= t$.

Therefore
$$\frac{d}{dt} (xt) = t \sin t$$

$$xt = \int t \sin t \, dt + c$$

To evaluate the integral on the right, we use the integration-by-parts formula of Section 10.4.

$$\int t \sin t \, dt = -t \cos t + \int \cos t \, dt$$
$$= -t \cos t + \sin t$$

Therefore
$$xt = -t \cos t + \sin t + c$$

or
$$x = \frac{1}{t} \sin t - \cos t + \frac{c}{t}$$

The boundary condition is $x = 0$ when $t = \pi$ and

therefore
$$0 = 1 + \frac{c}{\pi}$$

or
$$c = -\pi$$

It follows that

$$x = \frac{1}{t} \sin t - \cos t - \frac{\pi}{t}$$

Example 2.

$$\frac{dx}{dt} + f(t)x = x^n g(t)$$

This equation can be solved by means of an integrating factor if we first substitute $u = 1/x^{n-1}$. Division by x^n yields

$$\frac{1}{x^n} \frac{dx}{dt} + \frac{1}{x^{n-1}} f(t) = g(t)$$

Now
$$\frac{du}{dt} = \frac{du}{dx} \cdot \frac{dx}{dt} = -(n-1)x^{-n} \frac{dx}{dt}$$

Therefore
$$\frac{1}{x^n}\frac{dx}{dt} = -\frac{1}{n-1}\frac{du}{dt}$$

Therefore
$$-\frac{1}{n-1}\frac{du}{dt} + uf(t) = g(t)$$

and finally
$$\frac{du}{dt} - (n-1)uf(t) = -(n-1)g(t)$$

This can be solved for $u(t)$ by means of an integrating factor $\exp\left[-(n-1)\int f(t)\,dt\right]$ and, of course, $x(t) = u(t)^{-1/n-1}$.

Example 3. A differential equation relating net profits P and advertising effort x is given by

$$\frac{dP}{dx} + aP = b - ax$$

where a and b are constants. Find P as a function of x.

The integrating factor is given by $\exp\int a\,dx = e^{ax}$ and thus

$$Pe^{ax} = \int(b - ax)e^{ax}\,dx + c$$

$$= \frac{b}{a}e^{ax} - xe^{ax} + \frac{e^{ax}}{a} + c$$

$$P = \frac{b+1}{a} - x + ce^{-ax}$$

If $P = P_0$ at $x = 0$, we have

$$P_0 = \frac{b+1}{a} + c, \quad c = P_0 - \frac{b+1}{a}$$

and
$$P = \alpha + \beta\exp(-ax) - x$$

where
$$\alpha = \frac{b+1}{a}, \quad \beta = P_0 - \frac{b+1}{a}$$

We observe that the functional form for P is composed of two terms, gross profits, $g(x)$, and advertising expenditure, x, where

$$g = \alpha + \beta\exp(-ax)$$

Exercises

1. Find the solutions of the following differential equations:

(a) $\dfrac{dy}{dx} - 2y = 1 - 2x$

(b) $\dfrac{dy}{dx} - y = -2e^{-x}$

(c) $x\dfrac{dy}{dx} - y = x \cos x$

2. The total cost C of ordering and holding is given by the following differential equation:

$$\frac{dC}{dq} + \frac{C}{q} = a$$

where q is the size of order, a is a constant, and $C = C_0$ when $q = q_0$. Find C as a function of q.

$Answer: C = \dfrac{aq}{2} + \dfrac{1}{q}\left(C_0 q_0 - \dfrac{aq_0^2}{2}\right).$

3. Manufacturing costs K are related to the number of items produced q by the equation

$$\frac{dK}{dq} + aK = b + cq$$

where a, b, and c are constants. If $K = 0$ when $q = 0$, find K as a function of q.

$Answer: K = \alpha(1 - e^{-aq}) + \beta q, \ \alpha = \dfrac{ba - c}{a^2}, \beta = \dfrac{c}{a}.$ The first term is the learning cost and the second term is the direct cost.

4. Equipment maintenance and operating costs C are related to the overhaul interval x by the equation

$$x^2\frac{dC}{dx} - (n - 1)xC = -na$$

where a and n are constants and $C = C_0$ when $x = x_0$. Find C as a function of x.

$Answer: C = \dfrac{a}{x} + bx^{n-1}, \ b = \dfrac{C_0 x_0 - a}{x_0^n}.$

■ 11.5   The General Linear Differential Equation with Constant Coefficients

If D is an *operator* equivalent to d/dt we may interpret $D^n x$ as $d^n x/dt^n$. The general equation to be discussed in this section can be written:

$$(8) \qquad\qquad L(D)x = g(t)$$

where $L = L(D)$ is an operator given by $L = L(D) = a_n D^n + a_{n-1} D^{n-1} + \cdots + a_1 D + a_0$.

The general solution to equations of the form (8) relies on two facts:

(i) If $x = f(t)$ satisfies (8) and $x = h(t)$ satisfies $Lx = 0$, then $x = f(t) + h(t)$ is also a solution of (8).

(ii) If $x = f_1(t)$ and $x = f_2(t)$ are solutions of $Lx = 0$, then $x = Af_1(t) + Bf_2(t)$ (where A, B are constants) satisfies $Lx = 0$.

Both these statements follow from the fact that L is a *linear operator*. That is, if $u(t)$ and $v(t)$ are any functions of t, then

$$(9) \qquad\qquad L(Au + Bv) = ALu + BLv$$

We can prove (9) by observing that D is a linear operator. It follows by induction that D^n is a linear operator, and it is easy to see that if H and K are each linear operators, then $(A_1 H + A_2 K)$ is also a linear operator. The reader can now verify (i) and (ii).

The general solution of equation (8) consists of two parts: the *complimentary function* and a *particular solution*, where the complimentary function is a general solution of $Lx = 0$ and a particular solution is a function that satisfies $Lx = g(t)$. To find the general solution of $L(D)x = 0$ we observe that

$$L(D)e^{mx} = e^{mx} L(m)$$

where $L(m)$ is the polynomial obtained by replacing D by m. Since $e^{mx} \neq 0$, we must have

$$(10) \qquad\qquad L(m) = 0$$

If equation (10) has n distinct roots, $m_1, m_2, \ldots, m_n$, we see that $x = e^{m_i t}$ is a solution of $Lx = 0$. It follows from (9) that $x = A_1 e^{m_1 t} + A_2 e^{m_2 t} + \cdots + A_n e^{m_n t}$ is also a solution. Since it contains n independent functions and n arbitrary constants, we conclude it is the general solution. If $L(m) = 0$ has repeated roots, some modification is necessary.

Methods of finding particular solutions depend on the form of $g(t)$. Details are given in the Appendix.

Example .   In this economic model due to Samuelson * it is assumed that a deficiency of capital below a certain equilibrium level K_e leads to an increase in the rate of capital investment and a surplus of capital leads to a decrease in the rate of capital investment.

Let $K(t)$ = amount of capital at time t

   $k(t)$ = excess of capital over equilibrium amount K_e

   $I(t)$ = rate of investment at time t

We have

(11) $$\frac{dk(t)}{dt} = I(t)$$

(12) $$k(t) = K(t) - K_e$$

Using Samuelson's assumption,

(13) $$\frac{dI(t)}{dt} = - ak(t), \qquad a > 0$$

Initial conditions for $t = 0$ are: $I(0) = I_0$, $k(0) = k_0$.
Differentiating (11), and using (12) and (13),

(14) $$\frac{d^2k(t)}{dt^2} = \frac{dI(t)}{dt} = - ak(t)$$

Equation (14) may be written as

$$(D^2 + a)k(t) = 0$$

If we set $k(t) = e^{mt}$, we must have

$$m^2 + a^m = 0$$

and the roots are $i\sqrt{a}$ and $-i\sqrt{a}$. The general solution is

$$k(t) = c_1 e^{i\sqrt{a}\,t} + c_2 e^{-i\sqrt{a}\,t}$$

$$= c_1(\cos \sqrt{a}\,t + i \sin \sqrt{a}\,t) + c_2(\cos \sqrt{a}\,t - i \sin \sqrt{a}\,t)$$

(15) $$k(t) = (c_1 + c_2) \cos \sqrt{a}\,t + i(c_1 - c_2) \sin \sqrt{a}\,t$$

At $t = 0$, $k_0 = c_1 + c_2$, from equation (15).   Differentiating equation (15), we have

* H. S. Ellis (Ed.), *A Survey of Contemporary Economics*, Blackston, Philadelphia, 1948, p. 363.

$$\frac{dk(t)}{dt} = I(t) = -(c_1 + c_2)\sqrt{a} \sin \sqrt{a}\, t + i(c_1 - c_2)\sqrt{a} \cos \sqrt{a}\, t$$

At $t = 0$, $\quad I_0 = i(c_1 - c_2)\sqrt{a}$, $\quad k_0 = c_1 + c_2$.
Hence

$$k(t) = k_0 \cos \sqrt{a}\, t + \frac{I_0}{\sqrt{a}} \sin \sqrt{a}\, t = A \sin (\sqrt{a}\, t + \epsilon)$$

where $$A^2 = \frac{I_0^2}{a} + k_0^2, \quad \tan \epsilon = \frac{k_0 \sqrt{a}}{I_0}$$

Thus the variation of k with t is oscillatory with period equal to $2\pi/\sqrt{a}$ and the amplitude equals $(I_0^2/a + k_0^2)^{\frac{1}{2}}$.

Exercises

1. Show that the following linear differential equations have solutions as given:

(a) $\dfrac{d^2x}{dt^2} - \dfrac{dx}{dt} - 2x = 0$; $\quad x = c_1 e^{-t} + c_2 e^{2t}$

(b) $\dfrac{d^2x}{dt^2} - \dfrac{dx}{dt} - 2x = 4t$; $\quad x = c_1 e^{-t} + c_2 e^{2t} + 1 - 2t$

(c) $\dfrac{d^2x}{dt^2} - k^2 x = a \cos kt$; $\quad x = c_1 e^{kt} + c_2 e^{-kt} - \dfrac{a}{2k^2} \cos kt$

2. In Samuelson's model the total capital investment is given by

$$K(t) = K_e + A \sin (\sqrt{a}\, t + \epsilon)$$

Examination of this function shows that

$$K_e - A \leq K(t) \leq K_e + A$$

Thus $K(t)$ cannot grow indefinitely. This is contrary to experience in most countries. Consider the following extension of Samuelson's model. Suppose that the rate of investment consists of two parts:

1. an amount depending only on $K(t)$, say $rK(t)$.
2. an amount whose rate of change depends upon how much the total capital differs from an equilibrium level.

Thus

$$\frac{dI}{dt} = \frac{r\, dK}{dt} - a(K - K_e)$$

Suppose further that $K_e = K_0 e^{bt}$. Show that these assumptions lead to a modification of equation (14), given by the equation

$$\frac{d^2K}{dt^2} - r\frac{dK}{dt} + aK = (a - b^2)K_0 e^{bt}$$

Find the complimentary function, and by assuming a particular solution of the form $K = Ae^{bt}$, find the constant A. Discuss the behavior of the system as t varies.

3. An economic model of national income is given as

$$\frac{d^2N}{dt^2} + a\frac{dN}{dt} - b = 0$$

where a and b are positive constants and $N(t)$ is the national income at time t. At $t = 0$, $N = 0$, $dN/dt = n_0$. Show that

$$N = \frac{b}{a}t + \frac{n_0 a - b}{a^2}[1 - \exp(-at)]$$

■ **11.6   Simultaneous Linear Equations**

We will introduce this subject by considering marketing and maintenance models each of which lead us to two simultaneous equations.

Example 1. Suppose two companies A and B, which share a large market between them, have a fraction x and y of the total sales respectively ($x + y = 1$). Each company wishes to increase its market share and endeavors to do so by spending money on advertising. Let S_1, S_2 be their respective advertising expenditures and let us postulate that the rate at which A gains market share is proportional to A's relative advertising expenditure times the competitor's share of market, less the rate at which the competitor attracts A's customers. A's rate of increase of market share at some future time t is dx/dt and we have

(16)
$$\frac{dx}{dt} = \frac{k_1 S_1 y}{S_1 + S_2} - \frac{k_2 S_2 x}{S_1 + S_2}$$

Similarly, from B's point of view,

(17)
$$\frac{dy}{dt} = \frac{k_2 S_2 x}{S_1 + S_2} - \frac{k_1 S_1 y}{S_1 + S_2}$$

Equations (16) and (17) are *simultaneous linear differential equations* that must be solved in order to determine the future market shares. A solution of such equations consists of expressing x and y as functions of t in such a way as to satisfy the equations and at the same time satisfy initial conditions at $t = 0$, say $x(0) = X$, $y(0) = Y$. The solution of such equations requires a combination of knowledge of the general form of solution and intelligent guesswork.

Let us start by adding equations (16) and (17). We obtain

$$\frac{dx}{dt} + \frac{dy}{dt} = 0$$

that is, $d/dt(x + y) = 0$ and integrating both sides yields

$$x + y = c \qquad (c \text{ is a constant})$$

Since x, y are market share fractions, their sum is unity, so that $x + y = 1$.

This is in accordance with our intuitive notions. Whatever functions satisfy the equations, their sum will be unity.

Now we have seen that the exponential function $w = Ae^{at}$, (A, a are constants) satisfies the equation $dw/dt = aw$ and this suggests trying to find a solution to (16) and (17) of the form $x = Ae^{at}$, $y = Be^{at}$, (A, B, and a are constants).

Substitution in (16) and (17) yields

$$Aae^{at} = \frac{k_1 S_1}{S_1 + S_2} Be^{at} - \frac{k_2 S_2}{S_1 + S_2} Ae^{at}$$

$$Bae^{at} = \frac{k_2 S_2}{S_1 + S_2} Ae^{at} - \frac{k_1 S_1}{S_1 + S_2} Be^{at}$$

For brevity we write

$$\alpha = \frac{k_1 S_1}{S_1 + S_2} \qquad \text{and} \qquad \beta = \frac{k_2 S_2}{S_1 + S_2}$$

and after dividing through by e^{at} we have

$$Aa = \alpha B - \beta A, \quad A(a + \beta) = \alpha B, \quad B = \frac{a + \beta}{\alpha} A$$

$$Ba = \beta A - \alpha B, \quad A\beta = (\alpha + a)B, \quad B = \frac{\beta}{\alpha + a} A$$

Thus either $A = B = 0$, which is a trivial solution, *or*

(18)
$$\frac{\alpha}{a + \beta} = \frac{\alpha + a}{\beta}$$

Equation (18) is called the *secular* equation and leads us to the only values of a that will yield functions satisfying (16) and (17).

From (18)

$$\alpha\beta = \alpha\beta + a(\alpha + \beta) + a^2$$

or
$$a^2 + a(\alpha + \beta) = 0$$

Thus
$$a = 0 \quad \text{or} \quad a = -(\alpha + \beta)$$

We now have two possible solutions:

$$x = A_1, y = \frac{\beta}{\alpha} A_1, \text{ if } a = 0$$

and
$$x = A_2 e^{-(\alpha+\beta)t}, y = -A_2 e^{-(\alpha+\beta)t}, \text{ if } a = -(\alpha+\beta)$$

It is easy enough to see that a third solution may be found by adding the first two. Thus the *general* solution is

$$x = A_1 + A_2 e^{-(\alpha+\beta)t}$$

$$y = A_1 \frac{\beta}{\alpha} - A_2 e^{-(\alpha+\beta)t}$$

Note that whatever values of A_1 and A_2 are chosen

$$x + y = A_1(1 + \beta/\alpha) = \text{constant}$$

To find the values of A_1 and A_2 we use the boundary conditions

$$x(0) = X$$

$$y(0) = Y$$

Therefore
$$X = A_1 + A_2$$

$$Y = A_1 \frac{\beta}{\alpha} - A_2$$

Hence $A_1 = (X + Y) \dfrac{\alpha}{\alpha + \beta} = \dfrac{\alpha}{\alpha + \beta}$ (since $X + Y = 1$)

$$A_2 = X - \frac{\alpha}{\alpha + \beta}$$

Finally,
$$x = \frac{\alpha}{\alpha + \beta} + \left(X - \frac{\alpha}{\alpha + \beta}\right) e^{-(\alpha+\beta)t}$$

and
$$y = \frac{\beta}{\alpha + \beta} - \left(X - \frac{\alpha}{\alpha + \beta}\right) e^{-(\alpha+\beta)t}$$

are solutions to equations (16) and (17). Now $\alpha + \beta > 0$ so that when t is very large we can ignore the exponential term and obtain

$$x = \frac{\alpha}{\alpha + \beta} = \frac{k_1 S_1}{k_1 S_1 + k_2 S_2}, \quad y = \frac{\beta}{\alpha + \beta} = \frac{k_2 S_2}{k_1 S_1 + k_2 S_2}$$

When this situation exists, the system is said to have reached a *steady state*. Although individual customers may switch brands, the *net change* in customers is zero, and the market shares will stay constant until k_1, k_2 or S_1, S_2 are changed. We see that the steady state market shares are given by the advertising effectiveness market shares.

Example 2. In considering profit from a machine that is subject to breakdown, the following equations occur:

$$\frac{dx}{dt} + \lambda x - \lambda y = c_2 - \lambda c_1, \quad \frac{dy}{dt} - \mu x + \mu y = -c_3$$

where $x(t)$ is the net return up to time t if the machine was running at time zero; $y(t)$ is the net return if it was broken down at time zero; c_1 is the setup cost that arises when a breakdown occurs; c_2 is the gross profit per hour while the machine is running, and c_3 is cost per hour of repair; λ is the rate at which breakdowns occur and $1/\mu$ is the average time of repair.

For brevity we will write $c_2 - \lambda c_1 = \alpha$ and $-c_3 = \beta$ and as usual $D = d/dt$. Our equations are

$$Dx + \lambda x - \lambda y = \alpha, \qquad Dy - \mu x + \mu y = \beta$$

We solve these by treating D as an algebraic quantity

$$(D + \lambda)x - \lambda y = \alpha$$

$$-\mu x + (D + \mu)y = \beta$$

Multiplying the first equation by μ, the second by $D + \lambda$ and adding

$$-\lambda \mu y + (D + \mu)(D + \lambda)y = \alpha\mu + (D + \lambda)\beta$$

Therefore
$$[D^2 + (\mu + \lambda)D]y = \alpha\mu + \lambda\beta$$

We now have a single equation of the second order in y. The complimentary function is $A + Be^{-(\lambda+\mu)t}$. A particular solution is found from

$$y = \frac{1}{(\lambda + \mu)D[1 + D/(\mu + \lambda)]} (\alpha\mu + \lambda\beta)$$

$$= \frac{1}{(\lambda + \mu)D}\left[1 - \frac{D}{\mu + \lambda} \cdots\right](\alpha\mu + \lambda\beta)$$

$$= \frac{\alpha\mu + \lambda\beta}{\lambda + \mu} t$$

The general solution for y is

$$y = A + Be^{-(\lambda+\mu)t} + \frac{\alpha\mu + \lambda\beta}{\lambda + \mu} t$$

But
$$x = \frac{(D + \mu)y - \beta}{\mu}$$

$$= A + \frac{\alpha - \beta}{\lambda + \mu} - \frac{\lambda}{\mu}Be^{-(\lambda+\mu)t} + \frac{\alpha\mu + \lambda\beta}{\lambda + \mu} t$$

To find A and B we note that when $t = 0$, there is no time to make any profit, and so $x(0) = y(0) = 0$.

Therefore
$$A + B = 0$$

$$A + \frac{\alpha - \beta}{\lambda + \mu} - \frac{\lambda}{\mu}B = 0$$

Therefore
$$A = \frac{(\beta - \alpha)\mu}{(\lambda + \mu)^2}$$

$$B = \frac{(\alpha - \beta)\mu}{(\lambda + \mu)^2}$$

Note that the average rate of profit is x/t or y/t as the case may be; for large t,

$$\frac{x}{t} = \frac{y}{t} = \frac{\alpha\mu + \lambda\beta}{\lambda + \mu}$$

Thus in the long run the net *rate* of profit is

$$\frac{\alpha\mu + \lambda\beta}{\lambda + \mu} = \frac{\mu(c_2 - \lambda c_1) - \lambda c_3}{\lambda + \mu}$$

Exercises for Chapter 11

1. Show that the solutions to the following differential equations are

(a) $\dfrac{dy}{dx} + y = \exp(-x);\quad y = (x + c)\exp(-x)$

(b) $\dfrac{dy}{dx} = \dfrac{2y^2 - x^2}{2xy};\quad y^2 + x^2 \log cx = 0$

(c) $\dfrac{d^2x}{dt^2} - 2\dfrac{dx}{dt} - 3x = \exp(2t);\quad y = c_1\exp(3t) + c_2\exp(-t) - \dfrac{1}{3}\exp(2t)$

(d) $\dfrac{d^2y}{dx^2} + y = 0;\quad y = c_1\sin(x + c_2)$

2. Solve the following differential equations:

(a) $(y^2 + 1)\,dx + (2xy + 1)\,dy = 0$

(b) $(x^2 + x - y)\,dx + x\,dy = 0$

(c) $\dfrac{d^2y}{dx^2} + \dfrac{dy}{dx} = x$

(d) $\dfrac{d^2y}{dx^2} - y = e^x$

(e) $\dfrac{d^4y}{dx^4} + 81y = 0$

3. Show that the solution to the *total differential equation*

$$a\frac{dx}{x} + b\frac{dy}{y} - \frac{dz}{z} = 0$$

is given by $z = cx^a y^b$, where c is an arbitrary constant.

4. Show that the solutions to the system of differential equations

$$\frac{dx}{dt} = \frac{x}{t} \quad\text{and}\quad \frac{dy}{dt} = \frac{y}{t}, \qquad x(0) = 0,\quad y(0) = 0$$

are $x = at$ and $y = bt$.

5. Sketch the graphs of the solutions of Examples 1 and 2 of Section 11.4.

6. In a military situation the rate of destruction of opposing forces is proportional to the number of friendly forces n_i $(i = 1, 2)$ in use at a given time. Each unit of force i destroys k_i of the opposing forces, and initial forces at time, $t = 0$, are N_i $(i = 1, 2)$.

(a) Show that the differential equations are given by

$$\frac{dn_1}{dt} = -k_2 n_2, \qquad \frac{dn_2}{dt} = -k_1 n_1; \qquad k_1, k_2 > 0$$

(b) Show that

$$\frac{d^2 n_1}{dt^2} = k_1 k_2 n_1, \quad \frac{d^2 n_2}{dt^2} = k_1 k_2 n_2$$

and $\quad n_i = A_i \exp(\sqrt{k_1 k_2}\, t) + B_i \exp(-\sqrt{k_1 k_2}\, t), \quad i = 1, 2$

$N_1 = A_1 + B_1, \quad N_2 = A_2 + B_2$

(c) Show that the values of the constants are

$$A_1 = \tfrac{1}{2}[N_1 - \sqrt{k_2/k_1}\, N_2], \quad B_1 = \tfrac{1}{2}[N_1 + \sqrt{k_2/k_1}\, N_2]$$

$$A_2 = \tfrac{1}{2}[N_2 - \sqrt{k_1/k_2}\, N_1], \quad B_2 = \tfrac{1}{2}[N_2 + \sqrt{k_1/k_2}\, N_1]$$

(d) Show that force 1 is the ultimate victor if $k_1 N_1{}^2 > k_2 N_2{}^2$.

7. Suppose that the demand and supply (per unit time) of a product is given by x and y respectively, where

$$x = ap + b$$
$$y = \alpha p + \beta$$

and p is the unit price. Suppose that the price changes so as to decrease the excess of demand over supply at a rate proportional to the excess. Show the following:

(a) $\dfrac{d}{dt}(x - y) = -k(x - y)$

(b) $\dfrac{dp}{dt} + k(p - \bar{p}) = 0$

where $\qquad \bar{p} = \dfrac{b - \beta}{\alpha - a}$

(c) The unit price tends to an equilibrium value $\bar{p}$, and

$$p(t) = \bar{p} + (p_0 - \bar{p}) \exp(-kt)$$

where p_0 is the initial price at $t = 0$.

12

Probability Theory and Stochastic Models

■ 12.1 Introduction

We saw in Chapter 1 that the decision maker is faced with the problem of maximizing the extent to which he achieves his goals or objectives. We say he has a measure of effectiveness, which can be computed once all the relevant variables are known. In symbols we write

$$E = f(x, y)$$

where E is the measure of effectiveness, x stands for the variables, x_1, x_2, ..., x_n, which the decision maker controls by his decisions, and y stands for uncontrolled variables, y_1, y_2, ..., y_m, which cannot be set by the decision maker but may vary from time to time under the control of others. In addition, there may be restrictions on possible values of the x_i and y_i that prevent a completely free choice of x_1, ..., x_n. However, if the values of y are known *before* the decisions are to be made, it is possible to compute a set of x's—$x^0 = (x_1{}^0, x_2{}^0, \ldots, x_n{}^0)$—as functions of $y = (y_1, \ldots, y_m)$ and which maximize E. If we denote the dependence of x^0 on y by writing $x^0 = x^0(y)$, then we determine $x^0(y)$ from

$$E_0 = f(x^0(y), y) \geq f(x, y)$$

for all x that satisfy the restrictions.

Unfortunately there are many cases (perhaps the majority of cases) where the nature of the situation forces us to determine x *before* we know y. For example, suppose the cost of holding inventory is c per unit in stock per month and that the gross profit is $p > c$ per unit; suppose further that if we cannot supply a customer from stock, we lose the sale and that excess stock at the end of the month is scrap at a net loss, c'. If we are permitted to order once a month for immediate delivery and our objective is to maximize profit over the month, then the control variable, x, is the total stock after receipt of order, and the effectiveness depends on the uncontrolled variable y, sales demand. In fact, the profit E is given by * $E = f(x, y)$, where

$$f(x, y) = \begin{cases} py - c\left(x - \dfrac{y}{2}\right) - c'(x - y) & \text{if } y \leq x \\[3mm] px - \dfrac{cx^2}{2y} & \text{if } y > x \end{cases}$$

It is easy enough to see that if y is known, we should choose $x = y$ in order to maximize profit. However, x must be chosen at the beginning of the month, and y cannot be known until the end. Of course there may be additional complications in that the sales price or the costs c and c' may not be known precisely.

Problems in which all the relevant variables are not known in advance are so common that we are forced to invent a theory to handle such situations. Fortunately, while we may not know y, we usually have some information to assist us. Thus we know that $y \geq 0$, and perhaps past experience tells us that y has never been less than 20 or more than 50.

If we are pessimistic, we might assume that "nature," who chooses y, will always make the worst choice (from our point of view) once she knows our choice of x. Thus nature chooses y to minimize:

$$E = f(x, y) = \begin{cases} y\left(p + \dfrac{c}{2} + c'\right) - x(c + c'), & 20 \leq y \leq x \\[3mm] px - \dfrac{cx^2}{2y}, & 50 \geq y \geq x \end{cases}$$

If $20 \leq y \leq x$, then nature chooses y as small as possible, that is, $y = 20$, and the profit is $E_1 = 20(p + c/2 + c') - x(c + c')$. If $50 \geq y \geq x$, then nature chooses $y = x$, and the profit is $E_2 = (p - c/2)x$. Now $E_1 - E_2 = 20(p + c/2 + c') - x(p + c/2 + c') \leq 0$ as long as $x \geq$

---

* We assume that if the sales demand during a month is y, then it occurs uniformly over the month, that is, stock at time t is $x - ty$ or zero, whichever is larger. The cost of holding inventory is thus

$$\int_{t=0}^{1} c(x - ty)\, dt = c\left(x - \frac{y}{2}\right) \qquad \text{or} \qquad \int_{t=0}^{x/y} c(x - ty)\, dt = \frac{cx^2}{2y}$$

according to whether $y \leq x$ or $y > x$.

20. Thus E_1 is smaller, and nature selects $y = 20$, no matter what value we choose for x, which means x is to be as small as possible, and so $x = 20$, and our profit is $20(p - c/2)$. In other words, no matter what the sales are (in excess of 20), we can ensure a profit of at least $20(p - c/2)$ by choosing $x = 20$. Mathematically we have chosen $x = x^0$, $y = y^0$, such that

$$f(x^0, y^0) = \max_{x \geq 0} \min_{y \geq 0} f(x, y)$$

This approach may be all we can do if we really believe in the perversity of nature, but often it is unduly pessimistic because past experience shows that nature usually does not do her worst. Perhaps we have kept records of the last N months and these show that during n_y months, sales demand was y where

$$\sum_{y=20}^{50} n_y = N; y = 20, 21, 22, \ldots, 50$$

If, in each of the N months, we had started with a stock of x, our total profit would have been

$$\sum_{y=20}^{50} f(x, y) n_y$$

and our average profit per month would have been

$$\frac{1}{N} \sum_{y=20}^{50} f(x, y) n_y = \sum_{y=20}^{x} \left[y \left(p + \frac{c}{2} + c' \right) - x(c + c') \right] \frac{n_y}{N}$$

$$+ \sum_{y=x+1}^{50} \left[px - \frac{cx^2}{2y} \right] \frac{n_y}{N}$$

$$= g(x)$$

If we believe that the relative frequency of future sales will be the same as in the past, it is reasonable to choose x so as to maximize $g(x)$. To do so we observe that $g(x)$ increases with x as long as $g(x + 1) - g(x) = \Delta g(x) > 0$; that is,

$$\Delta g(x) = - \sum_{y=20}^{x} (c + c') \frac{n_y}{N} + \sum_{y=x+1}^{50} \left[p - \frac{c}{2y} (2x + 1) \right] \frac{n_y}{N} > 0$$

Now $$\sum_{y=x+1}^{50} \frac{n_y}{N} = 1 - \sum_{y=20}^{x} \frac{n_y}{N}$$

Hence $\Delta g(x) > 0$ implies

$$(c + c' + p) \sum_{y=20}^{x} \frac{n_y}{N} + \left(x + \frac{1}{2}\right) c \sum_{y=x+1}^{50} \frac{n_y}{N_y} < p$$

Thus x^0 is the largest value of x that satisfies this inequality. It should be noted that we are only concerned with the *relative* values of n_{20}, n_{21}, ..., n_{50} and not the actual values. We often use the symbol $p_y = n_y/N$ and call it the *empirical probability* that sales demand is equal to y.

In order to understand problems of this type it is necessary to have a mathematical theory of probability. Any theory that purports to be a model of reality must start with axioms that are intuitively in accord with experience and must lead to conclusions that also agree with observations. In the remainder of this chapter we shall see how such a theory of probability can be developed and applied to management system problems.

■ 12.2   The Axiomatic Approach to Probability

Intuitive notions suggest our theory must have the following structure. In certain specified circumstances (known as *trials*), various *events* may occur. If we conduct a large number of similar trials, different events occur with different relative frequencies. We think of these relative frequencies as "the probabilities that the various events occur." If the event A is more likely than the event B, then A's probability must be larger than B's. If A cannot occur, its probability is zero, and if A occurs at every trial, its probability is one. We thus set up the following axioms:

1. For a given trial, the set S comprises the totality of possible outcomes, that is, the elements $\{E_1, E_2, \ldots\}$ of S are the possible events that can occur when we perform the trial. S is called the *sample space*.

2. One and only one of the events E_1, E_2, ... must occur, that is, $E_i \cap E_j = 0$ if $i \neq j$. E_1, E_2, ... are known as *elementary events* to distinguish them from *events*, which will be defined below.

3. To each elementary event E_i, there corresponds a nonnegative number p_i known as the *probability that E_i occurs*, written $\Pr\{E_i\} = p_i$.

4. If an elementary event cannot occur, its probability is zero.

5. If an elementary event is certain to occur, its probability is one.

Consider an automobile dealer whose weekly sales vary up to 20 cars. A trial consists of a week, and the possible elementary events, E_0, E_1,

..., E_{20}, are sales of 0, 1, 2, ..., 20 cars. If the dealer always sells at least 3 cars, we would set the probability of sales of 0, 1, and 2 cars equal to zero.

The notion (Chapter 2) of the union of sets lends itself in a natural way to the definition of more elaborate events. Suppose the event E occurs whenever one of the elementary events E_1, E_2, ... E_k occurs. (E might be the event "fewer than 5 cars sold," which occurs whenever E_0, E_1, ..., E_4 occur.) Then we say E is the union of E_1, E_2, ..., E_k and write

$$E = \bigcup_{i=1}^{k} E_i \quad \text{or} \quad E = \bigcup_{E_i \in E} E_i$$

It is thus seen that the events which may occur comprise the totality of subsets of S.

To find the probability of an event $E = \bigcup_{E_i \in E} E_i$, where $\{E_i\}$ are elementary events, we use axiom (6):

6. If $E = \bigcup_{E_i \in E} E_i$, where $\{E_i\}$ are elementary events, then

$$\Pr \{E\} = \sum_{E_i \in E} \Pr \{E_i\}$$

In order to be able to use these axioms for all subsets of S we adopt the convention that $\Pr \{\phi\} = 0$, where ϕ is the empty subset. We also have the obvious extensions of axioms (4) and (5):

4a. If an event cannot occur, its probability is zero.

5a. If an event is certain to occur, its probability is one.

We could, of course, infer (4a) from (6) as follows. If an event E cannot occur, there are no elementary events that imply the occurrence of E. Hence the subset $E = \phi$, and so $\Pr \{E\} = 0$.

From (5a) we can infer the important result that

$$\Pr \{S\} = \sum_{E_i \in S} \Pr \{E_i\} = 1$$

Since one of the events $\{E_i\}$ must occur, the event S is certain, and so its probability is one. It follows that the probability of any event, E (elementary or not), satisfies the inequality

$$0 \leq \Pr \{E\} \leq 1$$

The reader should consider how these results fit our intuitive notions of relative frequency. It is often helpful to think of the elementary

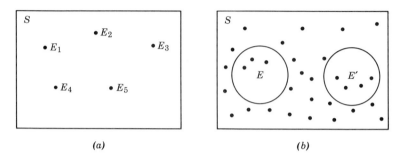

Figure 12.1   (a) Elementary units.   (b) The events E and E'.

events as points in the sample space S and to draw Venn diagrams
(Chapter 2) to show other events, as in Figures 12.1a and 12.1b.

■ 12.3   Events Expressible in Terms of Other Events

If E and F are subsets of S, they correspond to two events; we now wish
to consider two further events that may be derived from them.   These
are

$H = E \cup F$ (the event that occurs when E *or* F *or* both occur)

$K = E \cap F$ (the event that occurs when E *and* F occur)

The event H is called the union of the events E and F; K is called
their intersection.   Exactly the same reasoning used in Chapter 2 for
the number of elements in the union of two subsets shows that

$$\mathrm{Pr}\,\{H\} = \mathrm{Pr}\,\{E \cup F\}$$

$$= \mathrm{Pr}\,\{E\} + \mathrm{Pr}\,\{F\} - \mathrm{Pr}\,\{E \cap F\}$$

and $\mathrm{Pr}\,\{E \cup F \cup G\} = \mathrm{Pr}\,\{E\} + \mathrm{Pr}\,\{F\} + \mathrm{Pr}\,\{G\} - \mathrm{Pr}\,\{E \cap F\}$

$$- \mathrm{Pr}\,\{E \cap G\} - \mathrm{Pr}\,\{F \cap G\}$$

$$+ \mathrm{Pr}\,\{E \cap F \cap G\}$$

The reader should verify these results with the aid of the Venn diagrams in Figures 12.2a and 12.2b.

It should be noted that if E, F, G, ..., K are *mutually exclusive* events
(i.e., no two can occur at once, which implies that for any pair of events
X, Y we have $X \cap Y = \phi$), then

$$\mathrm{Pr}\,\{E \cup F \cup G \cup \ldots \cup K\} = \mathrm{Pr}\,\{E\} + \mathrm{Pr}\,\{F\} + \cdots + \mathrm{Pr}\,\{K\}$$

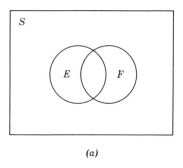 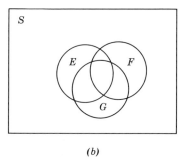

(a)   (b)

Figure 12.2   Venn diagrams.   (a) $E \cup F$.   (b) $E \cup F \cup G$.

Further, if either E or F but not both must occur, i.e., $E \cup F = S$ and $E \cap F = \phi$, then

$$\Pr \{F\} = 1 - \Pr \{E\}$$

Frequently our assessment of probability is changed by the receipt of additional information.   For example, if next year's sales depend on the amount of advertising effort in the early portion of next year, then our assessment of the chance of a good sales year will change once we know what the advertising effort was.   Our theory must take this into account and it does so by defining *conditional probability*.

Definition.   Let $\Pr \{E | F\}$ be the probability that E occurs once we know that F has occurred.   (Read "probability of E given F.")   As long as $\Pr \{F\} \neq 0$, we define:

$$\Pr \{E | F\} = \frac{\Pr \{E \cap F\}}{\Pr \{F\}}$$

If $\Pr \{F\} = 0$, then $\Pr \{E | F\} = 0$.

This is frequently used to find $\Pr \{E \cap F\}$ as often it is easy to find the probability of E once we know F has occurred.   The reader should again consider how this definition fits in with the intuitive notion of relative frequency.

There are occasions when $\Pr \{E | F\} = \Pr \{E\}$.   In this case it is easy to show that $\Pr \{F | E\} = \Pr \{F\}$.   When this occurs, the events E and F are said to be *independent*, and $\Pr \{E \cap F\} = \Pr \{E\} \times \Pr \{F\}$.

■ **12.4   Empirical Determination of Probability**

We now have a theory that enables us to compute the probability for any event once we know the probabilities of the elementary events that are contained in it.   There are two methods of measuring the probabilities of elementary events.   In the first place, if we have a list of all elementary events in the sample space S and if we believe them all to be equally likely (principle of equal likelihood), then the probability of any one is simply $1/n$, where n is the number of events.   It is this reasoning that assigns the probability $\frac{1}{2}$ to "heads" when we flip a coin or $\frac{1}{6}$ to the probability of an ace when we throw a die.   Although many elegant and interesting examples of this reasoning can be constructed, particularly in analyzing card and dice games, it does not appear to be very useful in management problems.

The most common approach in business is to use the concept of relative frequency.   That is, we determine the probability of an event E by observing a large number N of independent trials and counting the number n of occasions when the event occurred.   We then estimate its probability as n/N.   Apart from the intuitive appeal of this approach, it may be justified by the *law of large numbers*.   This says, in effect, that if $p = \Pr \{E\}$ and if N is large, then n/N is almost certain to be close to p.   We can assume that n/N is arbitrarily close to p by selecting large values of N.   The law of large numbers can be proved as a consequence of the axioms already given, which we will do in Theorem 5, Section 12.9.

■ 12.5   Examples on the Axioms of Probability

Example 1.   Let p be the probability that a part produced is defective. If we make n parts, what is the probability that none are defective? That they are not all good?

We assume that the parts are produced independently, so that the fact that we have had a run of several good parts does not affect the probability that the next part manufactured is defective.   Consider the sample space consisting of two points:

$$E \equiv \text{the part is defective}$$

$$\bar{E} \equiv \text{the part is good}$$

Since $\Pr \{E\} + \Pr \{\bar{E}\} = 1$, we see $\Pr \{\bar{E}\} = 1 - p$, and for brevity we will write $1 - p = q$.

Now the event "n good parts" $= \bigcap\limits_{i=1}^{n} \{$the ith part produced is good$\}$.   Therefore $\Pr \{n \text{ good parts}\} = q^{n}$.

If we regard the production of n parts as a trial, we can think of the corresponding sample space as comprising two points: "all parts are good" and "not all parts are good." We thus see that the probability of at least one defective part is $1 - q^n$.

Example 2. With the data of Example 1, what is the probability that the first defective part is the kth part to be made? The event "part k is the first defective" is the intersection of the two independent events: "the first $(k - 1)$ parts are good" and "part k is defective." Its probability is thus the product of the two probabilities and is equal to $q^{k-1}p$. (Note $k > 0$.)

Example 3. With the data of Example 1, what is the probability that there are exactly k defectives when we make n parts?

Let us think of the sample space corresponding to the making of n parts as all the collections of good and bad parts that might occur. Since each part may be good or bad, there are 2^n points in this space, and a typical point might be

$$G\,G\,G\,D\,G\,G\,G\,G\,G\,D \ldots D\,G\,G$$

which represents three good parts, followed by a defective, then five good parts, another defective and so on. The event "exactly k defectives" is the union of all points containing exactly k D's and $(n - k)$ G's. It is not hard to see that the probability of any particular one of these points is $p^k q^{n-k}$ and that no two can occur together. Hence the probability that any such point occurs is found by adding their individual probabilities. As there are $n!/[k!(n - k)!]$ of them, all with probability $p^k q^{n-k}$, we see that the required probability is $\{n!/[k!(n - k)!]\} \times p^k q^{n-k}$. Notice that this is the term in p^k in the expansion of $(p + q)^n = 1^n = 1$. Thus if we add these probabilities over all values of k between 0 and n, we obtain 1, which is what we would expect.

Example 4. A safety manager has observed the following statistics of head injuries among construction workers. Do they provide evidence that injuries decrease when safety helmets are worn?

Total number of workers	1000
Number wearing helmets	600
Total number of head injuries	37
Head injuries among those wearing helmets	14

First we estimate the probability of a head injury among all workers as $\frac{37}{1000} = 0.037$. Next we estimate the conditional probability of a head injury, if the worker wears a helmet, as $\frac{14}{600} = 0.023$. Since this is much lower than for all workers, we conclude helmets are effective in reducing head injuries. It is possible to devise statistical tests to assess the probability of such a difference being due to chance, even if the underlying probabilities are the same. The reader is referred to any elementary text on mathematical statistics.

Note that the probability of a worker wearing a helmet is $\frac{600}{1000}$ = 0.6. The probability of wearing a helmet *and* suffering a head injury is $\frac{14}{1000}$ = 0.014, and so the conditional probability of a head injury, if the man wears a helmet, is $\frac{0.014}{0.6}$ = 0.023, as before. We have assumed that all workers, regardless of whether they wear helmets or not, are subject to the same chance of suffering an accident which could cause a head injury.

Exercises

1. In the economic lot-size formula, total costs were given in Section 7.2 by

$$K = \frac{c_1 q}{2} + \frac{c_3 R}{q}$$

Suppose we know only that c_3 lies between c_3' and c_3'' without knowing its precise value. Use the arguments of the introduction to find the value of q which will ensure that the largest cost incurred will be as small as possible. What will the costs be if nature does her worst? What will they be if nature picks the most favorable value from our viewpoint? (Remember we must choose q *before* nature chooses c_3.)

2. A newspaper boy has observed the following probabilities of sales.

Sales demand	29	30	31	32	33	34	35	36	37	38	39	40	41
Probability	0.01	0.02	0.03	0.06	0.10	0.12	0.15	0.13	0.11	0.08	0.08	0.06	0.05

It costs him 5¢ for each paper he buys and he sells them for 7¢. He is not allowed refunds on unsold papers.

(a) What is the greatest profit he can be sure of making, and how many papers must he buy to do so?

(b) What is the largest number of papers he can buy while still ensuring that he will not incur a loss?

(c) How many papers should he buy to maximize his probability of making a profit in excess of 70¢. With this stock, what is the probability he fails to make 70¢?

(d) What is the conditional probability of selling one more paper, assuming he has one left, and has already sold 36?

(e) What is the probability he sells out if he has sold 36 papers and has 3 left?

(f) The marginal cost of buying one more paper is always 5¢. The marginal return from one more paper is 7¢ times the probability it is sold. Construct a table showing the probability of selling one more paper (assuming it is in stock), given previous sales of 29, 30, 31, ... 41.

(g) If the boy believes the economic doctrine that profits are increasing as long as marginal returns exceed marginal costs, how many papers will he buy?

3. In Example 2 we saw that the probability that the first defective occurs when we make the kth part is $q^{k-1}p$. By summing over all possible values of k, show that unless $p = 0$, we are certain to have a defective part eventually.

4. Using reasoning similar to that of Examples 2 and 3, find the probability that the 2nd defective occurs when we make the kth part. Consider two cases (i) $k < 2$ and (ii) $k \geq 2$. Generalize for the probability that the rth defective occurs on part k.

5. Use the results of exercise 4 to show that unless $p = 0$, we are eventually certain to make r defectives, no matter how large r may be.

■ 12.6 Distributions

We have seen that many events naturally have numbers associated with them. (The number of defectives, the number of units sold, etc.) If we draw up a table showing the probabilities of various numbers occurring, we have what is known as a *distribution function*. Certain distribution functions occur frequently and have received names. We list a few below.

Binomial Distribution

This gives the probability that an event occurs k times in n independent trials. It may be expressed as

$$\Pr\{k\} = \frac{n!}{k!(n-k)!} p^k q^{n-k}$$

where $p = \Pr\{$the event occurs in a single trial$\}$ and $q = 1 - p$. (See Example 3, Section 12.5.)

Geometric Distribution

This gives the probability that the event occurs for the *first* time on the kth trial.

$$\Pr \{k\} = q^{k-1}p$$

(See Example 2, Section 12.5.)

Negative Binomial Distribution

This gives the probability that the event occurs for the rth time on the kth trial, $k \geq r$.

$$\Pr \{r, k\} = \frac{(k-1)!}{(r-1)!(k-r)!} p^r q^{k-r}$$

(See exercise 4, Section 12.5.)

Note that when $r = 1$, we have the Geometric Distribution.

Uniform Distribution

This gives the distribution of a variable equally likely to take any integral value between a and b inclusive, where a and b are integers and $a \leq b$.

$$\Pr \{n\} = 0, \qquad n < a \quad \text{or} \quad n > b$$

$$\Pr \{n\} = \frac{1}{b - a + 1}, \, a \leq n \leq b$$

Poisson Distribution

Suppose in the binomial distribution the number n of trials becomes very large, and the probability p of the event occurring becomes very small in such a way that np remains equal to a constant λ. We then have

$$\Pr \{k\} = \lim_{n \to \infty} \left\{ \frac{n!}{k!(n-k)!} \left(\frac{\lambda}{n}\right)^k \left(1 - \frac{\lambda}{n}\right)^{n-k} \right\}$$

$$= \lim_{n \to \infty} \left\{ \frac{n(n-1) \ldots (n-k+1)}{n^k} \times \frac{\lambda^k}{k!} \left(1 - \frac{\lambda}{n}\right)^n \left(1 - \frac{\lambda}{n}\right)^{-k} \right\}$$

It is easy to see that the first and last factors tend to 1 and that $(1 - \lambda/n)^n$ tends to $e^{-\lambda}$ (Section 5.7). Thus in the limit

$$\Pr\{k\} = e^{-\lambda} \frac{\lambda^k}{k!}$$

This is called a *Poisson Distribution*. For the time being it may be thought of as a useful approximation to the Binomial Distribution when n is large, but we shall see (Sections 12.8 and 12.11) that it is very useful in its own right.

■ **12.7   Mean and Variance**

The amount of information contained in a distribution is very large, and it is often difficult to appreciate its significance when it is all presented at once. As an aid to understanding we can draw diagrams such as the one shown in Figure 12.3. We erect rectangles whose heights are proportional to the probabilities.

It is convenient to summarize the information in the distribution function by means of two parameters—the *mean* and *variance*. If p_x is the probability that the variable X has the value x, we define the mean of X as

$$\bar{x} = \sum_x x p_x$$

This is in accord with our usual concept of a mean or average, because if there is a large number N of occasions on which we observe X, we would expect it to have the value x a total of $N p_x$ times. When we add up the values of the observations, we find a total of

$$\sum_x N p_x x$$

and on dividing by N to obtain the average, we have the result above.

We call $\bar{x}$ a *measure of location* because it gives a rough idea of the general location of the distribution. Sometimes $\bar{x}$ is called the *expected value of X* and is written $\mathcal{E}(X)$. Other measures of location are the *mode*, which is the value of x that maximizes p_x and the *median m*, which is such that $\Pr\{X < m\} = \Pr\{X > m\} \simeq \frac{1}{2}$, or more precisely, the median is any value such that

$$\Pr\{X < m\} \leq \tfrac{1}{2} \qquad \text{and} \qquad \Pr\{X < m + 1\} \geq \tfrac{1}{2}$$

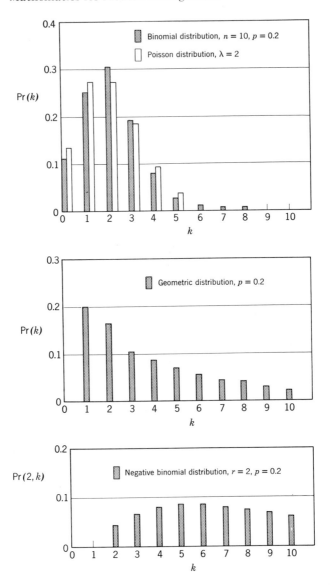

Figure 12.3   Binomial, Poisson, geometric, and negative binomial distributions.

Since X is a variable, we may have to consider a function of X, say $f(X)$. The probability that $f(X)$ has the value $f(x)$ is simply the probability that X takes the value * x.

The expected value of $f(X)$ is thus

$$\mathcal{E}\{f(X)\} = \sum_x f(x)p_x$$

Probably the most common function of x used in this formula is $(x - \bar{x})^2$. We define the *variance* of x as

$$\sigma^2 = \mathcal{E}\{(X - \bar{x})^2\} = \sum_x (x - \bar{x})^2 p_x$$

The variance is a *measure of dispersion* because it indicates how far the distribution is spread on either side of the mean. The square root of the variance is called the *standard deviation*.

Let us now compute the mean and variance of the newspaper boy's sales demand in exercise 2, Section 12.5. We have mean $= 29 \times 0.01 + 30 \times 0.02 + 31 \times 0.03 + 32 \times 0.06 + \cdots + 40 \times 0.05 = 35.73$.

To compute the variance we observe that

$$\sum_x (x - \bar{x})^2 p_x = \sum_x (x^2 - 2\bar{x}x + \bar{x}^2)p_x$$

$$= \sum_x x^2 p_x - 2\bar{x} \sum_x x p_x + \bar{x}^2 \sum_x p_x$$

$$= \sum_x x^2 p_x - \bar{x}^2$$

since $\qquad\qquad \sum_x p_x = 1, \quad \sum_x x p_x = \bar{x}$

Furthermore, we can move the origin for both x and $\bar{x}$ without affecting the variance (see Theorem 1, Section 12.9). Let us deduct 35 from every value of x and from $\bar{x}$. We then compute

$$\sigma^2 = (-6)^2 \times 0.01 + (-5)^2 \times 0.02 + \cdots + 0^2$$

$$\times 0.15 + \cdots + 6^2 \times 0.05 - (0.73)^2$$

$$= 7.74$$

The standard deviation is $\sqrt{7.74} = 2.78$.

The mode for these data is obviously 35 and the median any number between 35 and 36. In this example all three measures of location are

---

* We are assuming that to each value of $f(x)$ there corresponds exactly one value of x; if not, we would have to add probabilities over $x_1, x_2, \ldots, x_k$, where $f(x_1) = f(x_2) = \cdots = f(x_k) = f(x)$, and no other values of x give the same value for $f(x)$.

about the same size, but this need not always be the case, as, for example, in the geometric distribution, where the mode is one but the mean obviously is not (see Figure 12.3).

The easiest way of finding the mean and variance when the distribution is given by an algebraic expression is often by means of the *generating function*.

Definition.   Let $p_x = \Pr\{X = x\}$ and let $P(z) = \sum_x z^x p_x$.   Then $P(z)$ is called the *generating function* of the sequence $\{p_x\}$.

When we know $P(z)$ we can find $\{p_x\}$ by means of Taylor's Theorem. Now $P'(z) = \sum_x xz^{x-1}p_x$ and we see $P'(1) = \sum_x xp_x = \bar{x}$. In addition,

$$P''(z) = \sum_x x(x-1)z^{x-2}p_x$$

so

$$P''(1) = \sum_x x(x-1)p_x = \sum_x x^2 p_x - \sum_x xp_x$$

Hence

$$\sigma^2 = \sum_x x^2 p_x - \bar{x}^2 = P''(1) + \bar{x} - \bar{x}^2$$

Table 12.1 shows the generating function, the mean, and the variance for each of the distributions named in Section 12.6.   The reader should verify all the results stated.

In business problems the expected value is of great importance because it helps to solve the problem posed at the beginning of this chapter, namely:

If the effectiveness is given by $E = f(x, y)$ and we can only know y, subject to a probability function p_y, we cannot choose x so as to optimize $f(x, y)$.   Frequently we choose x so as to optimize the *expected value of*

TABLE 12.1 GENERATING FUNCTION, MEAN, AND VARIANCE OF SOME COMMON DISTRIBUTIONS

Name	Form	Range	Generating Function	Mean	Variance
Binomial	$p_k = \dfrac{n!}{k!(n-k)!}p^k q^{n-k}$	$0 \leq k \leq n$	$(q + pz)^n$	np	npq
Geometric	$p_k = q^{k-1}p$	$k \geq 1$	$\dfrac{pz}{1-qz}$	$\dfrac{1}{p}$	$\dfrac{q}{p^2}$
Negative binomial	$p_k = \dfrac{(k-1)!}{(r-1)!(k-r)!}p^r q^{k-r}$	$k \geq r$	$\dfrac{(pz)^r}{(1-qz)^r}$	$\dfrac{r}{p}$	$\dfrac{rq}{p^2}$
Uniform	$p_k = \dfrac{1}{b-a+1}$	$a \leq k \leq b$	$\dfrac{z^a - z^{b+1}}{1-z}$	$\dfrac{b-a}{2}$	$\dfrac{(b-a)^2}{12} + \dfrac{b-a}{6}$
Poisson	$p_k = e^{-\lambda}\dfrac{\lambda^k}{k!}$	$k \geq 0$	$e^{-\lambda(1-z)}$	λ	λ

$f(x, y)$. That is, we select $x^0(y)$ such that

$$\sum_y f(x, y)p_y \leq \sum_y f(x^0, y)p_y$$

Note that (1) neither of these expressions depends on the value of y, but both depend on the distribution of y, p_y, and (2) this is *not* the same procedure as optimizing $f(x, \bar{y})$.

Example. How many papers should the newspaper boy order if he wishes to maximize his expected profit? (See exercise 2, Section 12.5.) Let p_y be the probability that he has a demand for y papers, and let P be the sales price and C the cost. Suppose he buys x papers. The profit is

$$Py - Cx \qquad \text{if } y \leq x$$
$$(P - C)x \qquad \text{if } y \geq x$$

Therefore the expected profit is

$$f(x) = \sum_{y=29}^{x} (Py - Cx)p_y + \sum_{y=x+1}^{41} (P - C)xp_y$$

Profit is increasing with x as long as $\Delta f(x) > 0$.

$$\Delta f(x) = -C \sum_{y=29}^{x} p_y + (P - C) \sum_{y=x+1}^{41} p_y$$

$$= P - C - P \sum_{y=29}^{x} p_y \qquad (\text{recall } \sum_{y=x+1}^{41} p_y = 1 - \sum_{y=29}^{x} p_y)$$

Thus $\Delta f(x) > 0$ as long as

$$\sum_{y=29}^{x} p_y < \frac{P - C}{P}$$

The reader should verify that this leads to the boy ordering 33 papers.

■ 12.8 The Poisson Distribution

We have seen that if we take a series of n independent trials, in each of which the probability of the event E is p, then as n tends to infinity, the probability of k occurrences tends to the Poisson Distribution, $p_k = e^{-\lambda} \dfrac{\lambda^k}{k!}$, where we allow p to tend to zero in such a way that pn remains equal to the constant λ. Now pn is the mean of the Binomial Distribution and λ is the mean of the Poisson Distribution. In other words, if we have a Binomial Distribution where n tends to infinity in such a way that the mean stays constant, we obtain a Poisson Distribution. This situation frequently occurs in practice. For example, the number of occasions a worker is exposed to risk of accident must be large. On the other hand, the risk on any one occasion is small. Hence we might expect the probability of a worker suffering 0, 1, 2, . . . accidents in a given period of time to follow a Poisson Distribution. Another example is found in the number of customers who request sales in a fixed time period. A third example is the number of aircraft arriving over a field in a period of, say, 5 minutes. The essential feature of the Poisson Distribution is the *independence* of the events that occur. If some workers are accident prone (i.e., the probability of an accident is greater, given that there have been previous accidents), then we will not find that the distribution of workers suffering 0, 1, 2, . . . accidents follows the Poisson form.

Since the parameter λ is the expected number of occurrences, if we measure λ over a unit time period, we can describe λ as the *rate* at which the event occurs. Thus in time t we should have an expected number of occurrences equal to λt and a distribution given by

$$p_k(t) = e^{-\lambda t}\frac{(\lambda t)^k}{k!}$$

We will show that if this is true for all k and t, then for small h, the conditional probability of the event in the interval t to $t + h$, given the event has not occurred in 0 to t, is approximately λh. The probability that the event has not occurred in 0 to t is $e^{-\lambda t}$. The probability that it has not occurred in the interval 0 to $t + h$ is $e^{-\lambda(t+h)}$, and the difference between these two is the probability that it occurs for the first time in t to $t + h$, given by

$$e^{-\lambda t} - e^{-\lambda(t+h)} = e^{-\lambda t}(1 - e^{-\lambda h}) \simeq e^{-\lambda t}\lambda h \qquad \text{(by Taylor's Theorem)}$$

But the probability that it occurs for the first time in t to $t + h$ is the intersection of two events:

1. It occurs in t to $t + h$ and not in 0 to t.
2. It did not occur in 0 to t.

The probability of (2) is $e^{-\lambda t}$; thus the required conditional probability is λh.

It follows that the conditional probability of occurrence in any small interval is independent of when the previous occurrence took place.

Conversely we can show that if the probability of an occurrence in t to $t + h$ is always λh, then the distribution is Poisson.

■ 12.9   Some Theorems on Means and Variances

Theorem 1.   If $Y = aX$, where a is a constant, then

$$\bar{y} = a\bar{x} \qquad \text{and} \qquad \sigma_y^{\,2} = a^2 \sigma_x^{\,2}$$

If $Y = aX + b$, where a and b are constants, then

$$\bar{y} = a\bar{x} + b \qquad \text{and} \qquad \sigma_y^{\,2} = a^2 \sigma_x^{\,2}$$

In particular, if $Y = X + b$, then

$$\bar{y} = \bar{x} + b \qquad \text{and} \qquad \sigma_y^{\,2} = \sigma_x^{\,2}$$

These results are often useful and their proofs are almost obvious. The reader should verify them for himself.

Theorem 2.   If $Z = X + Y$, then $\mathcal{E}(Z) = \mathcal{E}(X) + \mathcal{E}(Y)$.   Let

$$\Pr\{X = x \text{ and } Y = y\} = p_{xy}$$

then
$$\Pr\{Z = z\} = \sum_{x+y=z} p_{xy}$$

where the sum is over all x and y, which add to z.   Therefore

$$\mathcal{E}(Z) = \sum_z z \sum_{x+y=z} p_{xy} = \sum_{x,y} (x + y)p_{xy}$$

$$= \sum_x x \sum_y p_{xy} + \sum_y y \sum_x p_{xy}$$

But the event $X = x$ is the union over y of the events $\{X = x \text{ and } Y = y\}$.

Therefore
$$\Pr\{X = x\} = \sum_y p_{xy}$$

Similarly,
$$\Pr\{Y = y\} = \sum_x p_{xy}$$

Thus
$$\mathcal{E}(Z) = \sum_x x \Pr\{X = x\} + \sum_y y \Pr\{Y = y\}$$

$$= \mathcal{E}(X) + \mathcal{E}(Y)$$

Corollary.   If $Z = X_1 + X_2 + \cdots + X_n$,   then $\mathcal{E}(Z) = \sum_i \mathcal{E}(X_i)$.
(Prove by mathematical induction.)

Theorem 3.   If $Z = X + Y$, then $\sigma_z{}^2 = \sigma_x{}^2 + \sigma_y{}^2 + 2\rho\sigma_x\sigma_y$ where $\sigma_x{}^2$, $\sigma_y{}^2$, $\sigma_z{}^2$ are the variances of X, Y, Z respectively and

$$\rho = \sum_{x,y} (x - \bar{x})(y - \bar{y})p_{xy}/\sigma_x\sigma_y$$

and ρ is called the *correlation coefficient of x and y.*

Let us write $X' = X - \bar{x}$, $Y' = Y - \bar{y}$ and $Z' = Z - \bar{z}$. Then it is clear that $\mathcal{E}(X') = \mathcal{E}(Y') = \mathcal{E}(Z') = 0$ and that the variances of the new variables equal the variances of the corresponding old variables. Therefore

$$\sigma_z{}^2 = \sum_{x,y} (X' + Y')^2 p_{X'Y'}$$

$$= \sum_{x,y} X'^2 p_{X'Y'} + \sum_{x,y} Y'^2 p_{X'Y'} + 2 \sum_{x,y} X'Y' p_{X'Y'}$$

$$= \sum_{x} X'^2 \sum_{y} p_{XY} + \sum_{y} Y'^2 \sum_{x} p_{XY} + 2\rho\sigma_x\sigma_y$$

$$= \sigma_x{}^2 + \sigma_y{}^2 + 2\rho\sigma_x\sigma_y$$

Note that if $\Pr\{X = x \text{ and } Y = y\} = \Pr\{X = x\} \times \Pr\{Y = y\}$, we say X and Y are *independent.* The reader should show that in this case $\rho = 0$. (*Hint:* write $p_{x'y'} = p_{x'} \times q_{y'}$).

Corollary.   If X and Y are independent and if

$$Z = X + Y \qquad or \qquad Z = X - Y$$

then
$$\sigma_z{}^2 = \sigma_x{}^2 + \sigma_y{}^2$$

Theorem 4 (Chebychev's Inequality).   For any distribution, the probability that $|x - \bar{x}|$ exceeds k times the standard deviation is less than $1/k^2$, that is,

$$\Pr\{|x - \bar{x}| \geq k\sigma\} \leq \frac{1}{k^2}$$

Let x_1 be the least integer not less than $\bar{x} + k\sigma$ and let x_2 be the greatest integer not greater than $\bar{x} - k\sigma$. Then our theorem states

$$\Pr\{X \leq x_2 \quad or \quad X \geq x_1\} \leq \frac{1}{k^2}$$

or
$$\sum_{x \leq x_2} p_x + \sum_{x \geq x_1} p_x \leq \frac{1}{k^2}$$

Now

$$\sigma^2 = \Sigma(x - \bar{x})^2 p_x$$

$$= \sum_{x \leq x_2} (x - \bar{x})^2 p_x + \sum_{x=x_2+1}^{x_1-1} (x - \bar{x})^2 p_x + \sum_{x \geq x_1} (x - \bar{x})^2 p_x$$

For the first and last of these sums, $(x - \bar{x})^2 \geq k^2 \sigma^2$.
Therefore

$$\sigma^2 \geq \left[\sum_{x \leq x_2} p_x + \sum_{x \geq x_1} p_x \right] k^2 \sigma^2 + \sum_{x=x_2+1}^{x_1-1} (x - \bar{x})^2 p_x$$

$$\geq \left[\sum_{x \leq x_2} p_x + \sum_{x \geq x_1} p_x \right] k^2 \sigma^2$$

Therefore
$$\sum_{x \leq x_2} p_x + \sum_{x \geq x_1} p_x \leq \frac{1}{k^2}$$

that is,
$$\Pr \{ \, |x - \bar{x}| \geq k\sigma \} \leq \frac{1}{k^2}$$

It is possible to construct an example to show that this is the best we can do if we wish to have a theorem that is true for *all* distributions of X. However, in most practical cases $1/k^2$ is very much greater than the probability on the left.

Examination of the distributions in Section 12.7 shows that if we know their means and, in some cases, their variances, we can compute probabilities for all possible values of the variables. Very often we know the form of a distribution but have insufficient data to estimate the probabilities. However, we can usually estimate the mean and variance from a relatively small amount of data and then use the estimates to compute the distribution. Various criteria are used to decide whether an estimate is a good one, but one obvious property is that if we base our estimate on a large number of observations, it should have a high probability of being close to the true value. Theorem 5 shows that m/n satisfies this requirement when used as an estimate of p. Theorem 6 shows that the average of a sample of n independent observations satisfies this requirement when used as an estimate of a mean.

Theorem 5 (The law of large numbers). Suppose we have n independent trials such that the probability that the event E occurs on each trial is p. Let $\eta > 0$, $\epsilon > 0$ be given freely; then we can always find a number $n_{\epsilon\eta}$ such that if $n > n_{\epsilon\eta}$ and if m is the number of times E occurs in n trials, then

$$\Pr\left\{\left|\frac{m}{n} - p\right| < \epsilon\right\} > 1 - \eta$$

The theorem may be put in a less precise form by saying that if n is large, the ratio m/n is almost certain to be close to p. We rely on this result when we conduct a large number of trials in order to estimate p.

We have seen that $\mathcal{E}(m) = np$ and that $\sigma_m{}^2 = npq$, where $q = 1 - p$ (Table 12.1).

By Theorem 1 of this section it follows that $\mathcal{E}(m/n) = p$ and the variance of m/n is $pq/n = \sigma^2$.

By Chebychev's Inequality,

$$\Pr\left\{\left|\frac{m}{n} - p\right| > k\sigma\right\} \leq \frac{1}{k^2}$$

Let $k\sigma = \epsilon$ or

$$k = \frac{\epsilon}{\sigma} = \frac{\sqrt{n}\epsilon}{\sqrt{pq}}$$

Then

$$\Pr\left\{\left|\frac{m}{n} - p\right| > \epsilon\right\} \leq \frac{pq}{n\epsilon^2} \leq \frac{1}{4n\epsilon^2}$$

since

$$pq = p(1 - p) \leq \frac{1}{4} \text{ for } 0 \leq p \leq 1$$

Now choose $n_{\epsilon\eta} > \dfrac{1}{4\eta\epsilon^2}$ so that if $n > n_{\epsilon\eta}$ we have $\dfrac{1}{4n\epsilon^2} < \eta$.

Then

$$\Pr\left\{\left|\frac{m}{n} - p\right| > \epsilon\right\} < \eta$$

and the result follows.

Theorem 6. Suppose that we take n independent observations x_1, $x_2, \ldots, x_n$ of a variable X and that $\dfrac{1}{n}\sum_{i=1}^{n} x_i = \bar{x}$. If the true value of $\mathcal{E}(X) = \bar{\bar{x}}$, then, given $\eta > 0$, $\epsilon > 0$, we can always find $n_{\epsilon\eta}$ such that if $n > n_{\epsilon\eta}$, then

$$\Pr\left\{|\bar{x} - \bar{\bar{x}}| < \epsilon\right\} > 1 - \eta$$

The proof is very similar to that of Theorem 5. We note that

$$\mathcal{E}(\bar{x}) = \frac{1}{n}\sum_{i=1}^{n}\mathcal{E}(x_i) = \frac{1}{n}\sum_{i=1}^{n}\bar{x} = \bar{x}$$

and that as $\bar{x} = \dfrac{1}{n}\sum_{i=1}^{n} x_i$ its variance is $\dfrac{1}{n^2}$ times the sum of the variance of the x_i's (the x_i are independent). But each x_i has a variance σ_x^2 so that the variance of $\bar{x}$ is $\dfrac{\sigma_x^2}{n}$. We can now obtain the required result with the aid of Chebychev's Inequality.

The two critical points in establishing Theorems 5 and 6 are

1. The expected value of the estimate is equal to the parameter we are estimating. Such estimates are said to be *unbiased*.

2. The estimate is an average value for the sample, and the variance for a sample of one is finite.

It is easy to see that the law of large numbers applies to an estimate of any parameter which is of this type.

Theorem 7. If we take n independent observations $x_1, \ldots, x_n$ of a variable X, then $s^2 = \dfrac{1}{n-1}\sum_{i=1}^{n}(x_i - \bar{x})^2$ is an unbiased estimate of σ^2 (as before, $\bar{x} = \dfrac{1}{n}\sum_{i=1}^{n}x_i$).

To prove this, note that

$$(n-1)s^2 = \sum_{i=1}^{n}(x_i - \bar{x})^2 = \sum_{i=1}^{n}x_i^2 - n\bar{x}^2$$

Therefore $\qquad \mathcal{E}\{(n-1)s^2\} = \sum_{i=1}^{n}\mathcal{E}(x_i^2) - n\mathcal{E}(\bar{x}^2)$

But $\qquad x_i^2 = [(x_i - \bar{x}) + \bar{x}]^2 = (x_i - \bar{x})^2 + \bar{x}^2 + 2\bar{x}(x_i - \bar{x})$

Therefore $\qquad \mathcal{E}(x_i^2) = \mathcal{E}\{(x_i - \bar{x})^2\} + \mathcal{E}(\bar{x}^2) + 2\bar{x}\mathcal{E}(x_i - \bar{x})$

$$= \sigma^2 + \bar{x}^2$$

and $\qquad\qquad\qquad n\bar{x} = \sum_{i=1}^{n}x_i$

The variance of $n\bar{x}$ is $n\sigma^2$, and the variance of $\bar{x}$ is σ^2/n. Applying the result for $\mathcal{E}(x_i^2)$ to $\mathcal{E}(\bar{x}^2)$, we see

$$\mathcal{E}(\bar{x}^2) = \frac{\sigma^2}{n} + \bar{x}^2$$

Hence

$$\mathcal{E}\{(n-1)s^2\} = n(\sigma^2 + \bar{x}^2) - n\left(\frac{\sigma^2}{n} + \bar{x}^2\right) = (n-1)\sigma^2$$

and $\qquad \mathcal{E}(s^2) = \sigma^2$

To summarize Theorems 6 and 7, we can say that the arithmetic mean of a sample can be used to estimate an expected value, and

$$s^2 = \frac{1}{n-1} \sum_{i=1}^{n} (x - \bar{x})^2$$

can be used to estimate a variance. In both cases we are assured of accuracy if the sample is large. It would be beyond our scope to discuss what we mean by large; the reader who is interested in the effect of sample sizes should refer to a standard text on the theory of mathematical statistics.

Exercises

1. Let p be the probability of the event E in a single trial. Define a variable X by

$$X = 1 \text{ if the event occurs}$$

$$0 \text{ if the event does not occur}$$

Show that $\mathcal{E}(X) = p$ and $\sigma_x^2 = p(1-p)$. Hence show that if Y is the number of occurrences of E in n independent trials, then

$$\mathcal{E}(Y) = np \qquad \text{and} \qquad \sigma_y^2 = npq$$

2. Let p be the probability of a defect in manufacturing a part. Suppose the first defect occurs in part x_1, the second in part $x_1 + x_2$, and the rth defect on part $x_1 + x_2 + \cdots + x_r$. Assume that the occurrence of a defect in a given part is independent of the sequence of defects among all preceding parts.

    (a) Find the expected value and variance of x_1, without using the generating function.

    (b) If $y_r = x_1 + x_2 + \cdots + x_r$, find the mean and variance of y_r, using part (a).

3. Show that if $\Pr\{X = x\} = p_x$, $\Pr\{Y = y\} = q_y$, X and Y are independent, and if we define $Z = X + Y$, $P(u) = \sum_x p_x u^x$, $Q(u) = \sum_y q_y u^y$ and $R(u) = \sum_z u^z s_z$, where $s_z = \Pr\{Z = z\}$, then $R(u) = P(u)Q(u)$. (*Hint:* $R(u) = \sum_{x,y} u^{x+y} p_x q_y$.)

4. Compute the mean, mode, and median in the following examples:

   (a) Binomial Distribution: $p = \frac{1}{2}$, $n = 6$
   (b) Binomial Distribution: $p = \frac{1}{5}$, $n = 5$
   (c) Poisson Distribution: $\lambda = 1$
   (d) Geometric Distribution: $p = \frac{1}{3}$
   (e) Uniform Distribution: $a = 0$, $b = 9$
   (f) Negative Binomial Distribution: $r = 4$, $p = \frac{1}{3}$

5. Given the table below, compute tables of $\Pr\{X = x\}$ and $\Pr\{Y = y\}$, and hence find $\bar{x}$ and $\bar{y}$, σ_x^2 and σ_y^2.

$$\Pr\{X = x \text{ and } Y = y\}$$

	x			
y	0	1	2	3
1	0.03	0.05	0.04	0.02
2	0.21	0.15	0.13	0.08
3	0.08	0.13	0.05	0.03

6. With the data of exercise 5, compute $\Pr\{X = x \mid Y = 2\}$ and $\Pr\{X = x \mid Y \geq 2\}$. Hence find the expected value of x, given $Y = 2$; given $Y \geq 2$.

7. In exercise 5 find the expected value of $Z = X + Y$ and σ_z^2.

8. We wish to estimate the probability that the event E occurs on a single trial by conducting a series of n trials and using the ratio m/n as an estimate of p (m = number of occurrences). Use Chebychev's Inequality to find a value of n so that the probability that our estimate is within 0.01 is greater than 0.95.

9. The variable m has a binomial distribution, with parameters n and p. If $n = 10$ and $p = 1/10$, use Chebychev's Inequality to estimate the probability $m/10 \geq 0.5$. Compare with the result of direct calculation.

10. The probability that a patient is scheduled to arrive at a hospital ward during any given 15-minute period is a constant p. Suppose that a nurse is allowed to leave the ward only if no patient is scheduled to

arrive during the next hour. Find the probability that the nurse has to wait for exactly 0, 15, 30, 45, and 60 minutes.

11. For the Poisson Distribution, show that the term p_k is maximum when k is the largest integer not exceeding λ.

12. Let $b(k; n, p)$ and $p(k; \lambda)$ denote the kth term of the binomial and Poisson Distributions, respectively. Show that as k increases, the terms $b(k; n, p)$ are first smaller, then larger, and then again smaller than $p(k; \lambda)$.

13. The following sales data were obtained from 11 automobile dealers for a period of 50 days:

Number sold, k	0	1	2	3	4	5
Number of days k automobiles were sold by a dealer	190	212	96	32	9	2

(a) Find the average number λ of automobiles sold daily by a dealer.

(b) Find the Poisson Distribution $p(k; \lambda)$, and compare with the empirical probabilities found from the table.

■ 12.10   Continuous Variables

So far we have confined our discussion to variables that only take on discrete values. We have thought of them as taking on integral values $(0, 1, 2, \ldots)$, but most of our remarks apply equally well to variables that take values $0, h, 2h, \ldots$.   However, there are many examples where such models are inadequate because the variables can take continuous values. Thus if we are concerned with next month's rainfall, or the output of continuous manufacturing processes, such as the volume of steel produced, there is no reason why we should limit such variables to discrete values.

Let us start by considering the *cumulative function* for a distribution.

Definition.   The *cumulative function* is a function P_x such that

$$P_x = \Pr\{X \leq x\}$$

It is clear that for discrete variables, if we write $[x]$ for the greatest integer, not larger than x, then

$$P_x = \sum_{u \leq [x]} p_u \quad \text{where} \quad p_u = \Pr\{X = u\}$$

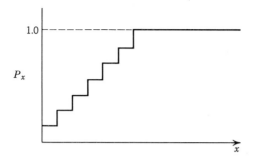

Figure 12.4   The cumulative function P_x.

It should be noted that whereas p_u is only defined when u is an integer, P_x is defined for all values of x. Further, P_x is nondecreasing and as x increases, P_x tends to one because X must take some value. A graph of P_x would look like Figure 12.4.

Now suppose that X can vary continuously. It is still meaningful to talk of the event $\{X \le x\}$ and the associated probability, $\Pr\{X \le x\}$. Suppose for such a variable we define a function

$$F(x) = \Pr\{X \le x\}$$

Then $F(x)$ will be an increasing nonnegative function with $\lim_{x \to \infty} F(x) = 1$.

It should be apparent that we then have, for $y \ge x$,

$$\Pr\{x < X \le y\} = F(y) - F(x)$$

and
$$\Pr\{x < X \le x + h\} = F(x + h) - F(x)$$

Now, if $F(x)$ possesses a derivative $F'(x) = f(x)$, say, then by the mean-value theorem:

$$\Pr\{x < X \le x + h\} = f(x + \theta h)h, \text{ where } 0 \le \theta \le 1$$

If h is small, we have

$$\lim_{h \to 0}\left[\frac{\Pr\{x < X < x + h\}}{h}\right] = f(x)$$

or for small h,
$$\Pr\{x < X \le x + h\} \simeq hf(x)$$

Definition. If $\Pr\{X \le x\} = F(x)$ and $f(x) = F'(x)$ exists, then $f(x)$ is called the *density function* of X and $F(x)$ is called the *distribution function* or sometimes the *cumulative distribution function*.

Note that this is not quite consistent with the terminology for the discrete case. Modern usage favors the definition of distribution function given above, which is applicable to both discrete and continuous variables. However, we still refer to the Binomial Distribution and other discrete functions.

It will be seen that $\Pr\{X = x\} = \lim_{h \to 0} hf(x) = 0$, unless $f(x)$ possesses a discontinuity. However, the event $\{X = x\}$ must occur for some x, so we see that although it is one of our axioms that an impossible event has probability zero, the converse is not necessarily true. Now

$$\Pr\{x \leq X \leq y\} = \Pr\{X = x\} + \Pr\{x < X \leq y\} = \Pr\{x < X \leq y\}$$

(again assuming $f(x)$ does not possess a discontinuity).

Hence $\qquad \Pr\{x \leq X \leq y\} = F(y) - F(x) = \int_x^y f(u)\, du$

The density function owes its importance to this integral.

Since $\lim_{x \to \infty} F(x) = 1$, we see $\int_{-\infty}^{\infty} f(u)\, du = 1$, and since $F(x)$ is non-decreasing, $f(x) \geq 0$. (We have specified the range of integration from $-\infty$ to $+\infty$; in practice the range is such as to include all nonzero values of $f(u)$.)

We now state definitions for the mean, variance, and expected value of any function of a continuous variable. They are analogous to those given earlier for a function of a discrete variable.

Definition. Let $f(x)$ be the density function of a continuous variable, and let $g(x)$ be any other function of x. Then the expected value of $g(x)$ is $\int_{-\infty}^{\infty} g(x)f(x)\, dx$. In particular, if $g(x) = x$, we define the mean by

$$\bar{x} = \int_{-\infty}^{\infty} xf(x)\, dx$$

and if $g(x) = (x - \bar{x})^2$, we define the variance as

$$\sigma^2 = \int_{-\infty}^{\infty} (x - \bar{x})^2 f(x)\, dx = \int_{-\infty}^{\infty} x^2 f(x)\, dx - \bar{x}^2$$

As in the case of discrete variables, the mean is a measure of location and the variance of dispersion. The mode is the value of x that maximizes $f(x)$, and the median m is defined by

$$\int_{-\infty}^{m} f(x)\,dx = \int_{m}^{\infty} f(x)\,dx = \frac{1}{2}$$

For continuous variables we do not have the ambiguity that occurred with the median in the discrete case.

■ 12.11   Special Distributions

There are several distributions that have received names. Probably the most common of all distributions is the *Normal or Gaussian Distribution* for which

$$f(x) = \frac{1}{\sqrt{2\pi}\sigma} \exp\left[-\frac{(x-\mu)^2}{2\sigma^2}\right], \qquad -\infty < x < \infty$$

The graph of $f(x)$ for $\mu = 0$, $\sigma = 1$ is shown in Figure 12.5.

It is apparent that $f(x)$ is symmetric about the value $x = \mu$, and it follows that μ is the mean value of x. To find the variance we have

$$\text{Variance} = \int_{-\infty}^{\infty} \frac{1}{\sqrt{2\pi}\sigma} (x-\mu)^2 \exp\left[-\frac{(x-\mu)^2}{2\sigma^2}\right] dx$$

Substitute

$$\frac{x-\mu}{\sqrt{2}\sigma} = y$$

and the integral becomes

$$\text{Variance} = \int_{-\infty}^{\infty} \frac{2\sigma^2}{\sqrt{\pi}} y^2 e^{-y^2}\,dy = \int_{-\infty}^{\infty} \frac{2\sigma^2}{\sqrt{\pi}} y \cdot (ye^{-y^2})\,dy$$

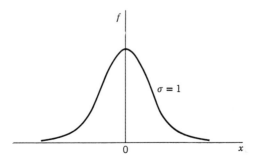

Figure 12.5   Normal distribution with $\mu = 0$ and $\sigma = 1$.

Integrating by parts, and, recalling that $\int 2ye^{-v^2}\,dy = -e^{-v^2}$, we have

$$\text{Variance} = \left[\frac{-\sigma^2}{\sqrt{\pi}}\,ye^{-v^2}\right]_{-\infty}^{\infty} + \int_{-\infty}^{\infty}\frac{\sigma^2}{\sqrt{\pi}}\,e^{-v^2}\,dy = \sigma^2\int_{-\infty}^{\infty}\frac{1}{\sqrt{\pi}}\,e^{-v^2}\,dy$$

Now, if $f(x)$ is a density function, its integral from $-\infty$ to $+\infty$ must be 1. (It can be proven that for $f(x)$ as defined this is so.) We see that the remaining integral is similar to that of $f(x)$ when $\sigma = 1$ and $\dfrac{x-\mu}{\sqrt{2}} = y$. It follows that the variance of x is σ^2.

One of the reasons that the Normal Distribution is important is that it can be used as an approximation to the Poisson and Binomial Distributions. We have the following theorem, stated without proof.

Theorem. Let x_1, x_2, ..., x_n be independent observations from any distribution with finite variance σ and mean μ. Then if n is large, $\bar{x} = \dfrac{1}{n}\sum_{i=1}^{n}x_i$ is distributed approximately as the Normal Distribution, with mean μ and variance σ^2/n. That is,

$$\Pr\{\bar{x} \le y\} = \int_{-\infty}^{y}\frac{1}{\sqrt{2\pi}(\sigma/\sqrt{n})}\exp\left[-\frac{(x-\mu)^2}{2(\sigma^2/n)}\right]dx$$

To perform numerical calculations we utilize tables of the integral

$$\int_{-\infty}^{u}\frac{1}{\sqrt{2\pi}}\,e^{-x^2/2}\,dx = \Phi(u)$$

To find $\Pr(\bar{x} < y)$, we express $y - \mu$ in units of $\sigma/\sqrt{n}$, that is, we find $u = \dfrac{y-\mu}{(\sigma/\sqrt{n})}$ and use the tables.

If we are dealing with a Binomial Distribution and m is the number of occurrences in n trials, then m/n is the average number of occurrences and for large n it is normally distributed with mean p and variance pq/n.

For the Poisson Distribution we can use the Normal tables with mean and variance equal to λ.

In the Poisson and Binomial cases negative observations are impossible. In the Normal Distribution, negative values can occur, and the approximation is only useful when the probability of negative observations is negligibly small. In practice this means that the mean must be at least three times the standard deviation. For the Binomial Distribution we must have

$$p > 3\sqrt{\frac{pq}{n}} \qquad \text{or} \qquad n > 9\frac{q}{p}$$

and for the Poisson Distribution we must have

$$\lambda > 3\sqrt{\lambda} \quad \text{or} \quad \lambda > 9$$

In practice many variables have been found to have Normal Distributions, and it is commonly assumed to "fit" whenever a distribution is known to be symmetric. A discussion of "goodness of fit" is beyond our scope, but the following story may serve as a warning against the popular habit of assuming normality without due consideration. "It is alleged that the Normal Distribution is used by physicists under the assumption that mathematicians have proved it as a mathematical law. On the other hand, the mathematicians use it because they believe the physicists have demonstrated that it is an empirical fact."

When a distribution is known to be asymmetric, there is another class of functions, which usually fit better than the Normal. This is the *Gamma Distribution*, for which

$$f(x) = \frac{b^{a+1}x^a e^{-bx}}{\Gamma(a+1)}, \quad x \geq 0$$

Here a and b are constants, with $a > -1$ and $b > 0$. $\Gamma(a+1)$ is the Gamma function of $(a+1)$. For our purposes it is merely a constant designed to make

$$\int_0^\infty f(x)\, dx = 1$$

The Gamma function is defined by

$$\Gamma(x) = \begin{cases} \displaystyle\int_0^\infty s^{x-1} e^{-s}\, ds, & x > 0 \\ 1 & x = 0 \end{cases}$$

If x is a positive integer, then $\Gamma(x) = (x-1)!$

The reader should use integration by parts to show that the mean and variance of the Gamma Distribution are

$$\text{Mean:} \quad \bar{x} = \frac{a+1}{b}$$

$$\text{Variance:} \quad \sigma^2 = \frac{a+1}{b^2}$$

Gamma Distributions are graphed in Figure 12.6.

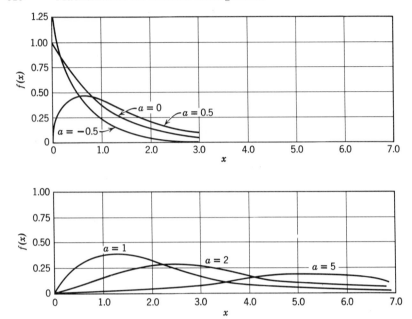

Figure 12.6   Gamma distributions with unit *b* but different values of *a*.

The Gamma Distribution is often useful for describing sales demands. If we tabulate weekly or monthly demands, we find that demands are never negative, that low demands are comparatively rare and that occasionally there is a good week with extremely high demands. This is precisely the shape of the Gamma Distribution. All we need to know is the observed mean and variance. We can then estimate *a* and *b* from the equations,

$$a = \frac{\bar{x}^2 - \sigma^2}{\sigma^2}$$

$$b = \frac{\bar{x}}{\sigma^2}$$

A special case of the Gamma Distribution is when $a = 0$ (Figure 12.6) and we have $f(x) = be^{-bx}$. This is called the *Exponential Distribution*. It has a close connection with the Poisson Distribution. It will be recalled that if the probability of an event occurring k times during a time interval, 0 to t, is given by $p_k(t) = e^{-\lambda t}(\lambda t)^k / k!$, then the probability of the event failing to occur in 0 to t is $p_0(t) = e^{-\lambda t}$. Thus the probability that the event does occur (one or more times) is $1 - e^{-\lambda t}$. This is a distribution function for the time until the event occurs. If we differentiate, we obtain $\lambda e^{-\lambda t}$ for the density function of t. It can be shown that the following processes are equivalent.* For convenience we refer to the event occurring as an *arrival*.

1. The conditional probability of an arrival in the interval t to $t + h$, given no arrival in 0 to t, is approximately λh, for all t. More precisely, if $p(h)$ is the probability of an arrival in time t to $t + h$, then

$$\lim_{h \to 0} \frac{p(h)}{h} = \lambda \text{ for all } t$$

2. The density function of the interval t between consecutive arrivals is $g(t) = \lambda e^{-\lambda t}$.

3. The probability of k arrivals in time t is $e^{-\lambda t} \frac{(\lambda t)^k}{k!}$ for all k and t.

Arrivals that occur in this way are often described as *random* arrivals.

Exercises for Chapter 12

1. The rectangular distribution has the density function

$$f(x) = \begin{cases} \dfrac{1}{b - a}, & a \leq x \leq b \\ 0, & \text{otherwise} \end{cases}$$

Find the mean and variance and the distribution function.

2. If X and Y both have independent rectangular distributions lying between $\pm a$ and $Z = X + Y$, find the distribution function for Z.
[Let $G(z) = \Pr\{Z \leq z\}$. One way this can occur is for X to lie in the interval x to $x + h$, and Y to be less than $z - x(x \leq z)$. To find $G(z)$ we must add over all values of x, that is,

$$G(z) = \int_{-a}^{z} f(x) F(z - x) \, dx]$$

3. Find the mean and variance of Z, in exercise 2, by direct calculation from the density function.

4. Verify that the mean and variance of the Gamma Distribution are given by

$$\bar{x} = \frac{a + 1}{b}, \quad \sigma^2 = \frac{a + 1}{b^2}$$

Show that in the case of the exponential function with parameter λ,

$$\bar{x} = \frac{1}{\lambda}, \quad \sigma^2 = \frac{1}{\lambda^2}$$

* For a proof, see William Feller, *Probability Theory and Its Applications*, 2nd ed., p. 400 ff., John Wiley and Sons, 1957.

5. Why is it, if the time between equipment failures has an exponential distribution, there is no point in preventive maintenance or overhaul? (Preventive maintenance is the removal or renovation of parts in service before failure in the hope of avoiding expensive breakdowns.)

6. Verify that the following processes are equivalent:

(a) The conditional probability of an arrival in the interval t to $t + h$, given no arrival up to time t, is $p(h)$, where

$$\lim_{h \to 0} \frac{p(h)}{h} = \lambda \qquad \text{for all } t$$

(b) The density function for the interval t between consecutive arrivals is $\lambda e^{-\lambda t}$.

(c) The probability of k arrivals in time t is $e^{-\lambda t}(\lambda t)^k/k!$ for all k and t.

[Show (b) is a consequence of (a) by dividing the interval 0 to t into t/h subintervals of length h each. The probability of no arrival in any one of these intervals is $1 - \lambda h$ and in all of them $(1 - \lambda h)^{t/h}$. (b) is obviously a consequence of (c). To show (c) is also a consequence of (a), note that (c) follows from (a) via (b) in the case $k = 0$. Assume it follows for $k = 0, 1, 2, \ldots, r$. Then there will be $r + 1$ arrivals in time 0 to t if there are r arrivals in 0 to u, one arrival in u to $u + h$ and no arrival in $u + h$ to t.

Since these events are independent, the probability of them all occurring is the product of their separate probabilities. As we vary u from 0 to t, we obtain all possible ways of having $r + 1$ arrivals in 0 to t, so that the required probability of $(r + 1)$ arrivals is the integral of the product. The result follows by induction.]

7. In exercise 3, Section 10.6, we have considered variable demand, where c_1 and c_2 are the costs per unit of overestimation and underestimation, respectively. Now suppose that the cost of manufacturing is $a + bS$, where S is the quantity produced and a and b are constants. Then the total expected cost is given by

$$a + bS + c_1 \int_0^S (S - x)f(x)\, dx + c_2 \int_S^\infty (x - S)f(x)\, dx$$

(a) Show that the value of S that minimizes the total expected cost is given by

$$F(S) = \frac{c_2 - b}{c_1 + c_2}$$

where

$$F(S) = \int_0^S f(x)\, dx$$

(b) If $f(x) = \alpha e^{-\alpha x}$, show that the optimal S is given by

$$S = \frac{1}{\alpha} \log \left[\frac{c_1 + c_2}{c_1 + b} \right]$$

8. Suppose that an order of q units placed on January 1st is received February 1st. The stock level on January 1st, after receipt of delivery, is s units. The stock level on February 1st, after receipt of delivery of order placed on January 1st, is $s + q - x$ (shortages are not lost). The costs per unit of overestimation and underestimation of demand are c_1 and c_2, respectively. The one month sales demand density function is $f(x)$ and is independent of demand in other months.

(a) If y is the demand in February, show that the total expected cost in February is given by

$$\int_{x=0}^{S} \left[c_1 \int_{y=0}^{S-x} (S - x - y)f(y)\, dy + c_2 \int_{S-x}^{\infty} (y + x - S)f(y)\, dy \right] f(x)\, dx$$

$$+ c_2 \int_{x=S}^{\infty} \left[\int_{y=0}^{\infty} (y + x - S)f(y)\, dy \right] f(x)\, dx \quad \text{where } S = s + q$$

(b) Show that the optimal value S_0 is given by

$$\int_{x=0}^{S_0} F(S_0 - x)f(x)\, dx = \frac{c_2}{c_1 + c_2}$$

where $F(z) = \int_0^z f(x)\, dx$. (Note $s > S_0$, $q = 0$).

(c) Show that if $f(x) = \alpha e^{-\alpha x}$, the optimal value of S is

$$e^{-\alpha S}[1 + \alpha S] = \frac{c_1}{c_1 + c_2}$$

9. In exercise 8, suppose that shortages are lost.

(a) Show that the total expected cost is given by

$$\int_{x=0}^{S} \left[c_1 \int_{y=0}^{S-x} (S - x - y)f(y)\, dy + c_2 \int_{y=S-x}^{\infty} (y + x - S)f(y)\, dy \right] f(x)\, dx$$

$$+ \int_{x=S}^{\infty} \left[c_1 \int_{y=0}^{q} (q - y)f(y)\, dy + c_2 \int_{q}^{\infty} (y - q)f(y)\, dy \right] f(x)\, dx$$

(b) Show that the optimal value of S is given by

$$\int_{x=0}^{S} F(S - x)f(x)\, dx + F(q)[1 - F(s)] = \frac{c_2}{c_1 + c_2}$$

where $S = s + q$.

(c) Show that if $f(x) = \alpha e^{-\alpha x}$, the optimal value of S is given by

$$e^{-\alpha S}[1 + \alpha s] = \frac{c_1}{c_1 + c_2}$$

10. Compare the order policies in exercises 8 and 9 where $c_1 = 2$, $c_2 = 8$, $\alpha = .001$, and $s = 1100$.

11. Suppose the cost of holding inventory is c_1 per unit per month and that the cost of keeping a customer waiting because we are out of stock is c_2 per unit per month. Orders can be placed once a month, and lead time is negligible.

(a) If monthly sales demand x has a density function $f(x)$, and demand arises uniformly over the month, show that the expected costs per month are

$$K = \int_0^S c_1 \left(S - \frac{x}{2} \right) f(x)\, dx + \int_S^{\infty} \left\{ \frac{c_1 S^2}{2x} + \frac{c_2(x - S)^2}{2x} \right\} f(x)\, dx$$

where S is the stock at the start of the month, after delivery of the order placed (if any).

(b) Let s be the stock before delivery of the order. Show that the optimal ordering policy is to order nothing if $s \geq S_0$ and $S_0 - s$ if $s < S_0$, where S_0 satisfies the equation:

$$\int_0^{S_0} f(x)\, dx + S_0 \int_{S_0}^\infty \frac{f(x)}{x}\, dx = \frac{c_2}{c_1 + c_2}$$

(c) Find the value of S_0 in the case where $f(x) = \alpha^2 x e^{-\alpha x}$.

12. An aircraft radar is subject to failure at a rate which results in a life t with a density function $f(t)$. Show that the average life is given by

$$\bar{l} = \int_0^\infty G(t)\, dt$$

where $G(t)$ is the probability a set fails after time t, that is,

$$G(t) = 1 - F(t) = \int_t^\infty f(u)\, du$$

13. In order to avoid in-flight failures, the radar sets in exercise 12 are to be replaced after a life T if they have not failed previously. Show that the average life will be

$$\bar{T} = \int_0^T G(t)\, dt$$

14. In the case of exercise 13, it may be shown that in the long run replacements (either because of in-flight failure or reaching age T) will be at an average rate per set of $1/\bar{T}$. Show that failures in flight will be at the rate $F(T)/\bar{T}$ and replacements at age T will be at the rate $G(T)/\bar{T}$. If the cost of replacement is c_1 and the additional cost of an in-flight failure is c_2, show that the optimal value of T minimizes

$$\frac{1}{\bar{T}} \{ c_1 G(T) + (c_1 + c_2) F(T) \}$$

Evaluate this expression when $f(t) = \lambda e^{-\lambda t}$ and show that in this case the optimal value of T is infinite, no matter how large c_2 may be.

15. A manufacturer of automobile batteries offers a guarantee for a period T. If the battery fails at time $t < T$, he will allow a rebate of $(1 - t/T)P$ against a new battery, where P is the purchase price. Suppose that battery life has a density function $f(t)$ and that the cost of producing a battery is c. What should P be if the manufacturer wishes to make an average net profit of $k\%$ of his manufacturing price? How is the result affected if, among customers whose batteries fail at time t, only a proportion $r(t)$ accept the rebate?

16. A system contains a large number N of similar items. Each item has a density function $f(t)$ for failure at time t, that is the probability that an item fails at age t to $t + dt$ is $f(t)\, dt$.

In order to keep N live items in the system we replace every item on failure at a cost c_1 each. It sometimes happens that we can replace all items simultaneously for a total cost of $Nc_2 < Nc_1$. In such cases we may consider a group replacement policy which calls for the replacement of all items on failure and replacement of the entire system at intervals T.

(a) Assuming that T is sufficiently short that no item, replaced on failure, will fail again, show that

$$K(T) = \frac{N}{T}\left[(c_2 + c_1\int_0^T f(t)\,dt)\right]$$

where $K(T)$ is the cost per unit time using a group replacement policy.

(b) Find the equation to be satisfied by the value of T which minimizes $K(T)$.

17. Consider two systems of two components each.

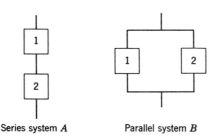

Series system A Parallel system B

where each component has a failure density function $f_i(t) = \lambda_i e^{-\lambda_i t}$, $i = 1, 2$. In system A the failure of *any* component causes the system to fail, whereas in system B the failure of both components is necessary for the system to fail.

(a) Show that the *system reliability*, the probability that the system does not fail in the interval $(0, t)$, is given by

$$R_A(t) = e^{-(\lambda_1 + \lambda_2)t}$$
$$R_B(t) = e^{-\lambda_1 t} + e^{-\lambda_2 t} - e^{-(\lambda_1 + \lambda_2)t}$$

(b) Show that the mean time between failures for each system is given by

$$m_A = \frac{1}{\lambda_1 + \lambda_2}$$

$$m_B = \frac{1}{\lambda_1} + \frac{1}{\lambda_2} - \frac{1}{\lambda_1 + \lambda_2}$$

(c) Show that the mean time between failures for series and parallel systems composed of n similar components (failure rates equal to λ) is given by

$$m = \frac{1}{n\lambda} \qquad \text{for the series system}$$

$$m = \frac{1}{\lambda}\sum_{j=1}^{n}\frac{1}{j} \qquad \text{for the parallel system}$$

Part Four

Linear Systems

13

Linear Equations and Matrices

■ 13.1 Systems of Linear Equations

In this chapter we develop graphical and algebraic methods for determining the solutions of systems of linear equations. We consider the effect of restrictions, in the form of inequalities on the space of admissible solutions to optimization problems.

Matrices (ordered arrays of numbers) are introduced to facilitate computational algorithms used to solve systems of linear equations. Rules for matrix operations are developed, including a method for determining the inverse of a matrix. The properties of matrix operations are applied in Chapters 14 and 15 to linear programming problems.

Example. A firm manufactures products X and Y, which require machines A and B. If the firm has 5 machines of type A and 14 machines of type B, find the number of units manufactured of each product in one week. The time required to produce one unit, using both machines, is as follows:

	Machine *	
Product	A	B
X	1 hr	2 hr
Y	2 hr	8 hr

* Machine hours available per week: 200 hr for machine A, 560 hr for machine B.

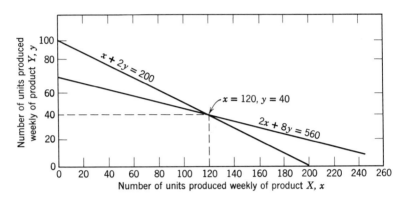

Figure 13.1

Let x = number of units produced per week of product X
$\quad\ y$ = number of units produced per week of product Y

We have the following equations.

$$1 \cdot x + 2 \cdot y = 200$$

$$2 \cdot x + 8 \cdot y = 560$$

If we graph the above equations and find the point of intersection of the two lines, then this point will be on both lines and hence will satisfy both equations. Referring to Figure 13.1, we see that the point (120, 40) is the point of intersection.

Exercises

1. Find the solutions of the following systems of linear equations:

(a) $5x_1 - 3x_2 = -14$ (c) $3x_1 + x_2 = 6$

$\quad\ x_1 + x_2 = 2$ $7x_1 - x_2 = 4$

(b) $x_1 - 5x_2 + x_3 = 11$ (d) $2x_1 + 8x_2 - x_3 = -5$

$\quad\ 3x_1 + x_2 - 2x_3 = 7$ $4x_1 - x_2 + 9x_3 = 1$

$\quad\ -x_1 + 6x_2 + 9x_3 = 8$ $5x_1 + 10x_2 + 2x_3 = -8$

2. A firm manufactures 3 products, X, Y, and Z, using 19 machines of type A, 13 machines of type B, and 15 machines of type C. If the

machining time requirements are given in the following table, find the production quantity of each product during a 40-hour week.

Product	Machine		
	A	B	C
X	2 hr	3 hr	5 hr
Y	3 hr	1 hr	2 hr
Z	4 hr	2 hr	1 hr

Find the number of machines of each type necessary to produce 120 items of product X, 80 items of product Y, and 80 items of product Z each week.

■ 13.2   Matrices: Notations and Definitions

If the reader will examine the way in which his knowledge of *numbers* progressed, he will observe the following sequence:

1. Positive integers and zero.

2. Positive fractions (required in order to make the operation of division feasible for all pairs of positive integers).

These two classes comprise the positive rationals.

3. Negative rational numbers (required to make the operation of subtraction feasible for all pairs of positive rational numbers).

4. Irrational numbers (required to establish the existence of a limit to all increasing and decreasing bounded sequences of rationals; in particular, so that equations of the type $x^n - A = 0$, where n is an integer and A is a positive rational can be solved).

Classes 1 through 4 comprise the *real* numbers.

5. Complex numbers, which consist of ordered pairs of real numbers (x, y) with the following properties:

(1) $$(x_1, y_1) + (x_2, y_2) = (x_1 + x_2, y_1 + y_2)$$

(2) $$(x_1, y_1) \times (x_2, y_2) = (x_1 x_2 - y_1 y_2, x_1 y_2 + x_2 y_1)$$

These apparently mystifying definitions become more reasonable when we define i to be a new type of number such that $i^2 = -1$ and then write our ordered pair as $x + iy$. The reader should verify equations

(1) and (2), using the ordinary laws of algebra and replacing i^2 by -1 whenever it appears. Complex numbers are needed in order to make the solution of *all* polynomial equations possible.

Each of the classes 1 through 5 includes all elements of previous classes, so each can be considered a further generalization. In this chapter we will introduce yet another generalization, *matrices* (singular matrix). The best way to think of matrices is as a mathematical shorthand (consider the economy of writing x^{10} instead of $x\,x\,x\,x\,x\,x\,x\,x\,x\,x$).

Let us take the set of linear equations

$$2x + 5y + 3z = 10$$

(3) $$x - 4y + 2z = 7$$

$$3x + y - 5z = 11$$

and observe that if we adopt the convention that the first number in each equation is to be the coefficient of x, the second that of y, and the third that of z, we do not need to write x, y, and z on each line. We only need the array

$$\begin{array}{ccc} 2 & 5 & 3 \\ 1 & -4 & 2 \\ 3 & 1 & -5 \end{array}$$

together with the column headings x, y, z to represent the left-hand side. Where should we place x, y, and z? The convention is to write them in a column to the right and to insert braces to remove ambiguity as to which symbol is a coefficient and which a variable. Later we will have letters to represent coefficients.

$$\begin{bmatrix} 2 & 5 & 3 \\ 1 & -4 & 2 \\ 3 & 1 & -5 \end{bmatrix} \begin{bmatrix} x \\ y \\ z \end{bmatrix} = \begin{bmatrix} 10 \\ 7 \\ 11 \end{bmatrix}$$

The column on the extreme right and the equality sign carry the obvious interpretations.

The reader is probably wondering why all this effort to avoid writing a few letters, but the notation allows further economies. Let $\mathbf{M}$ stand for the square array, $\mathbf{X}$ for the column x, y, z, and $\mathbf{B}$ for the column 10, 7, 11. We can now write our equations very compactly as

(4) $$\mathbf{MX} = \mathbf{B}$$

M is called a *matrix*, **X** and **B** are called *column vectors*, and **MX** can be considered a new type of multiplication. Two matrices are *equal* if they have the same number of rows and columns and if the corresponding elements are equal. Clearly the solution of (3) is equivalent to solving the matrix equation (4) for the unknown vector **X**. If (4) consisted of numbers instead of these new quantities, we would write

$$\mathbf{X} = \mathbf{M}^{-1}\mathbf{B}$$

where the number $\mathbf{M}^{-1}$ is such that $\mathbf{M}^{-1}\mathbf{M} = 1$. Is there a matrix that plays a similar role to a reciprocal in ordinary numbers? The answer is yes in certain circumstances. However, the details must wait until we have examined multiplication a little more closely.

Exercise. Write the matrix equation for each of the following:

(a) $x + 2y = 5$ (b) $3x - 5y + 4z = 7$

    $3x + 4y = 11$ $x + y + 2z = 13$

                  $x - y + z = 3$

■ **13.3   Matrix Operations**

Let us approach the problem from a different point of view. Suppose the variables y_1, y_2, ..., y_k are defined in terms of other variables x_1, x_2, ..., x_n by the equations

$$y_1 = a_{11}x_1 + a_{12}x_2 + \cdots + a_{1n}x_n$$

$$y_2 = a_{21}x_1 + \cdots\cdots\quad + a_{2n}x_n$$

(5)

$$\vdots$$

$$y_k = a_{k1}x_1 + \cdots\cdots\quad + a_{kn}x_n$$

If $\mathbf{A}_{kn}$ is the $k \times n$ (read k by n) array or matrix,

$$\begin{bmatrix} a_{11} & a_{12} & \cdots & a_{1n} \\ \vdots & & & \\ a_{k1} & \cdots\cdots\cdots\cdots & a_{kn} \end{bmatrix}$$

X *is* the *column matrix*,

$$\begin{bmatrix} x_1 \\ x_2 \\ \cdot \\ \cdot \\ \cdot \\ x_n \end{bmatrix}$$

and **Y** is the *column matrix*,

$$\begin{bmatrix} y_1 \\ y_2 \\ \cdot \\ \cdot \\ \cdot \\ y_k \end{bmatrix}$$

then in matrix notation

(5a)   **Y = AX**

Now suppose that each of the x's can be expressed in terms of z_1, z_2, ..., z_m by the equations

$$x_1 = b_{11}z_1 + \cdots + b_{1m}z_m$$

(6)

$$x_n = b_{n1}z_1 + \cdots + b_{nm}z_m$$

Then with obvious definitions we write

(6a)   **X = BZ**

and we ought to be able to substitute from (6a) into (5a) and obtain

(6b)   **Y = A(BZ)**

If we substitute from (6) into (5), we obtain

$$y_1 = c_{11}z_1 + c_{12}z_2 + \cdots + c_{1m}z_m$$

$$y_2 = c_{21}z_1 + \cdots \cdots + c_{2m}z_m$$

(7)

$$y_k = c_{k1}z_1 + \cdots \cdots + c_{km}z_m$$

or

(7a) $$Y = CZ$$

where $$c_{ij} = \sum_{r=1}^{n} a_{ir}b_{rj}$$

It is reasonable on comparing (7a) and (6b) to define the product **AB** as the matrix **C**.

Note that the definition only applies to **AB** and not to **BA**. Further, it would not work unless **A** has as many columns as **B** has rows.

We give the following formal definition:

Definition. The *product* **AB** of two matrices **A** and **B** is the matrix **C** = $[c_{ij}]$ provided

1. **A** has as many columns as **B** has rows, say n.

2. $c_{ij} = \sum_{r=1}^{n} a_{ir}b_{rj}$

3. $[c_{ij}]$ means the matrix with the element c_{ij} in the ith row, jth column position.

If (1) does not hold, the product **AB** is not defined. If (1) holds and **B** has as many columns as **A** has rows, the product **BA** is defined but in general it is not the same as **AB**. If we regard the columns **X**, **Y**, **Z** as matrices with one column and several rows, the definition of product coincides with our earlier notions of **MX**, **AX**, etc.

We define *addition* and *subtraction* of matrices as follows:

Definition
$$A \pm B = C$$

where $$A = [a_{ij}], \quad B = [b_{ij}], \quad C = [c_{ij}]$$

and $$c_{ij} = a_{ij} \pm b_{ij}$$

provided **A** has the same number of rows as **B** and **A** has the same number of columns as **B**.

Exercises

1. Multiply the following:

(a) $\begin{bmatrix} 1 & 2 & 3 \\ 4 & 5 & 6 \end{bmatrix} \begin{bmatrix} 4 & 5 & 7 \\ 2 & 3 & 1 \\ 6 & 5 & 8 \end{bmatrix}$ (b) $\begin{bmatrix} 1 & 4 \\ 3 & 5 \end{bmatrix} \begin{bmatrix} 3 & 1 \\ 5 & 6 \end{bmatrix}$ (c) $\begin{bmatrix} 3 & 1 \\ 5 & 6 \end{bmatrix} \begin{bmatrix} 1 & 4 \\ 3 & 5 \end{bmatrix}$

2. Verify that

$$\left(\begin{bmatrix} 1 & 4 \\ 3 & 5 \end{bmatrix} \begin{bmatrix} 3 & 1 \\ 5 & 6 \end{bmatrix} \right) \begin{bmatrix} 2 & 1 \\ 4 & 3 \end{bmatrix} = \begin{bmatrix} 1 & 4 \\ 3 & 5 \end{bmatrix} \left(\begin{bmatrix} 3 & 1 \\ 5 & 6 \end{bmatrix} \begin{bmatrix} 2 & 1 \\ 4 & 3 \end{bmatrix} \right)$$

Show the result is generally true, that is, $(\mathbf{AB})\mathbf{C} = \mathbf{A}(\mathbf{BC})$.

3. Verify that $\mathbf{A} + \mathbf{B} = \mathbf{B} + \mathbf{A}$

$$(\mathbf{A} + \mathbf{B}) + \mathbf{C} = \mathbf{A} + (\mathbf{B} + \mathbf{C})$$

and that $\mathbf{A} - \mathbf{A} =$ a *null* matrix, consisting only of zeros.

4. Show that if we partition two matrices into submatrices

$$\mathbf{M} = \begin{bmatrix} \mathbf{P} & \mathbf{Q} \\ \hline \mathbf{R} & \mathbf{S} \end{bmatrix}, \quad \mathbf{N} = \begin{bmatrix} \mathbf{U} & \mathbf{V} \\ \hline \mathbf{W} & \mathbf{T} \end{bmatrix}$$

then, provided all products exist,

$$\mathbf{MN} = \begin{bmatrix} \mathbf{PU} + \mathbf{QW} & \mathbf{PV} + \mathbf{QT} \\ \hline \mathbf{RU} + \mathbf{SW} & \mathbf{RV} + \mathbf{ST} \end{bmatrix}$$

5. As an example, verify the result numerically in the case below.

$$\mathbf{M} = \begin{bmatrix} 1 & 2 & 3 & 4 \\ 3 & 2 & 5 & 1 \\ \hline 4 & 1 & 6 & 3 \\ 3 & 2 & 4 & 1 \end{bmatrix}, \quad \mathbf{N} = \begin{bmatrix} 2 & 3 & 4 & 1 & 2 & 4 & 2 \\ 1 & 4 & 3 & 5 & 1 & 3 & 1 \\ \hline 4 & 2 & 1 & 3 & 6 & 1 & 5 \\ 1 & 2 & 1 & 4 & 7 & 9 & 8 \end{bmatrix}$$

6. Verify the distribution laws: $\mathbf{A}(\mathbf{B} + \mathbf{C}) = \mathbf{AB} + \mathbf{AC}$ and $(\mathbf{A} + \mathbf{B})\mathbf{C} = \mathbf{AC} + \mathbf{BC}$.

■ 13.4 The Zero and Identity Matrices

Having defined a product and a sum of two matrices, we see that there is some semblance of an arithmetic of matrices. We have a *zero*, which is defined as the null matrix,* consisting only of zeros. It is obvious that the null matrix $\mathbf{N}$ behaves similarly to zero in arithmetic in that

$$\mathbf{A} + \mathbf{N} = \mathbf{A}$$

and $\mathbf{AN}$ is also a null matrix, $\mathbf{N}$ consisting of n rows and m columns. Is

---

* When we talk of the null matrix we are thinking of matrices with given numbers of rows and columns.

there a matrix $\mathbf{I}$ which behaves similarly to one? That is, is there any matrix $\mathbf{I}$ such that

$$\mathbf{IA} = \mathbf{A}$$

for all $m \times n$ matrices $\mathbf{A}$ (matrices with m rows and n columns)? The answer is yes only when $\mathbf{A}$ is a square matrix (same number of rows as columns). In what follows, matrices will be assumed square unless the contrary is indicated.

We now show that there is only one matrix $\mathbf{I}_n$ such that for all $n \times n$ matrices, $\mathbf{A}$

$$(8) \qquad\qquad \mathbf{I}_n\mathbf{A} = \mathbf{AI}_n = \mathbf{A}$$

Suppose there is a second matrix $\mathbf{J}$ for which

$$(9) \qquad\qquad \mathbf{JA} = \mathbf{AJ} = \mathbf{A}$$

for all $\mathbf{A}$. Then from (9), $\mathbf{I}_n\mathbf{J} = \mathbf{I}_n$, and from (8) $\mathbf{I}_n\mathbf{J} = \mathbf{J}$, and thus $\mathbf{I}_n = \mathbf{J}$.

It is easy enough to verify that $\mathbf{I}_n$ is an $n \times n$ matrix consisting of zeros everywhere except along the $NW\text{-}SE$ (northwest-southeast) diagonal (called the main diagonal), which consists of ones,

$$\mathbf{I}_1 = [1], \quad \mathbf{I}_2 = \begin{bmatrix} 1 & 0 \\ 0 & 1 \end{bmatrix}, \quad \mathbf{I}_3 = \begin{bmatrix} 1 & 0 & 0 \\ 0 & 1 & 0 \\ 0 & 0 & 1 \end{bmatrix}$$

and so on. Where n is understood we write simply $\mathbf{I}$ and refer to $\mathbf{I}$ as the unit matrix.

■ 13.5 Matrix Inversion

We now turn to the problem of division in matrix arithmetic. In ordinary arithmetic we define a/b as a number x that satisfies the equation

$$bx = a$$

We next show that if b^{-1} is a number such that $bb^{-1} = 1$ (and of course $b^{-1}b = 1$), then

$$x = ab^{-1} = b^{-1}a$$

With matrices the situation is more involved. In the first place, if $\mathbf{B}^{-1}$ is such that $\mathbf{BB}^{-1} = \mathbf{I}$, it is not obvious that $\mathbf{B}^{-1}\mathbf{B} = \mathbf{I}$. However, it happens to be true.

Let $\mathbf{U}$ and $\mathbf{V}$ be such that

(10) $$\mathbf{UB} = \mathbf{I}$$

(11) $$\mathbf{BV} = \mathbf{I}$$

Then, from (10), $(\mathbf{UB})\mathbf{V} = \mathbf{IV} = \mathbf{V}$. But $(\mathbf{UB})\mathbf{V} = \mathbf{U}(\mathbf{BV}) = \mathbf{UI} = \mathbf{U}$, so that $\mathbf{U} = \mathbf{V}$ and it follows that, provided $\mathbf{B}^{-1}$ exists, it is unique and such that $\mathbf{B}^{-1}\mathbf{B} = \mathbf{BB}^{-1} = \mathbf{I}$. The reader should now prove that $(\mathbf{B}^{-1})^{-1} = \mathbf{B}$.

We can now define matrix division in two ways:

Definition

   (i) $\mathbf{A} \div \mathbf{B} = \mathbf{X}$ where $\mathbf{BX} = \mathbf{A}$
   (ii) $\mathbf{A} \div \mathbf{B} = \mathbf{Y}$ where $\mathbf{YB} = \mathbf{A}$

It is easy enough to verify that if we can find $\mathbf{B}^{-1}$, then $\mathbf{X} = \mathbf{B}^{-1}\mathbf{A}$, $\mathbf{Y} = \mathbf{AB}^{-1}$.

The context usually tells us which division is required. The only use of division is to operate on both sides of an equation and clearly we will treat both sides in the same way. Thus to solve

$$\mathbf{MX} = \mathbf{B}$$

we write

$$\mathbf{M}^{-1}(\mathbf{MX}) = \mathbf{M}^{-1}\mathbf{B}$$

$$\mathbf{X} = \mathbf{M}^{-1}\mathbf{B}$$

Obviously $\mathbf{BM}^{-1}$ will not be the solution for $\mathbf{M}(\mathbf{BM}^{-1}) \neq \mathbf{B}$ for the general matrices $\mathbf{M}$ and $\mathbf{B}$. When $\mathbf{B}^{-1}$ exists such that $\mathbf{BB}^{-1} = \mathbf{I}$, $\mathbf{B}^{-1}$ is called the *inverse* or *reciprocal* of $\mathbf{B}$.

We have frequently hedged on the issue of the existence of $\mathbf{B}^{-1}$, and the reader probably suspects that $\mathbf{B}^{-1}$ does not always exist. Conditions for the existence of an inverse can be stated in various ways. Perhaps the simplest involves the concept of determinants. We have carefully avoided this concept because we will have no use for it in this book.*

For our purpose it will be sufficient to state that if $\mathbf{B}$ is an $n \times n$ matrix, $\mathbf{X}$ is the column $x_1, x_2, \ldots, x_n$, and $\mathbf{C}$ the column $c_1, c_2, \ldots, c_n$,

---

* A formal solution of linear equations, known as Cramer's Rule, is given in most elementary texts. However, it is not a useful numerical method unless there are only two or three equations, in which case other simpler techniques are just as convenient. We do not consider that determinants have much application to elementary mathematics of management problems.

where not every c is zero, then $\mathbf{B}^{-1}$ exists whenever $\mathbf{B}$ is such that the equation

$$\mathbf{BX} = \mathbf{C}$$

has a unique solution.

One method of inverting $\mathbf{B}$ is to solve these equations in terms of the c's. The array of coefficients of c's will be the inverse of $\mathbf{B}$. The method is best illustrated numerically.

Example 1. Find the inverse of

$$\mathbf{B} = \begin{bmatrix} 4 & 2 & 3 \\ 1 & 3 & 2 \\ 2 & 1 & 5 \end{bmatrix}$$

Suppose $\mathbf{BX} = \mathbf{C}$, that is,

$$\begin{bmatrix} 4 & 2 & 3 \\ 1 & 3 & 2 \\ 2 & 1 & 5 \end{bmatrix} \begin{bmatrix} x_1 \\ x_2 \\ x_3 \end{bmatrix} = \begin{bmatrix} c_1 \\ c_2 \\ c_3 \end{bmatrix}$$

Divide the first equation by 4.

$$\begin{bmatrix} 1 & \frac{1}{2} & \frac{3}{4} \\ 1 & 3 & 2 \\ 2 & 1 & 5 \end{bmatrix} \begin{bmatrix} x_1 \\ x_2 \\ x_3 \end{bmatrix} = \begin{bmatrix} \frac{1}{4}c_1 \\ c_2 \\ c_3 \end{bmatrix}$$

Subtract the first equation from the second and twice the first from the third.

$$\begin{bmatrix} 1 & \frac{1}{2} & \frac{3}{4} \\ 0 & \frac{5}{2} & \frac{5}{4} \\ 0 & 0 & \frac{7}{2} \end{bmatrix} \begin{bmatrix} x_1 \\ x_2 \\ x_3 \end{bmatrix} = \begin{bmatrix} \frac{1}{4}c_1 \\ c_2 - \frac{1}{4}c_1 \\ c_3 - \frac{1}{2}c_1 \end{bmatrix}$$

Divide the second equation by $\frac{5}{2}$. Subtract $\frac{1}{2}$ the result from the first.

$$\begin{bmatrix} 1 & 0 & \frac{1}{2} \\ 0 & 1 & \frac{1}{2} \\ 0 & 0 & \frac{7}{2} \end{bmatrix} \begin{bmatrix} x_1 \\ x_2 \\ x_3 \end{bmatrix} = \begin{bmatrix} \frac{3}{10}c_1 - \frac{1}{5}c_2 \\ \frac{2}{5}c_2 - \frac{1}{10}c_1 \\ c_3 - \frac{1}{2}c_1 \end{bmatrix}$$

Divide the third equation by $\frac{7}{2}$ and subtract $\frac{1}{2}$ the result from the first and $\frac{1}{2}$ the result from the second.

$$\begin{bmatrix} 1 & 0 & 0 \\ 0 & 1 & 0 \\ 0 & 0 & 1 \end{bmatrix}\begin{bmatrix} x_1 \\ x_2 \\ x_3 \end{bmatrix} = \begin{bmatrix} \frac{13}{35}c_1 - \frac{1}{5}c_2 - \frac{1}{7}c_3 \\ -\frac{1}{35}c_1 + \frac{2}{5}c_2 - \frac{1}{7}c_3 \\ -\frac{1}{7}c_1 + 0c_2 + \frac{2}{7}c_3 \end{bmatrix}$$

$$= \begin{bmatrix} \frac{13}{35} & -\frac{1}{5} & -\frac{1}{7} \\ -\frac{1}{35} & \frac{2}{5} & -\frac{1}{7} \\ -\frac{1}{7} & 0 & \frac{2}{7} \end{bmatrix}\begin{bmatrix} c_1 \\ c_2 \\ c_3 \end{bmatrix}$$

or $\mathbf{IX} = \mathbf{B}^{-1}\mathbf{C}$.

The inverse of $\mathbf{B}$ is thus

$$\mathbf{B}^{-1} = \begin{bmatrix} \frac{13}{35} & -\frac{1}{5} & -\frac{1}{7} \\ -\frac{1}{35} & \frac{2}{5} & -\frac{1}{7} \\ -\frac{1}{7} & 0 & \frac{2}{7} \end{bmatrix}$$

The result should be verified by multiplying by $\mathbf{B}$. It is clear that we do not need to write the columns of x's every time; neither do we need the c's, provided we keep their coefficients separate. The easiest way to do this is to write them in separate columns. We can also drop the equality sign. The reader will see this amounts to writing a unit matrix alongside $\mathbf{B}$ and performing the following operations in succession on the rows of the "augmented matrix."

(i) Divide by constant.

(ii) Add or subtract multiples of rows to each other.

When the $\mathbf{B}$ matrix has been reduced to a unit matrix, the part corresponding to $\mathbf{I}$ is the inverse of $\mathbf{B}$.

Example 2. Solve the previous example without introducing $\mathbf{C}$ and $\mathbf{X}$.

$$\begin{bmatrix} 4 & 2 & 3 & 1 & 0 & 0 \\ 1 & 3 & 2 & 0 & 1 & 0 \\ 2 & 1 & 5 & 0 & 0 & 1 \end{bmatrix} \rightarrow \begin{bmatrix} 1 & \frac{1}{2} & \frac{3}{4} & \frac{1}{4} & 0 & 0 \\ 1 & 3 & 2 & 0 & 1 & 0 \\ 2 & 1 & 5 & 0 & 0 & 1 \end{bmatrix} \rightarrow$$

$$\begin{bmatrix} 1 & \frac{1}{2} & \frac{3}{4} & \frac{1}{4} & 0 & 0 \\ 0 & \frac{5}{2} & \frac{5}{4} & -\frac{1}{4} & 1 & 0 \\ 0 & 0 & \frac{7}{2} & -\frac{1}{2} & 0 & 1 \end{bmatrix} \rightarrow \begin{bmatrix} 1 & 0 & \frac{1}{2} & \frac{3}{10} & -\frac{1}{5} & 0 \\ 0 & 1 & \frac{1}{2} & -\frac{1}{10} & \frac{2}{5} & 0 \\ 0 & 0 & \frac{7}{2} & -\frac{1}{2} & 0 & 1 \end{bmatrix} \rightarrow$$

$$\begin{bmatrix} 1 & 0 & 0 & \frac{13}{35} & -\frac{1}{5} & -\frac{1}{7} \\ 0 & 1 & 0 & -\frac{1}{35} & \frac{2}{5} & -\frac{1}{7} \\ 0 & 0 & 1 & -\frac{1}{7} & 0 & \frac{2}{7} \end{bmatrix}$$

A possible snag may arise if at a given stage the diagonal element required for division is zero. In this case it is in order to bring a non-zero element to the appropriate point by interchanging rows. However, if no such rearrangement of rows is possible, no inverse exists. Then the equations do not have a unique solution. Either they have no solution or an infinity of solutions, depending on the particular values of **C**.

Example 3. Invert

$$\begin{bmatrix} 0 & 1 \\ 2 & 3 \end{bmatrix}$$

$$\begin{bmatrix} 0 & 1 & 1 & 0 \\ 2 & 3 & 0 & 1 \end{bmatrix} \rightarrow \begin{bmatrix} 2 & 3 & 0 & 1 \\ 0 & 1 & 1 & 0 \end{bmatrix} \rightarrow \begin{bmatrix} 1 & \frac{3}{2} & 0 & \frac{1}{2} \\ 0 & 1 & 1 & 0 \end{bmatrix} \rightarrow$$

$$\begin{bmatrix} 1 & 0 & -\frac{3}{2} & \frac{1}{2} \\ 0 & 1 & 1 & 0 \end{bmatrix}$$

Thus the inverse is

$$\begin{bmatrix} -\frac{3}{2} & \frac{1}{2} \\ 1 & 0 \end{bmatrix}$$

and this may be checked by multiplication.

Example 4. Solve the example of Section 13.1 by finding the inverse of matrices. We have the system of equations

$$x_1 + 2x_2 = 200$$

$$2x_1 + 8x_2 = 560$$

which can be written as

$$\begin{bmatrix} 1 & 2 \\ 2 & 8 \end{bmatrix} \begin{bmatrix} x_1 \\ x_2 \end{bmatrix} = \begin{bmatrix} 200 \\ 560 \end{bmatrix}$$

or **AX** = **C**, where

$$\mathbf{A} = \begin{bmatrix} 1 & 2 \\ 2 & 8 \end{bmatrix}, \quad \mathbf{X} = \begin{bmatrix} x_1 \\ x_2 \end{bmatrix}, \quad \text{and } \mathbf{C} = \begin{bmatrix} 200 \\ 560 \end{bmatrix}$$

and $X = A^{-1}C$. We first find A^{-1},

$$\begin{vmatrix} 1 & 2 & 1 & 0 \\ 2 & 8 & 0 & 1 \end{vmatrix} \rightarrow \begin{vmatrix} 1 & 2 & 1 & 0 \\ 0 & 4 & -2 & 1 \end{vmatrix}$$

$$\rightarrow \begin{vmatrix} 1 & 2 & 1 & 0 \\ 0 & 1 & -\frac{1}{2} & \frac{1}{4} \end{vmatrix} \rightarrow \begin{vmatrix} 1 & 0 & 2 & -\frac{1}{2} \\ 0 & 1 & -\frac{1}{2} & \frac{1}{4} \end{vmatrix}$$

$$A^{-1} = \begin{vmatrix} 2 & -\frac{1}{2} \\ -\frac{1}{2} & \frac{1}{4} \end{vmatrix}$$

and $$X = \begin{vmatrix} 2 & -\frac{1}{2} \\ -\frac{1}{2} & \frac{1}{4} \end{vmatrix} \begin{vmatrix} 200 \\ 560 \end{vmatrix} = \begin{vmatrix} 120 \\ 40 \end{vmatrix}$$

Hence $x_1 = 120$, $x_2 = 40$.

We can summarize our results so far by saying that there exists an arithmetic of matrices, one very similar to that of ordinary numbers. That is, we have a zero, a unit, and rules of multiplication, addition, and subtraction. The rules of operation obey the associative, commutative and distributive laws of ordinary numbers. In many cases matrices have an inverse or reciprocal. Matrix equations imply equality between corresponding elements on each side. Inequalities imply the same inequalities between corresponding elements. Equations can be manipulated as if the symbols in them were ordinary algebraic symbols, provided care is taken to preserve the order of multiplication. Division is often possible and is accomplished by multiplying by the inverse. Finally, the reader may verify that inequality signs are preserved by multiplying both sides by the same positive matrix (i.e., one in which all elements are greater than or equal to zero).

Exercises

1. Invert the following matrices:

(a) $\begin{bmatrix} 1 & 4 & 2 \\ 3 & 1 & 1 \\ 2 & 3 & 2 \end{bmatrix}$ (b) $\begin{bmatrix} 1 & 2 & 4 & 1 \\ 3 & 5 & 2 & 3 \\ 5 & 7 & 1 & 1 \\ 2 & 3 & 4 & 5 \end{bmatrix}$ (c) $\begin{bmatrix} 0 & 1 & 3 \\ 2 & 2 & 1 \\ 3 & 0 & 1 \end{bmatrix}$

2. Let M be the partitioned matrix

$$\begin{bmatrix} A_{mn} & I_m \\ \hline I_n & O \end{bmatrix}$$

where $\mathbf{A}_{mn}$ is an m row, n column matrix, $\mathbf{I}_m$, $\mathbf{I}_n$ are unit matrices of sides m and n, and $\mathbf{O}$ is an n row, m column matrix, all of whose elements are zero.

Assume $\mathbf{M}^{-1}$ may be partitioned as follows:

$$\begin{bmatrix} \mathbf{P}_{nm} & \mathbf{Q}_{nn} \\ \hline \mathbf{R}_{mm} & \mathbf{S}_{mn} \end{bmatrix} \qquad (\mathbf{P}_{nm} \text{ has } n \text{ rows, } m \text{ columns, etc.})$$

Multiply $\mathbf{M}$ and $\mathbf{M}^{-1}$ and, by equating the submatrices in the product, find $\mathbf{M}^{-1}$ (see also exercise 3).

3. If

$$\mathbf{M} = \begin{bmatrix} 2 & 3 & -1 & 1 & 0 \\ 1 & -2 & 3 & 0 & 1 \\ \hline 1 & 0 & 0 & 0 & 0 \\ 0 & 1 & 0 & 0 & 0 \\ 0 & 0 & 1 & 0 & 0 \end{bmatrix}$$

find $\mathbf{M}^{-1}$ by the methods of exercise 2 and verify the result by direct multiplication. (Such matrices occur in linear programming.)

4. A *diagonal* matrix is a square matrix in which all elements not along the *NW-SE* diagonal (called the *leading diagonal*) are zero. If $\mathbf{D}$ is such a matrix, with $d_{ij} = 0 (i \neq j)$, $d_{ii} = \alpha_i$, show that $\mathbf{DA}$ is equivalent to multiplying each row in $\mathbf{A}$ by the corresponding α_i and $\mathbf{AD}$ is equivalent to multiplying each column by the corresponding α_i. Show also that if no $\alpha_i = 0$, the inverse of $\mathbf{D}$ is a diagonal matrix whose diagonal consists of $1/\alpha_1$, $1/\alpha_2$, ..., $1/\alpha_n$.

5. Show that $(\mathbf{ABC} \dots \mathbf{PQR})^{-1} = \mathbf{R}^{-1}\mathbf{Q}^{-1}\mathbf{P}^{-1} \dots \mathbf{C}^{-1}\mathbf{B}^{-1}\mathbf{A}^{-1}$.

6. The matrix $\mathbf{U}$ can be partitioned as follows:

$$\mathbf{U} = \begin{bmatrix} \mathbf{B}_{mn} & \mathbf{D}_{mm} \\ \hline \mathbf{D}_{nn} & \mathbf{O} \end{bmatrix}$$

($\mathbf{D}_{mm}$, $\mathbf{D}_{nn}$ are diagonal matrices, none of whose diagonal elements are zero—see exercise 4.) Show that $\mathbf{U}$ may be reduced to the form of $\mathbf{M}$ in exercise 2 by pre-multiplying by $\mathbf{D}^{-1}$ where

$$\mathbf{D} = \begin{bmatrix} \mathbf{D}_{mm} & \mathbf{O} \\ \hline \mathbf{O} & \mathbf{D}_{nn} \end{bmatrix}$$

Thus $\mathbf{D}^{-1}\mathbf{U} = \mathbf{M}$ or $\mathbf{U} = \mathbf{DM}$. Hence show

$$\mathbf{U}^{-1} = \begin{bmatrix} \mathbf{O} & \mathbf{D}_{nn}^{-1} \\ \hline \mathbf{D}_{mm}^{-1} & -\mathbf{D}_{mm}^{-1}\,\mathbf{B}_{mn}\,\mathbf{D}_{nn}^{-1} \end{bmatrix}$$

Exercises for Chapter 13

1. Find the admissible regions defined by the following inequalities:

   (a) $-3 \leq x \leq 4, \quad 2 \leq y \leq 5$

   (b) $x + 2y \leq 50, \quad x + 4y \leq 60, \quad x, y \geq 0$

   (c) $-x + y \leq 5, \quad x + 3y \leq 60, \quad y \geq 5$

2. A firm manufactures two products X and Y with the following characteristics:

Product	Unit Cost	Unit Machine Hours	Maximum Sales Quantity
X	$1	2	4000
Y	$2	1	4000

Find the admissible region for production quantities, x, of X and y, of Y, if the total manufacturing cost budget is $10,000 and the total machine capacity is 15,000 hours.

3. Solve the following equation for x and y:

$$x \cos \theta - y \sin \theta = 1$$

$$x \sin \theta + y \cos \theta = 1$$

4. One thousand airline stewardesses, classified in the following age groups, are employed by an airline:

Age	20–24	25–29	30–34	35–39
Number	500	320	150	30

The probability that a stewardess in the ith group will leave by the end of the year is given by the column vector

$$\mathbf{p} = \begin{pmatrix} 0.20 \\ 0.15 \\ 0.10 \\ 0.05 \end{pmatrix}$$

Using matrix multiplication, find the number of stewardesses who are expected to leave in one year.

5. Solve the exercises of Section 13.2 by the method of matrix inversion.

6. Solve equations (3). Verify that the solution can be expressed in the form $\mathbf{X} = \mathbf{SB}$, where $\mathbf{S}$ is a 3×3 matrix. Let s_{ij} be the elements of $\mathbf{S}$. Then

$$\mathbf{SB} = \begin{bmatrix} 10s_{11} + 7s_{12} + 11s_{13} \\ 10s_{21} + 7s_{22} + 11s_{23} \\ 10s_{31} + 7s_{32} + 11s_{33} \end{bmatrix} = \begin{bmatrix} x \\ y \\ z \end{bmatrix}$$

(There are in fact many matrices $\mathbf{S}$. However, if we insist on an $\mathbf{S}$ matrix that will work for all vectors $\mathbf{B}$, there is only one.)

7. Find the inverse of the following matrices and show that the product of the original matrix and its inverse is the identity matrix:

(a) $\begin{vmatrix} 1 & -3 \\ -2 & 4 \end{vmatrix}$ (c) $\begin{vmatrix} \frac{1}{2} & \frac{1}{3} \\ \frac{1}{4} & \frac{1}{5} \end{vmatrix}$

(b) $\begin{vmatrix} 1 & -1 & 1 \\ -1 & 2 & 1 \\ 2 & 1 & -1 \end{vmatrix}$ (d) $\begin{vmatrix} 4 & 3 & -1 \\ 2 & 1 & 2 \\ 3 & -1 & 1 \end{vmatrix}$

14

Linear Programming: Simplex Method

■ **14.1 Introduction**

The planning of activities, such as the allocation of men, materials, or machines, is called *programming*. Programming problems occur in situations where the available resources may be limited or incapable of being utilized completely. The objective is to determine the most efficient method of allocating these resources to activities so that a measure of performance is optimized. Whenever this measure is a linear function of the controllable variables, and the restrictions on utilization or availability of resources are expressible as a system of linear equations or inequalities, we have a *linear programming problem*.

For example, in the case of manufacturing a variety of products on a group of machines, the production problem is to determine the most efficient utilization of available machine capacities to meet the required demand. The programming problem is to allocate the available machine resources to the various products so that the total production cost is a minimum. To solve this problem by the method of this chapter, information is required on the unit production cost, unit production time, machine capacity, and production requirements.

As another example, consider the production planning problem of determining a smooth pattern of production that meets specific weekly demands. The programming problem is to schedule weekly production and inventory changes so that total costs of production and inventory are a minimum. This is a linear programming problem, for the total costs and restrictions are linear functions of the quantity produced and stored. Input data required to solve this problem are the unit cost of manufacturing and storing, machine and warehouse space capacities, and demand levels.

This chapter formulates the linear programming problem in mathematical form. Since the number of variables in a linear programming problem may be very large, practical problems often require the use of electronic computers to determine numerical solutions. Geometric concepts are developed in this chapter and are used to form the basis of an algebraic method, the Simplex method, for solving general linear programming problems. A principle of duality is developed and applied to reduce the magnitude of computational effort. Applications are given in the form of examples and exercises.

■ 14.2 Formulation of Linear Programming Problems

Example 1. Consider the following problem faced by a production planner in a soft-drink plant. He has two bottling machines A and B. A is designed for 8-ounce bottles and B for 16-ounce bottles. However, each can be uesd on both types with some loss of efficiency. Given the data below, how should the bottling plant be used?

	8-ounce bottles	16-ounce bottles
Machine A	100/minute	40/minute
Machine B	75/minute	60/minute

The machines can be run 8 hours per day, 5 days per week. Profit on an 8-ounce bottle is 1 cent and on a 16-ounce bottle, 2.5 cents.

Weekly production of the drink cannot exceed 300,000 ounces, and the market can absorb 25,000 8-ounce bottles and 7000 16-ounce bottles.

The planner wishes to maximize his profit, subject, of course, to meeting all the production and marketing restrictions. Suppose he sets up the schedule below, where

x_1 = number of 8-ounce bottles produced on machine A
x_2 = number of 8-ounce bottles produced on machine B
x_3 = number of 16-ounce bottles produced on machine A
x_4 = number of 16-ounce bottles produced on machine B

	8-ounce bottles	16-ounce bottles
Machine A	x_1	x_3
Machine B	x_2	x_4

The weekly profit is $Z = x_1 + x_2 + 2.5x_3 + 2.5x_4$.

He wishes to maximize Z, subject to the following restrictions on x_1, x_2, x_3, x_4.

Nonnegativity. $x_1 \geq 0$, $x_2 \geq 0$, $x_3 \geq 0$, $x_4 \geq 0$ (He cannot bottle negative quantities.)

Time limitation. Only (60 minutes/hour)(8 hours/day)(5 days/week) = 2400 minutes available per week.

$$\text{For machine } A, \quad \frac{x_1}{100} + \frac{x_3}{40} \leq 2400$$

$$\text{For machine } B, \quad \frac{x_2}{75} + \frac{x_4}{60} \leq 2400$$

Capacity limitation. Total amount of drink available each week is 300,000 ounces.

$$8x_1 + 8x_2 + 16x_3 + 16x_4 \leq 300,000$$

Market limitation. Only 25,000 8-ounce bottles and 7000 16-ounce bottles can be sold.

$$x_1 + x_2 \leq 25,000$$

$$x_3 + x_4 \leq 7000$$

Thus the problem is to maximize the profit

$$Z = x_1 + x_2 + 2.5x_3 + 2.5x_4$$

subject to the restrictions

$$\frac{x_1}{100} + \frac{x_3}{40} \leq 2400$$

$$\frac{x_2}{75} + \frac{x_4}{60} \leq 2400$$

$$8x_1 + 8x_2 + 16x_3 + 16x_4 \leq 300,000$$

$$x_1 + x_2 \leq 25,000$$

$$x_3 + x_4 \leq 7000$$

It will be observed that all the restrictions and the Z function are *linear* in the x's.

Definition. Any problem of maximizing a linear function of n variables, subject to linear constraints is defined as a *linear programming problem*.

We saw in Section 7.3 that if we wish to find the maximum of $y = f(x)$ in the range $a \leq x \leq b$, we must examine the values of y at:

(i) any point for which $f'(x) = 0$ and $a \leq x \leq b$.
(ii) at the points $x = a$ and $x = b$.

We also saw that if $y = f(x_1, x_2, \ldots, x_n)$, and we wish to find the maximum, we must examine the values of y at all points for which $\partial f / \partial x_i = 0$, $i = 1, 2, \ldots, n$. We are now interested in finding the maximum of a function of several variables, where the independent variables are confined to a stated region.

The general method is to search for the maximum in two places: (i) where $\partial f / \partial x_i = 0$, $i = 1, 2, \ldots, n$, within the region of interest, and (ii) over points on the boundary of the region of interest.

In Example 1 we see that

$$\frac{\partial Z}{\partial x_1} = 1, \quad \frac{\partial Z}{\partial x_2} = 1, \quad \frac{\partial Z}{\partial x_3} = 2.5, \quad \frac{\partial Z}{\partial x_4} = 2.5$$

so we have no possibility of all derivatives vanishing and consequently must search for a solution somewhere on the boundary of the region defined by the restrictions. The difficulty is to envisage the appearance of this region, in order to examine its boundary. The region is in four dimensions, so we are going to need some mathematics to aid our intuition. We will start with a simple problem in two variables.

Example 2. Maximize $Z = 5x + 2y$ over all $x \geq 0$, $y \geq 0$ which satisfy:

$$x \leq 10$$

$$y \leq 12$$

$$3x + 2y \leq 40$$

We start by sketching the region defined by the restrictions (Figure 14.1). The nonnegativity restrictions confine us to the first quadrant, and the other conditions limit us to the shaded area $OABDE$.

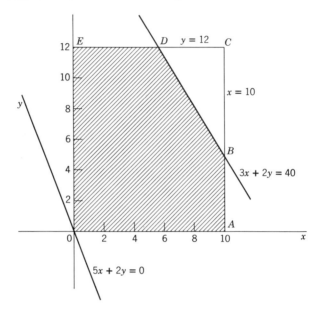

Figure 14.1

We say that any point P with coordinates (x, y) is *feasible* so long as P lies within or on the boundary of the admissible region. Note that not all points yield different values of Z. In fact, Z is the same for all points on the line parallel to $5x + 2y = 0$. All such lines have equations of the form $5x + 2y = k$, and along any such line, Z has the value k. We showed in Section 5.5 that the distance of the line from the origin is $k/(2^2 + 5^2)^{1/2}$, and so if we wish to maximize Z, we must move the line as far from the origin as possible.

It is easy enough to do this graphically. Draw the line $5x + 2y = 0$, place a ruler along it, and slide the ruler across the figure parallel to the initial line until further movement would leave no points within the admissible region. A little experimentation will show that as long as the ruler intersects two of the boundary lines in distinct points, it can be moved further, while still having points within the region. *We conclude that the maximum must lie at one of the corners.* It is easy to verify that the corner which yields the maximum value for Z is the point $B(10, 5)$ An alternative to the graphical method described above is to evaluate Z at each of the corners and to select the corner that yields the maximum value of Z. The corners occur at the intersections of pairs of lines forming the boundary and may be found by solving pairs of equations from the set:

$$x = 0, \; y = 0 \; \text{(point } O\text{)}$$

$$x = 10, \; y = 0 \; \text{(point } A\text{)}$$

$$x = 10, \; 3x + 2y = 40 \; \text{(point } B\text{)}$$

$$x = 10, \; y = 12 \; \text{(point } C\text{)}$$

$$3x + 2y = 40, \; y = 12 \; \text{(point } D\text{)}$$

$$x = 0, \; y = 12 \; \text{(point } E\text{)}$$

There are 6 such pairs, but not all of them yield points in the admissible region. For example, $x = 10$, $y = 12$ yields the point C in Figure 14.1. In two dimensions it is not very difficult to see which pairs yield feasible points by sketching the figure, but with three or more variables (our soft drink planner in Example 1 had four variables), this is not possible. Of course, we could find all points and then check to see which were feasible; but the labor is prohibitive, and we must look for a more efficient method.

Exercises. Maximize the following, over all $x \geq 0$, $y \geq 0$ which satisfy the stated restrictions:

1. $Z = 2x - y$
   $x + y \leq 5$
   $x + 2y \leq 8$

2. $Z = 4x + 7y$
   $x \leq 10$
   $y - x \leq 5$

3. $Z = 3x + 4y$
   $y - x \leq 5$
   $x + y \leq 10$

4. A manufacturer produces two types of bearings, A and B, utilizing three types of machines, lathes, grinders, drill presses. The machinery requirements for one unit of each product, in hours, is expressed in the following table.

Bearing	Lathe	Grinder	Drill Press
A	0.01	0.03	0.03
B	0.02	0.01	0.015
	Weekly Machine Capacity		
	40 hr	30 hr	36 hr

Unit profits are $0.10 and $0.15 for bearings A and B, respectively.

(a) Formulate the profit maximization problem as a linear programming problem.

(b) Find the region of feasible solutions graphically.

(c) Find the optimal weekly production of each bearing type.

■ 14.3   Geometrical Concepts

The computational procedures for solving linear programming problems are simple enough in the sense that we can write down a list of rules, which, if followed faithfully, will yield the solution.   On the other hand, the list is lengthy and almost impossible to remember without an understanding of how it is derived.   Many elementary texts merely state the rules, but the authors believe that slavishly following instructions is a task for an electronic computer, not for an intelligent human being.   A human has the unique gifts of comprehension and understanding, and his contribution can only exceed that of the computer if he uses them. Accordingly, we will develop the necessary rules; we warn the reader that the development consists of many stages and is lengthy.   However, no one step is difficult, and, taken a little at a time, the argument can easily be followed with the mathematics now at the reader's disposal.

The crucial result that furnishes the key to our problem is that, no matter how many variables are contained in the linear programming problem, the maximum always lies at a "corner."   Once we have proved this, all we need is an efficient procedure for performing the following steps:

(a) finding at least one corner.
(b) deciding whether it is the corner that yields the maximum.
(c) if it is not the best corner, finding another that is better.
(d) a guarantee that if steps (b) and (c) are repeated, they will eventually lead to *the* best corner.

Let us start with a formal statement of a linear programming problem.   Maximize $Z = c_1 x_1 + c_2 x_2 + \cdots + c_n x_n$ over the set of variables $\{x_1, x_2, \ldots, x_n\}$, where

$$(1) \qquad x_1 \geq 0, \quad x_2 \geq 0, \ldots, \quad x_n \geq 0$$

and

$$(2) \qquad \begin{aligned} a_{11}x_1 + a_{12}x_2 + \cdots + a_{1n}x_n &\leq b_1 \\ a_{21}x_1 + a_{22}x_2 + \cdots\cdots + a_{2n}x_2 &\leq b_2 \\ &\vdots \\ a_{m1}x_1 + a_{m2}x_2 + \cdots + a_{mn}x_n &\leq b_m \end{aligned}$$

In matrix notation (Chapter 13), we wish to maximize $Z = (\mathbf{C}, \mathbf{X})$ over all $\mathbf{X} \geq 0$ which satisfy

$$\mathbf{AX} \leq \mathbf{B}$$

where
$$(\mathbf{C}, \mathbf{X}) = \mathbf{CX} = (c_1 c_2 \cdots c_n) \begin{pmatrix} x_1 \\ x_2 \\ \cdot \\ \cdot \\ \cdot \\ x_n \end{pmatrix}$$

$$\mathbf{AX} = \begin{pmatrix} a_{11} & a_{12} & \cdots & a_{1n} \\ a_{21} & a_{22} & \cdots & a_{2n} \\ \cdot & \cdot & & \cdot \\ \cdot & \cdot & & \cdot \\ \cdot & \cdot & & \cdot \\ a_{m1} & a_{m2} & \cdots & a_{mn} \end{pmatrix} \begin{pmatrix} x_1 \\ x_2 \\ \cdot \\ \cdot \\ \cdot \\ x_n \end{pmatrix} \quad \text{and} \quad \mathbf{B} = \begin{pmatrix} b_1 \\ b_2 \\ \cdot \\ \cdot \\ \cdot \\ b_m \end{pmatrix}$$

Let us imagine the point P with coordinates $(x_1, x_2, \ldots, x_n)$ in n-dimensional space, and consider our problem as that of moving P about inside the region R, defined by the restrictions (1) and (2), until we find the maximum value of Z. We verify that the steps listed in (a)–(d) lead to the maximum by demonstrating the following results:

(i) The region R is *convex*. That is, if P and Q are two points of R, all points on the line between them belong to R. Let $P = (x_1, \ldots, x_n)$ and $Q = (y_1, \ldots, y_n)$ be any two points. Then any point, T, on the line between them has coordinates

$$(px_1 + qy_1, px_2 + qy_2, \ldots, px_n + qy_n)$$

where $0 \le p \le 1$, $q = 1 - p$.

It is obvious that if $(x_1, \ldots, x_n)$ and $(y_1, \ldots, y_n)$ satisfy (1) and (2), so do the coordinates of T. A convenient notation is to write

$$T = pP + qQ$$

(ii) If Z_P and Z_Q are the values of Z at P and Q, then the value of Z at T is given by

$$Z_T = pZ_P + qZ_Q$$

(iii) In Chapter 5 it was shown that any point H inside R can be expressed as

$$H = \alpha_1 P_1 + \alpha_2 P_2 + \cdots + \alpha_t P_t$$

where $P_1, P_2, \ldots, P_t$ are the corners of R, $\alpha_i \ge 0$, and $\alpha_1 + \alpha_2 + \cdots + \alpha_t = 1$.

(iv) If $Z_1, Z_2, \ldots, Z_t$ are the values of Z at the corners, then results (i), (ii) and (iii) can be used to show that the value of Z at any point within R is expressible as

$$Z = \alpha_1 Z_1 + \alpha_2 Z_2 + \cdots + \alpha_t Z_t$$

(v) Let $Z_M = \max \{Z_1, Z_2, \ldots, Z_t\}$. To maximize Z we must take $\alpha_M = 1$ and all other α's equal to zero. *Thus Z takes its maximum at the corner P_M.* It is possible for more than one corner to have the value Z_M, in this case any point in the edge or face in which the corners lie also yields Z_M. However, it is never possible for the maximum value of Z to occur inside R. *Thus our search for the maximum can be confined to the corners.*

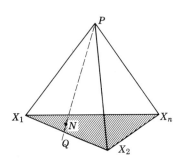

Figure 14.2

(vi) *If movement away from a corner, along all the edges through it, decreases Z, then Z attains its maximum at this corner.*

First of all, note that at such corner Z is greater than at any corner that can be reached by moving along the edges through it. If possible, suppose there are two such corners, say P and Q, and consider what happens to Z as we move from P toward Q along the line PQ. Let an $(n-1)$ dimensional hyperplane * cut the edges through P on the points $X_1, X_2, \ldots, X_n$ of Figure 14.2. Let PQ meet the hyperplane at N. First, as in (iii) and (iv), we can show

$$N = \alpha_1 X_1 + \alpha_2 X_2 + \cdots + \alpha_n X_n$$

and
$$Z_N = \alpha_1 Z_{X_1} + \alpha_2 Z_{X_2} + \cdots + \alpha_n Z_{X_n}$$

where none of the α's are negative and their sum is unity. But $Z_P > Z_{X_1}; Z_P > Z_{X_2}; \ldots, Z_P > Z_{X_n}$, and thus $Z_P > Z_N$.

Exactly the same argument shows $Z_Q > Z_P$. We conclude only one point can exist such that Z decreases along all edges through it.†

The above results suggest the procedures (a)–(d).

Example Find the nonnegative values of x, y, z that maximize the expression $Z = 3x + 5y + 4z$ subject to the restrictions:

$$2x + 3y \leq 8$$

(3)
$$2y + 5z \leq 10$$

$$3x + 2y + 4z \leq 15$$

---

* Here we ask the reader to use a little geometrical imagination. A hyperplane is a multidimensional analog of a plane in three dimensions. It consists of the points that satisfy a linear equation.

† We have not excluded equality all the way along an edge. This is possible.

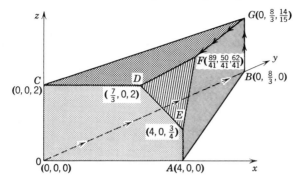

Figure 14.3 Region of admissible solutions in three dimensions (Example 3.)

If we consider x, y, and z to be coordinates in three-dimensional space, the nonnegativity restrictions mean that we are concerned only with the region consisting of points whose coordinates are all either positive or zero. However, we are not free to choose any point in this region because of the restrictions (3). In fact, we are limited to points that lie within or on the boundary of the solid enclosed by the six planes, whose equations are

$$2x + 3y = 8, \qquad x = 0$$

$$2y + 5z = 10, \qquad y = 0$$

$$3x + 2y + 4z = 15, \qquad z = 0$$

This solid $[OABCDEFG]$ is shown in Figure 14.3.

In order to perform steps (a)–(d) with reasonable algebraic simplicity we introduce the so-called *slack variables* u, v, w, defined by the equations,

$$2x + 3y + u = 8$$

(4) $$2y + 5z + v = 10$$

$$3x + 2y + 4z + w = 15$$

It will be realized that u, v, w are the deficiencies when the inequality signs hold in the original restrictions. Moreover, if x, y, z are to satisfy restrictions (4), u, v, w must be nonnegative.

If we rewrite (4) as

$$u = 8 - 2x - 3y$$

(5) $$v = 10 - 2y - 5z$$

$$w = 15 - 3x - 2y - 4z$$

we see that any two of the six equations, $u = 0$, $v = 0$, $w = 0$, $x = 0$, $y = 0$, $z = 0$, together represent one of the edges of the solid $OABC\text{-}DEFG$. Now suppose we start at the origin, which is clearly a corner of the solid. Thus we choose $x = y = z = 0$ and read off the corresponding values of u, v, w as 8, 10, 15.

The three edges through the origin are represented by the pairs of equations

$$\left.\begin{array}{l} x = 0 \\ y = 0 \end{array}\right\} \qquad \left.\begin{array}{l} x = 0 \\ z = 0 \end{array}\right\} \qquad \left.\begin{array}{l} y = 0 \\ z = 0 \end{array}\right\}$$

If we move along these lines, we increase z, y, x, respectively. Each unit increase in x, y, z increases Z by 3, 5, 4, respectively; so we decide to increase y as much as possible and, for the time being, leave x and z as zero.

Referring to (5) we see that we can increase y by $\frac{8}{3}$ without making u negative; we can increase y by 5 without making v negative, and we can increase y by $\frac{15}{2}$ without making w negative. Thus the maximum increase in y is $\frac{8}{3}$, and we move from the origin to the point $B(0, \frac{8}{3}, 0)$. Next we rearrange equations (4) so that we can read off the nonzero variables at B, just as previously we read off the nonzero variables at the origin. To do this we solve (4) for v, w, and y (the nonzero variables at B) in terms of x, z, and u (the zero variables at B). An easy way to do this is to solve the first equation of (5) for y and then substitute this expression for y in the other two equations of (5). We obtain

$$\tfrac{2}{3}x + y + \tfrac{1}{3}u = \tfrac{8}{3}$$

$$-\tfrac{4}{3}x + 5z - \tfrac{2}{3}u + v = \tfrac{14}{3}$$

$$\tfrac{5}{3}x + 4z - \tfrac{2}{3}u + w = \tfrac{29}{3}$$

or

$$y = \tfrac{8}{3} - \tfrac{2}{3}x - \tfrac{1}{3}u$$

(6)

$$v = \tfrac{14}{3} + \tfrac{4}{3}x - 5z + \tfrac{2}{3}u$$

$$w = \tfrac{29}{3} - \tfrac{5}{3}x - 4z + \tfrac{2}{3}u$$

The edges through B are given by

$$\left.\begin{array}{l} x = 0 \\ z = 0 \end{array}\right\} BO \qquad \left.\begin{array}{l} x = 0 \\ u = 0 \end{array}\right\} BG \qquad \left.\begin{array}{l} z = 0 \\ u = 0 \end{array}\right\} BA$$

We have just moved along BO; so we consider moving along BG and BA.

If we move along BA, we will have to increase x, and from the first equation in (6) we see we will have to decrease y by $\frac{2}{3}$ for every unit increase in x. Thus, for every unit increase in x, we will change Z by $3 \times 1 - 5 \times \frac{2}{3} = -\frac{1}{3}$. Thus we do not want to move along BA.

If we move along BG, we increase z, and we see from (6) that x and y do not change as z increases. Consequently, increasing z increases Z by 4 per unit. From the second of equations (6), we can increase z by as much as $\frac{14}{15}$ without making v negative; and, from the third equation, we can increase z by as much as $\frac{29}{12}$ without making w negative. Thus the maximum permissible increase in z is $\frac{14}{15}$, and we move from B to G.

Again we express the nonzero variables (y, z, and w) in terms of the zero variables:

$$\tfrac{2}{3}x + y + \tfrac{1}{3}u = \tfrac{8}{3} - \tfrac{4}{15}x + z - \tfrac{2}{15}u + \tfrac{1}{5}v = \tfrac{14}{15}$$

$$\tfrac{41}{15}x - \tfrac{2}{15}u - \tfrac{4}{5}v + w = \tfrac{89}{15}$$

or $\qquad y = \tfrac{8}{3} - \tfrac{2}{3}x - \tfrac{1}{3}u$

(7) $\qquad z = \tfrac{14}{15} + \tfrac{4}{15}x + \tfrac{2}{15}u - \tfrac{1}{5}v$

$\qquad w = \tfrac{89}{15} - \tfrac{41}{15}x + \tfrac{2}{15}u + \tfrac{4}{5}v$

and repeat the operations, arriving at the point F with coordinates $(\tfrac{89}{41}, \tfrac{50}{41}, \tfrac{62}{41})$. Here we discover that movement in any direction decreases Z, and we conclude that Z takes its maximum at the vertex F.

The geometric basis for the simplex method has been described here in order to motivate the algebraic presentation that follows and is not recommended as a calculational procedure, even in the three-dimensional case. From here on we will be thinking of the algebraic analog of the geometric method already discussed and will develop the simplex table which is used for calculation.

Exercise. Show that results (i) to (v) are valid.

■ 14.4 The Simplex Method

The first step in the simplex method for solving the general problem posed at the beginning of Section 14.3 is to convert the system of m linear inequalities in the k variables $x_1, x_2, \ldots, x_k$ given in (2) to a system of m linear equations. This is done by the insertion of the so-called "slack variables," $x_{k+1}, x_{k+2}, \ldots, x_{k+m}$, one for each of the displayed inequalities, so that (2) becomes

$$a_{11}x_1 + a_{12}x_2 + \cdots + a_{1k}x_k + x_{k+1} = b_1$$

$$a_{21}x_1 + a_{22}x_2 + \cdots + a_{2k}x_k + x_{k+2} = b_2$$

(8)
.

.

.

$$a_{m1}x_1 + a_{m2}x_2 + \cdots + a_{mk}x_k + x_{k+m} = b_m$$

The linear programming problem may now be restated as follows: to find, among all sets of points $(x_1, x_2, \ldots, x_{k+m})$ satisfying (8) with each x_j nonnegative, that point $(\bar{x}_1, \bar{x}_2, \ldots, \bar{x}_{k+m})$ which maximizes the linear function

(9) $$Z = C_1x_1 + C_2x_2 + \cdots + C_kx_k$$

Once the maximal $(\bar{x}_i, \bar{x}_2, \ldots, \bar{x}_{k+m})$ is found, the answer to the problem as originally stated is just the subset $(\bar{x}_1, \bar{x}_2, \ldots, \bar{x}_k)$. The slack variables are merely a device used in arriving at the optimal solution and may or may not have physical meaning in individual problems.

The key theorem underlying the simplex approach says, in effect, that the set $(x_1, x_2, \ldots, x_{k+m})$ which maximizes (9) subject to (8) must necessarily possess k elements which are zero. If we knew which coordinates were zero at the optimum, we could insert their values in (8); the latter system would then be a set of m equations in m unknowns and could be solved algebraically for the optimum. Without this knowledge we must be content to proceed in a step-by-step fashion toward solution. The procedure may be visualized as follows. We choose k of the $k + m$ coordinates and assign them the value zero. Using these values, we then solve the restriction equations for the remaining m coordinates. If any of the coordinates are negative, we discard this solution as violating the nonnegativity restriction and try another set of k coordinates for the zero variables. If none of the coordinates is negative, we have what is called a *feasible solution*, which is the starting point of the iterative process. The simplex technique permits us to test the feasible solution for optimality, and, if it is nonoptimal, to proceed directly to a different feasible soluti n with an improved Z. It can be shown that eventually the technique must take us to an optimal solution.*

A feasible solution for the nth stage is related to the feasible solution

---

* In practice each iteration leads to a new corner; as there are only a finite number of corners we must reach the optimum. There are some theoretical exceptions but they are not of practical importance.

for the $n + 1$st stage in the following way. One of the zero coordinates for the nth stage becomes nonzero in the $n + 1$st stage and is called an *entering variable*. To compensate, one of the nonzero coordinates in the nth stage becomes zero in the $n + 1$st stage and is called a *departing variable*. The other zero coordinates remain zero; and the other nonzero coordinates, in general, remain nonzero (though their values may change). The simplex routine is presented next. For definiteness, we shall give the table for the case of five original variables and four restrictions [$k = 5$, $m = 4$ in (8) and (9) above].

Step One

Convert the m restrictive inequalities to m equations, by the insertion of the nonnegative slack variables x_{k+1}, x_{k+2}, ..., x_{k+m}, one for each of the m restrictions. Write this system of equations in matrix form. Mark each column in some way so as to designate which variable is served by that column of coefficients. (Below, we mark the column of coefficients of x_i by P_i and use P_0 to designate the column of constant terms.) Insert also a row C_j, where C_j is the coefficient of x_j in the objective function Z.

P_1	P_2	P_3	P_4	P_5	P_6	P_7	P_8	P_9	P_0
a_{11}	a_{12}	a_{13}	a_{14}	a_{15}	1	0	0	0	b_1
a_{21}	a_{22}	a_{23}	a_{24}	a_{25}	0	1	0	0	b_2
a_{31}	a_{32}	a_{33}	a_{34}	a_{35}	0	0	1	0	b_3
a_{41}	a_{42}	a_{43}	a_{44}	a_{45}	0	0	0	1	b_4

$C_j \rightarrow$ C_1 C_2 C_3 C_4 C_5 0   0   0   0

Step Two

Read off a feasible solution and insert it as a row below the coefficient matrix. The feasible solution at any stage is read off by choosing the nonzero variables to be those whose columns consist of 1 and the rest zeros. Insert P-designations $P_{[i]}$ to the left of each row of the coefficient matrix, to indicate which nonzero coordinate value is read from that equation. Insert also a column of $C_{[i]}$, where $C_{[i]}$ is the coefficient of $x_{[i]}$ in Z.

If all the b_i are positive, a feasible solution is obviously $x_1 = x_2 =$

$x_3 = x_4 = x_5 = 0, \quad x_6 = b_1, \quad x_7 = b_2, \quad x_8 = b_3, \quad x_9 = b_4.$ The table becomes:

$C_{[i]}$	$P_{[i]}$	P_1	P_2	P_3	P_4	P_5	P_6	P_7	P_8	P_9	P_0
0	P_6	a_{11}	a_{12}	a_{13}	a_{14}	a_{15}	1	0	0	0	b_1
0	P_7	a_{21}	a_{22}	a_{23}	a_{24}	a_{25}	0	1	0	0	b_2
0	P_8	a_{31}	a_{32}	a_{33}	a_{34}	a_{35}	0	0	1	0	b_3
0	P_9	a_{41}	a_{42}	a_{43}	a_{44}	a_{45}	0	0	0	1	b_4

$$C_j \rightarrow \quad C_1 \quad C_2 \quad C_3 \quad C_4 \quad C_5 \quad 0 \quad 0 \quad 0 \quad 0$$

Solution. $\quad 0 \quad\ 0 \quad\ 0 \quad\ 0 \quad\ 0 \quad b_1 \quad b_2 \quad b_3 \quad b_4$

(If not all the b_i are positive, some preliminary manipulation is necessary before the feasible solution can be read off; see Example 2 of this section.)

Step Three

Test the solution for optimality. This is done by computing an *"evaluation"* Δ_j for each zero variable x_j, by the formula

$$(10) \qquad \Delta_j = C_j - \sum_{i=1}^{m} a_{ij} C_{[i]}$$

If one or more of the evaluations Δ_j are positive, the solution is nonoptimal, and we proceed to step four. If $\Delta_j \leq 0$ for each j, the solution is optimal. (*Note:* If none of the evaluations is positive, but if any are zero, other optimal solutions exist, with the same value for Z. If all the evaluations are less than zero, the achieved optimal solution is unique.)

The interpretation of the evaluations is as follows. Let Z_0 be the value of Z for the feasible solution under test, and let $Z_0^{(j)}$ be the value of Z that would result if the feasible solution were altered, namely, increase the zero coordinate x_j from 0 to 1, retain the other zero coordinates as zero, and adjust the nonzero coordinates so that the restriction equations remain satisfied. Then

$$(11) \qquad \Delta_j = Z_0^{(j)} - Z_0$$

The proof of (11) is left to the reader as an exercise. The table has now grown to:

$C_{[i]}$	$P_{[i]}$	P_1	P_2	P_3	P_4	P_5	P_6	P_7	P_8	P_9	P_0
0	P_6	a_{11}	a_{12}	a_{13}	a_{14}	a_{15}	1	0	0	0	b_1
0	P_7	a_{21}	a_{22}	a_{23}	a_{24}	a_{25}	0	1	0	0	b_2
0	P_8	a_{31}	a_{32}	a_{33}	a_{34}	a_{35}	0	0	1	0	b_3
0	P_9	a_{41}	a_{42}	a_{43}	a_{44}	a_{45}	0	0	0	1	b_4

$$C_j \rightarrow \quad C_1 \quad C_2 \quad C_3 \quad C_4 \quad C_5 \quad 0 \quad 0 \quad 0 \quad 0$$

$$\text{Solution.} \quad 0 \quad\ 0 \quad\ 0 \quad\ 0 \quad\ 0 \quad\ b_1 \quad b_2 \quad b_3 \quad b_4$$

$$\Delta_j \quad\ \Delta_1 \quad \Delta_2 \quad \Delta_3 \quad \Delta_4 \quad \Delta_5 \quad - \quad - \quad - \quad -$$

(At this stage, and indeed at any stage of a problem where the set of nonzero variables is just the set of slack variables, it is seen that $\Delta_j = C_j$ for each j. But such a relationship will not hold for later iterations.)

Step Four

Determine the entering variable x_r. Recall that the entering variable is that zero variable in the feasible solution which is to become nonzero in the next iteration. An entering variable x_j must have the following properties:

(i) It is zero in the present table.
(ii) $\Delta_j \geq 0$.
(iii) At least one of the a_{ij} in the column for x_j must be greater than zero.*

Any variable x_j with these properties could be used, in the sense that the resulting feasible solution in the next iteration will produce a value of Z at least as great as that in the present table. The following empirical rule for choosing the entering variable has been found to produce quick convergence. Choose from among the possible entering variables that zero coordinate x_j for which Δ_j is largest.

Step Five

Determine the departing variable x_s. The departing variable is that nonzero coordinate $x_{[i]}$ which is to become zero in the next iteration. The

---

* Any variable x_j which has no element a_{ij} in its column greater than zero may be increased indefinitely without violating the original restrictions. If such a variable also has a *positive* Δ_j, Z may be increased indefinitely merely by increasing x_j. Such cases can hardly arise in models of physical problems.

choice of the departing variable is, in general, determined by the choice of the entering variable, together with the nonnegativity restrictions on the coordinates. If x_r is the entering variable, the rule is: s will be that $[i]$ for which the quotient b_i/a_{ir} takes its smallest *nonnegative* value; and x_s will be the departing variable. (*Note:* Since we assumed earlier that the problem has been put into such a form that all the b_i are positive, we are really selecting from among positive a_{ir} in the rth column.)

We now have all the information we need to complete the simplex table for this stage of the iteration. For definiteness, let the entering variable be x_3 and the departing variable be x_7.

$C_{[i]}$	$P_{[i]}$	P_1	P_2	P_3	P_4	P_5	P_6	P_7	P_8	P_9	P_0
0	P_6	a_{11}	a_{12}	a_{13}	a_{14}	a_{15}	1	0	0	0	b_1
0	P_7	a_{21}	a_{22}	a_{23}	a_{24}	a_{25}	0	1	0	0	b_2
0	P_8	a_{31}	a_{32}	a_{33}	a_{34}	a_{35}	0	0	1	0	b_3
0	P_9	a_{41}	a_{42}	a_{43}	a_{44}	a_{45}	0	0	0	1	b_4

	$C_j \rightarrow$	C_1	C_2	C_3	C_4	C_5	0	0	0	0	
Solution.		0	0	0	0	0	b_1	b_2	b_3	b_4	
	Δ_j	Δ_1	Δ_2	Δ_3	Δ_4	Δ_5	–	–	–	–	

        ↑   ↓
   Entering   Departing
   variable   variable
    x_r x_s

The reason for distinguishing the element in the column labeled P_r and the row labeled P_s will become apparent in the next step.

Step Six

Calculate the new coefficient matrix by means of suitably chosen row operations on the old coefficient matrix. The new coefficient matrix is to have unity in the position distinguished in step five, and zero elsewhere in that column. When this is accomplished, the new matrix will be such that the new feasible solution can be read off immediately.

Computationally, we proceed as follows. Divide all elements of the distinguished row by the distinguished element of that row, thus obtaining unity in the distinguished position. Then subtract appropriate multiples of this new row from the other $m - 1$ rows, so as to obtain zeros in the remaining positions of the distinguished column.

If we use a'_{ij}, b_i' to denote the elements of the new coefficient matrix, the new matrix will be:

P_1	P_2	P_3	P_4	P_5	P_6	P_7	P_8	P_9	P_0
a'_{11}	a'_{12}	0	a'_{14}	a'_{15}	1	a'_{17}	0	0	b_1'
a'_{21}	a'_{22}	1	a'_{24}	a'_{25}	0	a'_{27}	0	0	b_2'
a'_{31}	a'_{32}	0	a'_{34}	a'_{35}	0	a'_{37}	1	0	b_3'
a'_{41}	a'_{42}	0	a'_{44}	a'_{45}	0	a'_{47}	0	1	b_4'

The b_i' will all be nonnegative because of the way the entering and departing variables were chosen.

Step Seven

Repeat steps one through six as needed, until an optimum is finally attained in step three.

The steps are performed, of course, on the new coefficient matrix so that, for example, equation (10) becomes

$$(12) \qquad \Delta'_j = C_j - \sum_{i=1}^{m} a'_{ij} C'_{[i]}$$

and so on. The complete second table, before entering and departing variables are chosen, is given below.

$C_{[i]}$	$P_{[i]}$	P_1	P_2	P_3	P_4	P_5	P_6	P_7	P_8	P_9	P_0
0	P_6	a'_{11}	a'_{12}	0	a'_{14}	a'_{15}	1	a'_{17}	0	0	b_1'
C_3	P_3	a'_{21}	a'_{22}	1	a'_{24}	a'_{25}	0	a'_{27}	0	0	b_2'
0	P_8	a'_{31}	a'_{32}	0	a'_{34}	a'_{35}	0	a'_{37}	1	0	b_3'
0	P_9	a'_{41}	a'_{42}	0	a'_{44}	a'_{45}	0	a'_{47}	0	1	b_4'

$$C_j \to \quad C_1 \quad C_2 \quad C_3 \quad C_4 \quad C_5 \quad 0 \quad 0 \quad 0 \quad 0$$

Solution. $\quad\quad 0 \quad\; 0 \quad\; b_2' \quad 0 \quad\; 0 \quad\; b_1' \quad 0 \quad\; b_3' \; b_4'$

$\quad\quad \Delta_j \quad\; \Delta_1' \;\; \Delta_2' \quad - \;\; \Delta_4' \;\; \Delta_5' \quad - \;\; \Delta_7' \quad - \quad -$

Example 1. Rework the example of Section 14.3 (the geometric example), by the simplex method.

Solution. To agree with the notation of the simplex routine presented above, we rename the variables x, y, z as x_1, x_2, x_3 and call the slack variables x_4, x_5, x_6. Then the problem becomes one of maximizing

$$Z = 3x_1 + 5x_2 + 4x_3$$

subject to the restrictions

$$2x_1 + 3x_2 \qquad + x_4 = 8$$

$$2x_2 + 5x_3 + x_5 = 10$$

$$3x_1 + 2x_2 + 4x_3 + x_6 = 15$$

The first table becomes

$C_{[i]}$	$P_{[i]}$	P_1	P_2	P_3	P_4	P_5	P_6	P_0
0	P_4	2	3	0	1	0	0	8
0	P_5	0	2	5	0	1	0	10
0	P_6	3	2	4	0	0	1	15

$C_j \rightarrow$ 3   ·5   4   0   0   0

Solution.   0   0   0   8   10   15 $(Z = 0)$

Δ_j 3   5   4   —   —   —

$\dfrac{b_i}{a_{i,2}}$ —   —   — $\dfrac{8}{3}$ $\dfrac{10}{2}$ $\dfrac{15}{2}$

                    ↑   ↓
              Entering Departing *
              variable   variable

To obtain the second table, we first calculate the intermediate coefficient matrix

$\frac{2}{3}$	1	0	$\frac{1}{3}$	0	0	$\frac{8}{3}$
0	2	5	0	1	0	10
3	2	4	0	0	1	15

and by row operations we get the coefficient matrix for the second table:

$\frac{2}{3}$	1	0	$\frac{1}{3}$	0	0	$\frac{8}{3}$
$-\frac{4}{3}$	0	5	$-\frac{2}{3}$	1	0	$\frac{14}{3}$
$\frac{5}{3}$	0	4	$-\frac{2}{3}$	0	1	$\frac{29}{3}$

* Remember that the entering variable x_2 is determined by the largest Δ_j, and the departing variable x_4 is determined by the smallest $b_i/a_{i,2}$.

In this example it turns out that four tables are needed before an optimum is reached. The second, third, and fourth are obtained in the manner described, and are set down below.

$C_{[i]}$	$P_{[i]}$	P_1	P_2	P_3	P_4	P_5	P_6	P_0
5	P_2	$\frac{2}{3}$	1	0	$\frac{1}{3}$	0	0	$\frac{8}{3}$
0	P_5	$-\frac{4}{3}$	0	5	$-\frac{2}{3}$	1	0	$\frac{14}{3}$
0	P_6	$\frac{5}{3}$	0	4	$-\frac{2}{3}$	0	1	$\frac{29}{3}$

$$C_j \to \quad 3 \quad 5 \quad 4 \quad 0 \quad 0 \quad 0 \quad 0$$

Solution.   0 $\frac{8}{3}$ 0   0 $\frac{14}{3}$ $\frac{29}{3}$ $(Z = \frac{40}{3})$

Δ_j $-\frac{1}{3}$ —   4 $-\frac{5}{3}$ —   —

$\dfrac{b_i}{a_{ir}}$ —   ∞   —   — $\frac{14}{15}$ $\frac{29}{12}$

↑ Entering variable   ↓ Departing variable

$C_{[i]}$	$P_{[i]}$	P_1	P_2	P_3	P_4	P_5	P_6	P_0
5	P_2	$\frac{2}{3}$	1	0	$\frac{1}{3}$	0	0	$\frac{8}{3}$
4	P_3	$-\frac{4}{15}$	0	1	$-\frac{2}{15}$	$\frac{1}{5}$	0	$\frac{14}{15}$
0	P_6	$\frac{41}{15}$	0	0	$-\frac{2}{15}$	$-\frac{4}{5}$	1	$\frac{89}{15}$

$$C_j \to \quad 3 \quad 5 \quad 4 \quad 0 \quad 0 \quad 0$$

Solution.   0 $\frac{8}{3}$ $\frac{14}{15}$ 0   0 $\frac{89}{15}$ $(Z = \frac{256}{15})$

Δ_j $\frac{11}{15}$ —   — $\frac{17}{15}$ $-\frac{4}{5}$ —

$\dfrac{b_i}{a_{ir}}$ —   4 $-\frac{7}{2}$ —   — $\frac{89}{41}$

↑ Entering variable   ↓ Departing variable

$C_{[i]}$	$P_{[i]}$	P_1	P_2	P_3	P_4	P_5	P_6	P_0
5	P_2	0	1	0	$\frac{15}{41}$	$\frac{8}{41}$	$-\frac{10}{41}$	$\frac{50}{41}$
4	P_3	0	0	1	$-\frac{6}{41}$	$\frac{5}{41}$	$\frac{4}{41}$	$\frac{62}{41}$
3	P_1	1	0	0	$-\frac{2}{41}$	$-\frac{12}{41}$	$\frac{15}{41}$	$\frac{89}{41}$

$$C_j \to \quad 3 \quad 5 \quad 4 \quad 0 \quad 0 \quad 0$$

Solution. $\frac{89}{41}$ $\frac{50}{41}$ $\frac{62}{41}$ 0   0   0 $(Z = \frac{765}{41})$

Δ_j —   —   — $-\frac{45}{41}$ $-\frac{24}{41}$ $-\frac{11}{41}$

Since all the Δ_j are nonpositive, the fourth table yields an optimum. The optimal solution is $(\frac{89}{41}, \frac{50}{41}, \frac{62}{41})$, giving a Z of $\frac{765}{41}$.

It has already been pointed out that the routine given above cannot even start if some of the constant terms b_i are negative. The reason is that if b_i is negative, the solution read off from the original coefficient matrix contains the negative coordinate $x_i(= b_i)$ and is therefore not feasible. Once a feasible solution is obtained, by ruse or inspiration, the simplex routine can proceed as given.

If a feasible solution is not readily apparent we can avoid searching for one by the device illustrated in the following example.

Example 2. Show how to maximize $Z = 5x_1 + 8x_2 + 3x_3$ over all nonnegative x_1, x_2, x_3 which satisfy

$$x_1 + x_2 + x_3 \leq 8$$

$$-x_1 - 2x_2 + x_3 \leq -2$$

We start by rewriting the second constraint as $x_1 + 2x_2 - x_3 \geq 2$ and then introduce two slack variables x_4 and x_5 together with an artificial variable x_6. The problem may now be stated as:

Maximize $Z = 5x_1 + 8x_2 + 3x_3$ over all nonnegative $x_1, x_2, \ldots, x_6$ which satisfy

$$x_1 + x_2 + x_3 + x_4 = 8$$

$$x_1 + 2x_2 - x_3 - x_5 + x_6 = 2$$

$$x_5 \geq x_6$$

The last restriction ensures that $x_1 + 2x_2 - x_3 \geq 2$. However, it is inconvenient to retain $x_5 \geq x_6$. Instead we omit $x_5 \geq x_6$ and modify the problem so as to maximize $Z' = 5x_1 + 8x_2 + 3x_3 - Mx_6$ where M is a very large positive number. A little reflection will show that the optimal solution to the modified problem will inevitably set $x_6 = 0$ and as $x_5 \geq 0$ such a solution will automatically satisfy $x_5 \geq x_6$. For hand computation we merely have to remember that M is far greater than the other coefficients in $Z(M = \infty)$. For machine computation we might set $M = 10^{20}$; we could then use the standard simplex routine.

Since the arithmetic of the simplex method is fairly lengthy, it may be advisable to perform certain checks on a table before proceeding to the next one. One obvious check is that the Z value obtained for a table should not be less than the Z value for the previous table. A more precise check relies on the fact (not proved here) that the row of evaluations Δ_j may be obtained from the Δ_j row of the previous table, in the same way that the rows of the coefficient matrix are obtained from the previous coefficient matrix. That is, to obtain the new row of evaluations we subtract from the old evaluation row the product of Δ_r times the distinguished row, divided by the distinguished element of that row. [This procedure could have been used to compute the new Δ_j; then the check would consist of the application of equation (10).]

The discussion of the text has been confined to problems where Z is to be *maximized* subject to restrictions, each requiring a linear function of the x_j to be *less than or equal to* some constant. However, this is no real limitation. If Z is to be minimized, we merely regard the problem as one of maximizing $(-Z)$. Further, any restriction of the form

$$\Sigma k_j x_j \geq b_j$$

can be rewritten as

$$\Sigma(-k_j)x_j \leq -b_j$$

■ 14.5 Duality in Linear Programming

An important concept in the theory of linear programming is that of *duality*. Given an original problem of maximizing a linear function of nonnegative variables, belonging to a convex set with linear boundaries, we will show that it is equivalent to the problem of minimizing another linear function of nonnegative variables over another convex set. We call the second problem the *dual* of the first.

The principal reason for considering duality in linear programming is that computational efforts may be reduced significantly as the simplex method solves both original and dual problems simultaneously, and we may have a choice of formulation at any stage of the simplex method.

We start with the problem of maximizing

$$Z = (\mathbf{C}, \mathbf{X})$$

over all $\mathbf{X} \geq 0$ which satisfy

(13) $$\mathbf{AX} \leq \mathbf{B}$$

where $$(\mathbf{C}, \mathbf{X}) = \mathbf{CX} = (c_1 c_2 \cdots c_n)\begin{pmatrix} x_1 \\ x_2 \\ \cdot \\ \cdot \\ \cdot \\ x_n \end{pmatrix}$$

$$\mathbf{AX} = \begin{pmatrix} a_{11} & a_{12} & \cdots & a_{1n} \\ a_{21} & a_{22} & \cdots & a_{2n} \\ \cdot & \cdot & & \cdot \\ \cdot & \cdot & & \cdot \\ \cdot & \cdot & & \cdot \\ a_{m1} & a_{m2} & \cdots & a_{mn} \end{pmatrix} \begin{pmatrix} x_1 \\ x_2 \\ \cdot \\ \cdot \\ \cdot \\ x_n \end{pmatrix} \quad \text{and} \quad \mathbf{B} = \begin{pmatrix} b_1 \\ b_2 \\ \cdot \\ \cdot \\ \cdot \\ b_m \end{pmatrix}$$

$\mathbf{X} = \mathbf{Y}$ is defined to mean $x_i = y_i$ for all i. $\mathbf{X} \geq \mathbf{Y}$ is defined to be $x_i \geq y_i$ for all i.

Let $\mathbf{W} \geq 0$ be a row vector (row matrix) with the same number of elements as $\mathbf{B}$. Then

$$(\mathbf{W}, \mathbf{AX}) \leq (\mathbf{W}, \mathbf{B})$$

Now let us choose $\mathbf{W}$ such that

(14) $$\mathbf{WA} \geq \mathbf{C}$$

Then we have

$$(\mathbf{W}, \mathbf{B}) \geq (\mathbf{W}, \mathbf{AX}) = (\mathbf{WA}, \mathbf{X}) \geq (\mathbf{C}, \mathbf{X})$$
or

(15) $$(\mathbf{W}, \mathbf{B}) \geq (\mathbf{C}, \mathbf{X})$$

for all $\mathbf{W} \geq 0$, $\mathbf{X} \geq 0$ satisfying (13) and (14). It follows that

(16) $$\min (\mathbf{W}, \mathbf{B}) \geq \max (\mathbf{C}, \mathbf{X})$$

where the minimum is over all $\mathbf{W} \geq 0$ such that $\mathbf{WA} \geq \mathbf{C}$, and the maximum is over all $\mathbf{X} \geq 0$ such that $\mathbf{AX} \leq \mathbf{B}$.

Let us assume that equality holds in (16); this requires that

(17) $$\text{if } \mathbf{WA}|_i > c_i, \text{ then } x_i = 0$$

and

(18) $$\text{if } \mathbf{AX}|_j < b_j, \text{ then } w_j = 0$$

where $\mathbf{WA}|_i$ is the ith element in the column vector of $\mathbf{WA}$, and $\mathbf{AX}|_j$ is the jth element in the row vector of $\mathbf{AX}$.

We now show that if we have two vectors $\mathbf{X}$, $\mathbf{W}$ which satisfy the restrictions (13) and (14) and equations (17) and (18), then $\mathbf{X}$ is the maximizing vector for $(\mathbf{C}, \mathbf{X})$ and $\mathbf{W}$ is the minimizing vector for $(\mathbf{W}, \mathbf{B})$.

First observe that when (17) and (18) are satisfied,

$$(\mathbf{W}, \mathbf{B}) = (\mathbf{C}, \mathbf{X})$$

Suppose $\mathbf{X}$, $\mathbf{W}$ satisfy all the requirements and that $\overline{\mathbf{X}}$ is such that $(\mathbf{C}, \overline{\mathbf{X}}) > (\mathbf{C}, \mathbf{X})$. From (16) $(\mathbf{C}, \overline{\mathbf{X}}) \leq (\mathbf{W}, \mathbf{B}) = (\mathbf{C}, \mathbf{X})$, so we obtain a contradiction. *Thus if* $\mathbf{X} \geq 0$, $\mathbf{W} \geq 0$ *satisfy* (13) *and* (14), (17) *and* (18) *then* $\mathbf{X}$ *maximizes* $(\mathbf{C}, \mathbf{X})$ *and* $\mathbf{W}$ *minimizes* $(\mathbf{W}, \mathbf{B})$. If the corresponding $\mathbf{W}$ has no negative elements, we have solutions to both the maximizing and minimizing problem. Such problems are each described as the *dual* of the other.

One important consequence of this result is that it enables us to check conjectured solutions. Suppose $\mathbf{X}$ is an alleged solution to the maximization problem. Statements (17) and (18) enable us to find the corresponding $\mathbf{W}$ immediately by solving a known set of linear equations. This fact is an improvement over our usual starting position when we only know we are looking for a corner, without knowing which set of equations gives it.

Example. Verify that $x_1 = 10$, $x_2 = 5$ is the vector which maximizes $Z = 5x_1 + 2x_2$, subject to

$$x_1 \leq 10$$

$$x_2 \leq 12$$

$$3x_1 + 2x_2 \leq 40$$

(This is the graphical problem, Example 2 of Section 10.2.)   Here

$$\mathbf{X} = \begin{bmatrix} 10 \\ 5 \end{bmatrix}, \quad \mathbf{B} = \begin{bmatrix} 10 \\ 12 \\ 40 \end{bmatrix}, \quad \mathbf{A} = \begin{bmatrix} 1 & 0 \\ 0 & 1 \\ 3 & 2 \end{bmatrix}, \quad \mathbf{C} = [5, 2]$$

The dual problem is to minimize $10w_1 + 12w_2 + 40w_3$ over all $\mathbf{W} \geq 0$ such that

$$w_1 + 3w_3 \geq 5$$

$$w_2 + 2w_3 \geq 2$$

Since $x_2 \leq 12$ is the only restriction out of the original set which yields a strict inequality ($x_2 = 5 < 12$) on substitution of the alleged solution, we conclude $w_2 = 0$, using (18).

Moreover, as neither x_1 nor x_2 is zero, we must have

$$w_1 + 3w_3 = 5$$

$$w_2 + 2w_3 = 2$$

whence $w_1 = 2$, $w_2 = 0$, $w_3 = 1$

and as $\mathbf{W}$ is nonnegative, we have that $\mathbf{X}$ is a solution to the maximization problem. Note that $\mathbf{X}$ is not a solution to the maximization of $2x_1 + 5x_2$ because we are led to

$$
\left.\begin{array}{r}
w_1 + 3w_3 = 2 \\
w_2 + 2w_3 = 5 \\
w_2 = 0
\end{array}\right\} \quad \text{or} \quad
\left[\begin{array}{l}
w_1 = -5.5 \\
w_2 = 0 \\
w_3 = 2.5
\end{array}\right.
$$

and the corresponding $\mathbf{W}$ is not nonnegative.

We now demonstrate the principal use of duality in solving linear programming problems. When we use the simplex method on the original maximization problem, the row Δ_j is actually the negative of the set of W's satisfying the dual problem. This means that the simplex method effectively solves both problems at once. We can use the algorithm on whichever problem we prefer in order to minimize computational effort.

In order to see this, we use partitioned matrices. On reaching the last simplex table let us relabel the elements of $\mathbf{X}$, which, of course, now includes slack variables and has $m + n$ elements, in such a way that $x_1 = x_2 = \cdots = x_n = 0; x_{n+1} > 0; x_{n+2} > 0; \ldots; x_{m+n} > 0.$

Our last table can be written in matrix form as

$$[\mathbf{M}_{mn}:\mathbf{I}_m]\mathbf{X} = \mathbf{K}$$

which, together with the fact that the first n elements are zero, enables us to determine $\mathbf{X}$.

Thus $\mathbf{X}$ is the solution of the matrix equation

$$
\left[\begin{array}{c:c}
\mathbf{M}_{m,n} & \mathbf{I}_m \\ \hdashline
\mathbf{I}_n & \mathbf{O}
\end{array}\right]
\left[\begin{array}{c}
\mathbf{X} \\ \\
\end{array}\right]
=
\left[\begin{array}{c}
\mathbf{K} \\ \hdashline
\mathbf{O}
\end{array}\right]
$$

(The column on the right consists of the m elements of $\mathbf{K}$, followed by n zeros.)

The solution of the dual problem is given by:

$$
[\mathbf{W}]
\left[\begin{array}{c:c}
\mathbf{M}_{m,n} & -\mathbf{I}_m \\ \hdashline
-\mathbf{I}_n & \mathbf{O}
\end{array}\right]
= \mathbf{C}'
$$

where $\mathbf{C}'$ is a row vector that differs from $\mathbf{C}$,

(a) by the addition of m zero elements so $\mathbf{C}'$ has as many elements as the product on the left.

(b) by rearrangement of the elements to correspond with the order of the elements of $\mathbf{X}$.

Thus

$$\mathbf{W} = \mathbf{C}' \left[\begin{array}{c:c} \mathbf{M}_{m,n} & -\mathbf{I}_m \\ \hdashline -\mathbf{I}_n & \mathbf{O} \end{array} \right]^{-1}$$

$$= \mathbf{C} \left[\begin{array}{c:c} \mathbf{O} & -\mathbf{I}_n \\ \hdashline -\mathbf{I}_m & -\mathbf{M}_{m,n} \end{array} \right]$$

Examination of this product shows that the elements of $\mathbf{W}$ are precisely those of the Δ_j row in the final simplex table, with the signs reversed. Thus we can read off the solution of the dual problem as soon as we have completed the original. Actually, we have a choice as to which problem we solve by the simplex method.

If we wish to solve the dual problem first, that is, minimize $(\mathbf{W}, \mathbf{B})$ over all $\mathbf{W} \geq 0$ which satisfy $\mathbf{W}\mathbf{A} \geq \mathbf{C}$, some preliminary manipulation may be necessary. It is easy enough to convert the problem into one of maximization, because

$$\min (\mathbf{W}, \mathbf{B}) = -\max (\mathbf{W}, -\mathbf{B})$$

We usually start our simplex table with the feasible solution $\mathbf{X} = 0$, but, assuming that at least some of the elements of $\mathbf{C}$ are positive, $\mathbf{W} = 0$ is not a feasible solution. We can, of course, reverse the signs of the inequalities by writing them as

$$\mathbf{W}(-\mathbf{A}) \leq -\mathbf{C}$$

but now some of the elements of $-\mathbf{C}$ are negative. The method of finding the optimal solution was discussed in example 2, Section 14.4.

Exercises for Chapter 14

1. Solve the following, using the simplex method:

    (a) Example 2, Section 14.2.
    (b) Exercise 4, Section 14.2.

2. Maximize $Z = 5x_1 - 2x_2 + 3x_3$, where x_1, x_2, and x_3 are nonnegative variables subject to the restrictions:

$$2x_1 + 2x_2 - x_3 \geq 2$$
$$3x_1 - 4x_2 \leq 3$$
$$x_2 + 3x_3 \leq 5$$

3. Maximize $Z = 2x_1 + 4x_2 + x_3$, where x_1, x_2, and x_3 are nonnegative variables subject to the restrictions:

$$x_1 + 2x_2 \leq 4$$
$$2x_1 + x_2 \leq 3$$
$$x_2 + 4x_3 \leq 3$$

4. Maximize

$$\sum_{i=1}^{3} \sum_{j=1}^{4} C_{ij} x_{ij}$$

subject to

$$\sum_{i=1}^{3} \sum_{j=1}^{4} x_{ij} \leq A_4$$

$$\sum_{i=1}^{3} \sum_{j=1}^{3} x_{ij} \leq A_3$$

$$\sum_{i=1}^{3} \sum_{j=1}^{2} x_{ij} \leq A_2$$

$$\sum_{i=1}^{3} x_{i1} \leq A_1$$

$$x_{ij} \geq 0, \quad i = 1, 2, 3$$

$$j = 1, 2, 3, 4$$

A_1, A_2, A_3, A_4 are any nonnegative constants and $C_{11} < C_{22} < C_{33} < C_{14} < C_{21} < C_{32} < C_{13} < C_{24} < C_{31} < C_{12} < C_{23} < C_{34}$.

(a) Write down the dual to this problem.
(b) Solve the dual problem.
(c) Obtain solution to the original problem.

5. A manufacturer wishes to cut several pieces from a bolt of cloth 36 inches wide with the minimum waste. The following lengths are needed:

12 feet by 20 inches wide

16 feet by 15 inches wide

20 feet by 13 inches wide

Each width may be cut in one or two pieces, but no piece shall be less than 6 feet long. How much cloth is needed to minimize total wastage, and how shall the cloth be cut?

6. In the manufacture of alloys, a certain alloy consisting of 3 metals in the following compositions is required.

Metal	Composition Required
1	60%
2	$\leq 20\%$
3	$\geq 20\%$

Five raw material sources containing the various metals and impurities are available. The percentage compositions of each metal, as well as impurities, are given below.

Raw Material Source

Metal	1	2	3	4	5
1	40	10	20	0	50
2	10	30	10	20	20
3	20	10	20	10	10
Impurities	30	50	50	70	20
Costs of processing one ton	$9	$7	$5	$6	$10

Determine how much of each source should be used in order to produce one ton of alloy at minimal cost.

7. A steel plant produces scrap in mixed lots of three different grades, 1, 2, and 3. The plant requires 200 tons of grade 1 scrap and 500 tons of grade 2 scrap and can produce any quantity from two sources. Previous experience has indicated that the sources have provided the following proportion of graded scrap:

Source	Grade 1	Grade 2	Grade 3
A	20%	40%	40%
B	40%	50%	10%

If the costs of source A is $30 per ton and source B is $50 per ton, find the amount to be produced from each source so as to minimize total costs.

8. A firm has five advertising media, TV, radio, newspaper, billboard (urban), billboard (rural). By means of advertising experiments the company has determined that the sales increase is $2.9, $2.7, $2.5, $2.7, $2.6 per dollar spent on advertisement by these media, respectively. The allocation of the advertising budget to the various media is subject to the following restrictions:

(a) The policy of the firm is to spend, at most, 30% of the total available budget on TV and radio together and at least 20% on billboards.
(b) Because of limited available time on TV, the firm has to spend at least $1\frac{1}{2}$ times on radio what it spends on TV.
(c) The firm desires to spend at least as much on billboards (rural) as on billboards (urban).
(d) For every dollar over $200,000 devoted to newspaper advertising, the company gets a rebate of 10%.

Find the optimal way of allocating a total budget of 1 million dollars to the various media.

Hint: First solve the problem by assuming that newspaper advertising is less than $200,000; then solve the problem by assuming that it is ≥$200,000, and compare the results.

9. A plant is equipped to produce six different products P_i, $i = 1, 2, 3, 4, 5, 6$ —all of which yield the same unit profit. Four different types of raw materials R_j, $j = 1, 2, 3, 4$ are required in the production process, as given below.

Raw Material	Requirement, in Tons, for Producing One Ton of						Total Tons Available
	P_1	P_2	P_3	P_4	P_5	P_6	
1	1	1	0	0	0	1	1
2	0	1	1	0	1	0	2
3	0	0	1	1	0	2	3
4	1	0	0	1	1	0	4

What should the production mix be so as to maximize the total profit?

(a) Set this up as a linear programming problem.
(b) Determine whether $P = (\frac{1}{3}, \frac{2}{3}, \frac{1}{3}, \frac{8}{3}, 1, 0)$ is (i) a feasible point, (ii) an extreme point, or (iii) an optimal point.
(c) Derive the general form for all optimal solutions.

10. A company makes two products A and B, which are sold at 8 cents and 12 cents per unit. The sketch shows the routing through the plant, where both products use the same raw material and packing facilities.

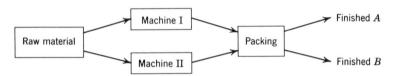

The following data are available as a result of cost and time studies. Raw material costs $100 per ton (2000 lb). Finished units of A weigh $\frac{1}{4}$ lb and units of B weigh $\frac{1}{3}$ lb.

Machine	Cost/hr	Yield (% input)	Input/hr	Available hr/day
I	$300	80	5000 lb	7
II	$350	75	4000 lb	8
Packing	$400	100	15,000 A-units or 8000 B-units	10

(a) Find an expression for the daily profit in terms of the input x_1, x_2 tons of raw material used for products A and B. Find also the restrictions that x_1 and x_2 must satisfy.
(b) What are the optimal values of x_1 and x_2? (Use a graphical method if you wish.)
(c) Which machine is the bottleneck? How much per hour could the company afford to pay for overtime on this machine?

15

Linear Programming —
The Transportation and
Assignment Problems

■ 15.1 Introduction

Although the simplex method will solve all linear programming problems, it is worthwhile to know certain special methods that apply to particular problems because they are more efficient than the simplex method. Suppose we have n factories (sources), which we will denote by $i = 1, 2, \ldots, n$ and m sales outlets (destinations), which we denote by $j = 1, 2, \ldots, m$. Furthermore, we are given that the cost of transportation from i to j is c_{ij} per unit. Let a_i be the output from factory i and b_j the amount required at outlet j. We may suppose that total output is just sufficient to meet requirements, that is,

$$\sum_{i=1}^{n} a_i = \sum_{j=1}^{m} b_j$$

If we ship x_{ij} from i to j, the total cost will be

$$Z = \sum_{i=1}^{n} \sum_{j=1}^{m} x_{ij} c_{ij}$$

We wish to choose from the x_{ij} which satisfy the following restrictions, those x_{ij} which minimize Z. The restrictions are:

$$x_{ij} \geq 0, \quad i = 1, \ldots, n, \quad j = 1, \ldots, m \quad \text{(We cannot ship negative quantities.)}$$

and

$$(1) \quad \sum_{j=1}^{m} x_{ij} = a_i, \quad i = 1, \ldots, n \quad \text{(We ship all the output from each factory.)}$$

(2) $\displaystyle\sum_{i=1}^{n} x_{ij} = b_j, \qquad j = 1, \ldots, m$ (Each outlet receives its exact requirements.)

Problems of this type are known as *transportation problems*. Table 15.1 illustrates the structure of the transportation problem.

TABLE 15.1 THE STRUCTURE OF THE TRANSPORTATION PROBLEM

From	1	2	To m
1	c_{11}	c_{12}	$\cdots$ c_{1m}
2	c_{21}	c_{22}	$\cdots$ c_{2m}
$\vdots$	$\vdots$	$\vdots$	$\vdots$
n	c_{n1}	$\cdot$	$\cdots$ c_{nm}

From	1	2	To m	Total
1	x_{11}	x_{12}	$\cdots$ x_{1m}	a_1
2	x_{21}	x_{22}	$\cdots$ x_{2m}	a_2
$\vdots$	$\vdots$	$\vdots$	$\vdots$	$\vdots$
n	x_{n1}	$\cdot$	$\cdots$ x_{nm}	a_n
Total	b_1	b_2	$\cdots$ b_m	

Cost matrix

c_{ij} = cost of shipping one unit from i to j

Routing matrix

x_{ij} = amount shipped from i to j

Note that we only have $m + n - 1$ *independent* equations among the x's. The reason is that if we add the n equations (1), we have

$$\sum_{ij} x_{ij} = \sum_{i} a_i$$

and if we add the m equations (2), we have

$$\sum_{ij} x_{ij} = \sum_{j} b_j = \sum_{i} a_i$$

This means that we can choose $mn - (m + n - 1)$ of the x's as equal to zero and solve equations (1) and (2) for the remaining $(m + n - 1)$ x's. In general, the $(m + n - 1)$ x's values found will not be zero. The variables found by solving the equations are said to form a *basic set*.* Can we choose any $(m + n - 1)$ x's for a basic set? Clearly not, because if $a_i \neq 0$, at least one of $x_{i1}, x_{i2}, \ldots, x_{im}$ must be nonzero. Similarly, if $b_j \neq 0$, at least one of $x_{1j}, x_{2j}, \ldots, x_{nj}$ must be nonzero (if $a_i = 0$, we would omit i from our considerations). If we write $\mathbf{X}$ for the matrix $[x_{ij}]$, we see that there must be at least one nonzero entry in each row

---

* It can be shown that the set of $\{x_{ij}\}$ which maximizes Z can have at most $m + n - 1$ nonzero values.

and column, with a total of not more than $(m + n - 1)$ nonzero entries. *We now show that there is at least one row or column with precisely one non-zero entry.* Moreover, if we delete such rows and columns, the reduced matrix has the same property. Suppose there were at least two nonzero entries in every row and column and that there are k such entries in all. Then $k \geq 2m$ and $k \geq 2n$. Therefore $2k \geq 2(m + n)$ and we see that $k \geq m + n$.

This is impossible, since we know $k = m + n - 1$. Suppose we set out to find the nonzero x's and that x_{ij} is the only nonzero entry in row i; then $x_{ij} = a_i$. If we delete row i, we have a similar problem, except that there is one row less and b_j is replaced by $b_j' = b_j - a_i$. Thus the reduced matrix has the same property of at least one entry in each row and column, with at least one row or column with a single entry. It follows that we can easily solve the equations for the basic set of x's by finding them one at a time. It also follows that if all the a's and b's are integers, then so are the basic x's. (Why?)

The set of equations for the basic x's are called *triangular*. It will be seen that by suitably relabeling the x's, the equations have the following form:

$$\alpha_{11}x_1 = \beta_1$$

$$\alpha_{21}x_1 + \alpha_{22}x_2 = \beta_2$$

$$\alpha_{31}x_1 + \alpha_{32}x_2 + \alpha_{33}x_3 = \beta_3$$

$$\vdots$$

$$\alpha_{k1}x_1 + \alpha_{k2}x_2 + \cdots + \alpha_{kk}x_k = \beta_k$$

The matrix $\mathbf{A} = [\alpha_{ij}']$ (where $\alpha_{ij}' = \alpha_{ij}$; $j \leq i$ and $\alpha_{ij}' = 0$, $j > i$) is also called triangular. As a matter of fact, in this particular case $\alpha_{ij}' = 1$ if $j \leq i$ and $\alpha_{ij}' = 0$ if $j > i$, and the equations can be solved with very little arithmetic.

In order to solve the minimization problem let us express Z in terms of the nonbasic x's only. Consider

$$Z = \sum_{ij} x_{ij}c_{ij} = \sum_{ij} x_{ij}c_{ij} + \sum_i u_i \left(\sum_j x_{ij} - a_i \right) + \sum_j v_j \left(\sum_i x_{ij} - b_j \right)$$

Since the quantities in brackets are zero, the equality is preserved, whatever values we give to the u's and v's. Thus we have

$$Z = \sum_{ij} x_{ij}(c_{ij} + u_i + v_j) - \sum_i u_i a_i - \sum_j v_j b_j$$

Now choose u_i and v_j so that

$$(3) \qquad\qquad c_{ij} + u_i + v_j = 0$$

whenever x_{ij} belongs to the basic set. It follows that the effect of increasing a nonbasic x_{ij} from zero to unity is to increase Z by an amount $c'_{ij} = c_{ij} + u_i + v_j$. Hence, if, for all nonbasic x_{ij}, we have $c'_{ij} \geq 0$, we have a minimum value for Z. Now equation (3) comprises $m + n - 1$ relationships with $m + n$ unknowns. We see that one u (or v) can be chosen arbitrarily, and we can then determine the remaining u's and v's uniquely. Furthermore, a little reflection will show that their equations are also triangular. In fact, the matrix of their coefficients is the *transpose* of the matrix $\mathbf{A}$ of coefficients of the x's. (The transpose of $\mathbf{A} = [\alpha'_{ij}]$ is merely $\mathbf{A}^T = [\alpha'_{ji}]$, i.e., interchange rows and columns.) Thus it is very easy to determine the values of the u's and v's.

As soon as we have the u's and v's we can compute the c'_{ij}. If any are negative, choose, from among the negative c''s, the largest $|c'_{ij}|$ and change the corresponding x_{ij} from zero to the largest possible value, say to x'_{ij}. Now when x_{ij} is increased to x'_{ij}, some other nonzero entry in row i, say x_{ij_1}, will have to be reduced by x'_{ij}; this will involve an increase of x'_{ij} somewhere in column j_1, say in $x_{i_1 j_1}$. There will be a decrease of x'_{ij} somewhere in row i_1, say in $x_{i_1 j_2}$, and so on, until we eventually balance all rows and columns by arriving back in column j. Since no entry can be negative, we see that x'_{ij} is merely the smallest of the entries where x'_{ij} is subtracted, and the corresponding entry becomes zero (and thus nonbasic).

Example. Solve the following transportation problem. First we must

TABLE 15.2

		To		
From	1	2	3	Available
1	2	7	4	5
2	3	3	1	8
3	5	4	7	7
4	1	6	2	14
Required	7	9	18	34

find a basic set. This can always be done by starting in the northwest corner [cell $(1, 1)$]. We see that, as the requirements for column 1 are 7 and the available at factory 1 is 5, we can make $x_{11} = 5$. This completes row 1. Now make $x_{21} = \min (7 - 5, 8) = 2$. This completes column 1. Now move to x_{22}. There are 6 more required in row 2 and 9 in column 2, so make $x_{22} = 6$. Continuing in this fashion we eventually arrive at the following matrix for x_{ij} (only nonzero entries shown).

TABLE 15.3

5			5
2	6		8
	3	4	7
		14	14

7	9	18

Now set $u_1 = 0$ and immediately $v_1 = -2$, for $u_1 + v_1 + c_{11} = 0$. Therefore $u_2 = -1$, for $u_2 + v_1 + c_{21} = 0$. Since $u_2 + v_2 = -c_{22} = -3$, $v_2 = -2$, and as $u_3 + v_2 = -c_{32} = -4$, we have $u_3 = -2$ and hence $v_3 = -5$, $u_4 = 3$. It is best to insert the u's and v's alongside the cost matrix, with the x's in the cell corners (upper left). Now

TABLE 15.4

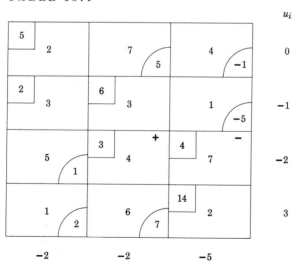

insert the $c'_{ij} = c_{ij} + u_i + v_j$ in the lower right corners. We see that x_{23} should be increased. If it becomes x'_{23}, then the entries in cells having a minus sign in the upper right corner will be decreased and those having a plus sign will increase by x'_{23}. Hence $x'_{23} = 4$; the new (and improved) basic set is shown in the next table. We now repeat the process until all $c'_{ij} \geq 0$. Note that c'_{ij} can also be found by adding and subtracting around the "pathway." Thus $c'_{23} = c_{23} - c_{33} + c_{32} - c_{22} = 1 - 7 + 4 - 3 = -5$. The reader may use whichever method he prefers for finding c'_{ij}. Note, also, that the triangular property of the equations for u_i and v_j guarantees that a suitable pathway will always exist.

The c'_{ij} in Table 15.5 show that x_{41} should be increased. If we

TABLE 15.5

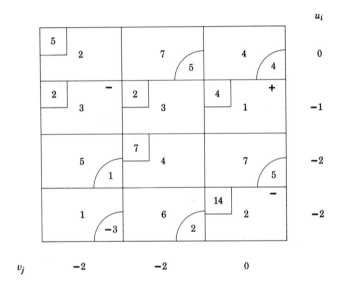

increase x_{41}, we see that $x'_{41} = 2$, and we obtain Table 15.6.

Since all $c'_{ij} \geq 0$, this is optimal. The final solution is $x_{11} = 5$, $x_{22} = 2$, $x_{23} = 6$, $x_{32} = 7$, $x_{41} = 2$, and $x_{34} = 12$. The minimum total cost is $Z = 5(2) + 2(3) + 6(1) + 7(4) + 2(1) + 12(2) = 76$.

It is clear that the number of iterations required will depend on how good our original basic set happened to be. It will pay us to take a little trouble to find a good starting set. If it were possible to use only the minimum cost routes in each row and column, we would obviously

TABLE 15.6

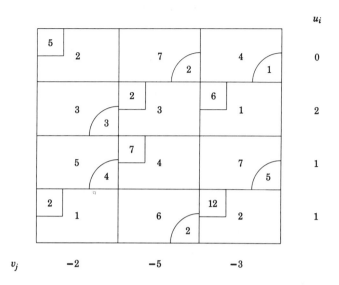

obtain the minimum value of Z. Usually this is not possible, so instead we examine the penalties for not using the row and column minima. The penalties are the differences between the two smallest costs in each row and column. We start the solution by using the route with *greatest* penalty. We then delete the row or column and continue to fill in routes on the reduced matrix. Let us apply this procedure to the example, Table 15.2. There are two equal largest penalties. We choose one, say cell (2, 3), and set $x_{23} = \min(8, 18) = 8$. This uses all the available resources for row 2 and leaves requirements of 10 in column 3. We now

TABLE 15.7

			Available	Penalty
2	7	4	5	2
3	3	1	8	2
5	4	7	7	1
1	6	2	14	1
Required 7	9	18		
Penalty 1	1	1		

write down the reduced problem

TABLE 15.8

			Available	Penalty
2	7	4	5	2
5	4	7	7	1
1	6	2	14	1
Required				
7	9	10		
Penalty				
1	2	2		

We make an entry in cell $(1, 1)$, setting $x_{11} = \min(5, 7) = 5$. The problem is now reduced to

TABLE 15.9

			Available	Penalty
5	4	7	7	1
1	6	2	14	1
Required				
2	9	10		
Penalty				
4	2	5		

We make an entry in cell $(4, 3)$, setting $x_{43} = \min(14, 10) = 10$. This leaves

TABLE 15.10

		Available	Penalty
5	4	7	1
1	6	4	5
Required			
2	9		
Penalty			
4	2		

We complete the solution with $x_{41} = 2$, $x_{42} = 2$, and $x_{32} = 7$. Thus we start our iterations with the set of Table 15.11. This initial solution

TABLE 15.11

Available

5 ⌐ 2	7	4	5
3	3	**8** ⌐ 1	8
5	**7** ⌐ 4	7	7
2 ⌐ 1	**2** ⌐ 6	**10** ⌐ 2	14

Required   7   9   18

results in a total cost of 80, whereas the optimal solution given previously yields a total minimum cost of 76.

Sometimes, for purposes of rough calculation, it is sufficient to find a lower bound for the value of Z; if a proposed solution is reasonably close to the lower bound, it may not be worth the trouble of improving it.

To obtain a lower bound we argue that Z cannot be less than the value obtained by ignoring what is available and assuming all requirements are met by shipping along the cheapest routes, using the column minima. With this assumption we see $Z_{min} \geq 7 \times 1 + 9 \times 3 + 18 \times 1 = 52$.

Similarly, if we ignore requirements and assume all available material is shipped by the cheapest route (row minima), we see $Z_{min} \geq 5 \times 2 + 8 \times 1 + 7 \times 4 + 4 \times 1 = 50$. Hence we conclude $Z_{min} \geq 52$. In general, we calculate two bounds in this fashion and use the larger one. In the example, $Z_{min} = 76$ so that the lower bound is a considerable underestimate.

■ 15.2 Solutions of Degenerate Cases

It may happen that at the start of the iteration (N-W corner rule), or at some later stage of iteration, the number of nonzero x's becomes less than $m + n - 1$. This can occur if we have two equal x'_{ij}, because, on subtraction of x'_{ij}, two additional zeros are introduced. Such cases are described as *degenerate*. When this happens, we cannot compute the

u's and v's because we have an insufficient number of equations. The technique for handling degeneracy is illustrated in the following example.

Example. Solve the following transportation problem, starting with the nonzero x's shown.

TABLE 15.12

To

From	1	2	3	4	Available
1	5 5	5	4	7	5
2	6	5 4	1	2	5
3	5	3 9	3 1	4	6
4	8	3	2	4 4	4
5	6	5	3	6 1	6
Requirements	5	8	3	10	

When we used the N-W rule, we started by setting $x_{11} = 5$, and this completed *both* row 1 and column 1, instead of only one of these, which would have been the case if the requirements for column 1 differed from the amounts available in row 1. We next set $x_{22} = \min (5, 8) = 5$, which completed row 2. Proceeding in the usual way we obtained the results shown in Table 15.12. Unfortunately, there are only 6 instead of 8 nonzero x's. Had we not completed row 1 and column 1 at the same time, we would have had a nonzero x at $(1, 2)$ or $(2, 1)$. We choose the smaller of c_{12} and c_{21}, that is, $\min (5, 6)$, and mark $x_{12} = \epsilon$, where we will treat ϵ as a very small quantity. Similarly, if we had not completed row 3 and column 3 at the same time, we would have had a nonzero x at $(3, 4)$ or $(4, 3)$. We select $\min (c_{34}, c_{43}) = c_{43} = 2$ and set $x_{43} = \epsilon'$.

We now proceed with the calculation of c'_{ij} in the usual way. The only difference is that, at any stage, ϵ and ϵ' are treated as smaller than any other value of x_{ij}. We also use the rules:

$$x_{ij} \pm \epsilon = x_{ij}, \qquad (x_{ij} > 0)$$

$$x_{ij} + \epsilon = \epsilon, \qquad (x_{ij} = 0)$$

$$\epsilon \pm \epsilon' = \epsilon$$

If it is ever necessary to compare two ϵ's, then we need a rule to decide which is smaller. Any rule to avoid ambiguity will do. A convenient rule is: If ϵ is above or to the left of ϵ', then $\epsilon < \epsilon'$. Of course, when the optimal solution is found, all reference to ϵ's is dropped.

The calculations are shown in Tables 15.13 and 15.14.

TABLE 15.13

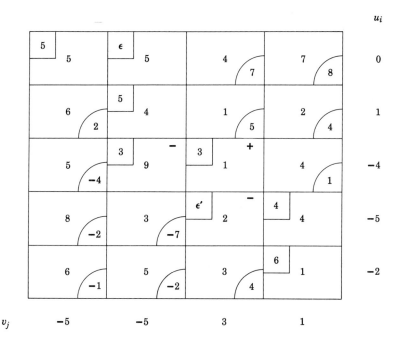

TABLE 15.14

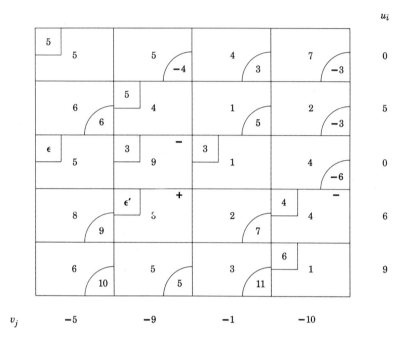

In Table 15.13 we first move ϵ' to $(4, 2)$; this has no effect on any other entry. It is then obvious from the pathway evaluation that ϵ should be moved to $(3, 1)$. Both moves have been made in Table 15.14. Since $c'_{34} = -6$, we make x_{34} as large as possible, and thus $x_{34} = 3$, $x_{32} = 0$, $x_{42} = 3 + \epsilon' = 3$, $x_{44} = 1$.

TABLE 15.15

u_i

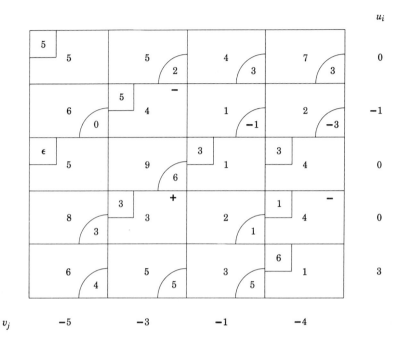

				u_i
5 5	5 2	4 3	7 3	0
6 0	5 4 −	1 −1	2 −3	−1

ε
  5
	9 6	3
		  1
			3
			  4
				0

8 3	3
	  3 +
		2 1	1
			  4 −
				0

6 4	5 5	3 5	6 1	3

v_j −5   −3   −1   −4

We have $c'_{24} = -3$, and thus $x_{22} = 4$, $x_{42} = 4$, and $x_{44} = 0$.

TABLE 15.16

				u_i
5 [−] 5	5 −1	4 3	7 3	0
6 3	4 [−] 4	1 2	1 [+] 2	2
ε [+] 5	9 3	3 1	3 [−] 4	0
8 6	4 3	2 4	4 3	3
6 4	5 2	3 5	6 1	3

v_j	−5	−6	−1	−4

We have that $c'_{12} = -1$, and thus $x_{12} = 3$, $x_{22} = 1$, $x_{24} = 4$, $x_{34} = 0$, $x_{31} = 3 + \epsilon = 3$, $x_{11} = 2$.

TABLE 15.17

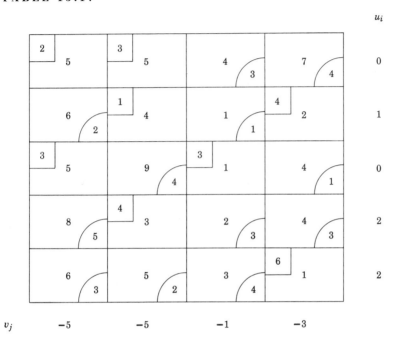

Since all $c'_{ij} > 0$, except where $x_{ij} > 0$, we conclude that this solution is optimal. Note that, despite starting with a degenerate solution, the final result is not degenerate. This is not necessarily the result in all cases.

■ 15.3 The Assignment Problem

Suppose we have n jobs to perform and n men, each of whom can perform each of the jobs, but with varying degrees of efficiency. Let c_{ij} be the cost when worker i performs job j. We wish to assign one job to each worker so as to minimize the total cost.

Let $x_{ij} = 1$ if worker i performs job j, and $x_{ij} = 0$ if he does not. Then the total cost is $\sum_{ij} x_{ij} c_{ij}$. This is to be minimized subject to the constraints:

$$\sum_{i=1}^{n} x_{ij} = 1, \qquad j = 1, 2, \ldots, n \quad \text{(job } j \text{ is performed by one worker)}$$

$$\sum_{j=1}^{n} x_{ij} = 1, \qquad i = 1, 2, \ldots, n \quad \text{(worker } i \text{ does one job)}$$

We also require that $x_{ij} = x_{ij}^2$ [this ensures $x_{ij} = 0$ or 1]. If we ignore the last constraint, we have a transportation problem, and we know that the solution of the transportation will be in nonnegative integers, for the a_i and b_j are integers. Since the sum of the x_{ij} is unity, the constraint $x_{ij} = x_{ij}^2$ will be automatically satisfied. However, there are only n (instead of $2n - 1$) nonzero x's. It is thus extremely degenerate; it could be solved by inserting $(n - 1)$ ϵ's, but we might spend a lot of time moving ϵ's around, even though the nonzero x's were in optimal positions. Instead we recommend a method that relies on two theorems:

Theorem 1. If all $c_{ij} \geq 0$, then $Z = \sum_{i,j} x_{ij} c_{ij} \geq 0$. Thus if some $c_{ij} = 0$, and we can find a set of x's that are all zero, except perhaps where $c_{ij} = 0$, then it must be optimal, for the corresponding $Z = 0$.

Theorem 2. If $X = [x_{ij}]$ is an optimal solution to the problem with costs $[c_{ij}]$, it is also optimal for costs $[c_{ij}']$, where

$$c_{ik}' = c_{ik} - c, \qquad i = 1, 2, \ldots, n$$

$$c_{ij}' = c_{ij}, \qquad i = 1, \ldots, n; k \neq j$$

The first theorem is obvious. To prove the second, note that

$$Z = \sum_{j=1}^{n} \sum_{i=1}^{n} x_{ij} c_{ij} = \sum_{\substack{j=1 \\ j \neq k}}^{n} \sum_{i=1}^{n} x_{ij} c_{ij} + \sum_{i=1}^{n} c_{ik} x_{ik}$$

and

$$Z' = \sum_{j=1}^{n} \sum_{i=1}^{n} x_{ij} c_{ij}' = \sum_{\substack{j=1 \\ j \neq k}}^{n} \sum_{i=1}^{n} x_{ij} c_{ij} + \sum_{i=1}^{n} (c_{ik} - c) x_{ik}$$

$$= \sum_{\substack{j=1 \\ j \neq k}}^{n} \sum_{i=1}^{n} x_{ij} c_{ij} + \sum_{i=1}^{n} c_{ik} x_{ik} - c$$

$$\left(\text{since } \sum_{i=1}^{n} x_{ik} = 1 \right)$$

$$= Z - c$$

Thus for any $\mathbf{X} = [x_{ij}]$, $Z' = Z - c$, and it follows that the same set of x's is optimal for both problems.

Example 1. Given the cost matrix below, solve the corresponding assignment problem.

TABLE 15.18

1	3	2	3	6
2	4	3	1	5
5	6	3	4	6
3	1	4	2	2
1	5	6	5	4

Start by subtracting the minimum of each row from every element in the row, and then do the same for the columns of the resulting matrix. This will not affect the optimal set of x's.

TABLE 15.19

0	2	1	2	4
1	3	2	0	3
2	3	0	1	2
2	0	3	1	0
0	4	5	4	2

We attempt to find a set of nonzero x's in the cells having zeros. Since we require one $x_{ij} = 1$ in each row and column, we start with any zero alone in its row (or column) and then cross out the row and column through it (their requirements have been satisfied). We then continue with the reduced matrix. It is seen that there is no solution among the zeros that have been developed so far, and we need to proceed as follows.

Draw the minimum number of lines through rows and columns which will cover all the zeros. For problems which are small enough for hand computation this can usually be done by inspection. (It can be shown that if we require n lines to cover all zeros, then there is a solution among the zeros.) The lines for Table 15.19 are shown in Table 15.20. Now find the minimum element not covered by a line.

TABLE 15.20

0	2	1	2	4
1	3	2	0	3
2	3	0	1	2
2	0	3	1	0
0	4	5	4	2

In this case it is 2. Subtract it from all elements not covered and add it to any element lying at the intersection of two lines. Theorem 2 can be used to show that the resulting cost matrix still has the same optimal solution as the original problem. (Why?) The cost matrix is

TABLE 15.21

0	0	1	2	2
1	1	2	0	1
2	1	0	1	0
4	0	5	3	2
0	2	5	4	0

We now have a solution among the zeros (shown in boxes). If we did not, we would repeat the process until we finally obtained a solution.

The method can be modified to solve the transportation problem, but the task of drawing lines is now more involved. The reader, after mastering the assignment exercises, should experiment with the transportation problem.

Exercises for Chapter 15

1. Solve the following transportation problems:

(a)

					a_i
2	3	5	7	5	17
4	1	2	1	6	13
2	8	6	1	3	16
5	3	7	2	4	20

| b_j | 16 | 20 | 13 | 12 | 5 |

(b)

						a_i
3	1	6	4	2	3	16
5	4	2	3	7	1	27
2	7	5	1	4	2	14

b_j 7   11   6   15   12   6

(c)

				a_i
1	2	5	3	5
3	4	−1	−2	7
−5	2	6	4	8
−1	5	3	8	11

b_j 6   6   9   10

2. The matrix $[c_{ij}]$ below shows the costs of shipment from plant i to warehouse j. Since regular time production a_i at plant i is 12, 14, 8, 16 units (total 50) and demand b_j at warehouse j is 15, 20, 12 and 15 units (total 62), it is decided to work overtime, which can raise production by as much as 50% at each plant. The additional costs of overtime are 3, 4, 5 and 3 per unit at plants 1, 2, 3, 4, respectively. Find the optimal production schedule.

$$[c_{ij}] = \begin{bmatrix} 5 & 7 & 3 & 8 \\ 6 & 2 & 5 & 3 \\ 4 & 7 & 2 & 5 \\ 8 & 3 & 2 & 6 \end{bmatrix}$$

Hint: Consider the overtime production as coming from 4 hypothetical factories 1′, 2′, 3′, and 4′. The costs of shipping from i' to j are $c_{i'j} = c_{ij} + k_i$, where k_i is the cost of overtime at i. Add a dummy warehouse 5, which will receive all the output of the unused capacity $(50 + \frac{50}{2} - 62 = 13 = b_5)$. The costs of shipping from i to 5 are zero $(i = 1, 2, 3, 4)$ and k_i for $i' = 1', 2', 3', 4'$.

Clearly the solution must have $x_{i'j} = 0$ unless $\sum_{j=1}^{4} x_{ij} = a_i$. Why will this constraint be automatically satisfied in the optimal schedule by the above method?

3. Solve the assignment problems for the cost matrices below.

(a) $\begin{bmatrix} 5 & 3 & 4 & 7 & 1 \\ 2 & 3 & 7 & 6 & 5 \\ 4 & 1 & 5 & 2 & 4 \\ 6 & 8 & 1 & 2 & 3 \\ 4 & 2 & 5 & 7 & 1 \end{bmatrix}$

(b) $\begin{bmatrix} 8 & 12 & 8 & 4 & 1 & 8 \\ 6 & 8 & 4 & 11 & 3 & 6 \\ 11 & -5 & 7 & 15 & 5 & 3 \\ 15 & 3 & 2 & -8 & 2 & 1 \\ 13 & 14 & 6 & 17 & -3 & 8 \\ 2 & -7 & -3 & 6 & 4 & 5 \end{bmatrix}$

4. A company owns three plants A, B, and C. Their respective production costs are \$265, \$233, and \$224 per unit, and their capacities are 6000, 3000, and 3000 units. The company has a contract to supply 1500, 2500, 2700, and 3300 units at cities W, X, Y, Z. Given the transportation costs below draw up the optimal production schedule. (Consider the total costs of manufacturing and shipping; assign excess production capacity to a dummy city with zero costs.)

		From		
		A	B	C
To	W	14	87	66
	X	39	17	14
	Y	6	17	68
	Z	86	77	26

5. Cities A, B, C, and D are used as central warehouses in a national distribution system for television sets. At a given time the corresponding inventories are 500, 2000, 800, and 600 units. A demand occurs at cities X, Y, Z, U, and V for 300, 400, 200, 200, and 400 units, respectively. The shipping costs per item between the various cities is given in the following cost matrix. How should shipments be made so as to minimize the total cost of transportation?

From	To				
	X	Y	Z	U	V
A	1	8	8	9	4
B	8	3	5	6	2
C	5	6	7	8	6
D	6	3	9	12	8

6. An airline operates the following schedule between two cities A and B.

Flight	Leave A	Arrive B	Flight	Leave B	Arrive A
1	8.00	10.00	101	7.00	9.00
2	9.00	11.00	102	8.00	10.00
3	14.00	16.00	103	13.00	15.00
4	18.00	20.00	104	19.00	21.00
5	19.00	21.00	105	20.00	22.00

The schedule operates 7 days a week. It is desired to pair flights so as to minimize time away from base. First draw up a table assuming all flights based at A and showing the lay-over times at B for each pairing [for example, if we pair flights 1 and 101, the layover at B is from 10.00 to 7.00 the following day, i.e., 21 hours]. Do the same for all flights based at B. If these times are t'_{ij} and t''_{ij}, then a pair of flights will be based at A or B according to whether $t'_{ij} >$ or $< t''_{ij}$. Let $t_{ij} = \min (t'_{ij}, t''_{ij})$. Use the assignment method to pair flights so as to minimize $\sum_{ij} x_{ij} t_{ij}$.

How many aircraft are required to operate this schedule?

7. Two factories can each make four products A, B, C, D. Their total capacities for all four products are 70,000 and 90,000 pounds per week. If overtime is worked the capacities can be increased by up to 14,000 and 18,000 pounds per week. The table below shows costs and sales demands. Which factory should make which products on normal and overtime production?

Cost per lb

Product	Factory I		Factory II		Weekly Demand (lb)
	Normal	Overtime	Normal	Overtime	
A	$1.30	$1.40	$1.30	$1.50	30,000
B	1.40	1.50	1.40	1.50	40,000
C	1.40	1.50	1.50	1.70	50,000
D	1.20	1.40	1.40	1.70	60,000

8. In the transportation problem we assumed that a shipment from factory i to warehouse j would go directly without transshipment at some intermediate point. Now let us assume it is possible to transship at any factory or warehouse if this proves cheaper than direct shipment. It is best to renumber so that the factories have numbers $i = 1, 2, \ldots, n$ and the warehouse, $i = n + 1, n + 2, \ldots, n + m$. Assume that for $i \neq j$ we know the cost of direct shipment $c_{ij}^{(0)}$ per unit from i to j and that a transshipment t i costs c_i per unit.

Let $c_{ij}^{(1)} = \min\{c_{ik}^{(0)} + c_k + c_{kj}^{(0)}; c_{ij}^{(0)}\}$, where the minimum is over $k = 1, 2, \ldots, m + n$, but $k \neq i$ and $k \neq j$. Then we will transship at k if $c_{ij}^{(1)} < c_{ij}^{(0)}$.

Furthermore, if we define $c_{ij}^{(n)} = \min\{c_{ik}^{(0)} + c_k + c_{kj}^{(n-1)}; c_{ij}^{(n-1)}\}$, where again the minimum is over $k = 1, 2, \ldots, m + n$ and $k \neq i$, $k \neq j$, then c_{ij}^n will be the minimum cost with not more than n transshipments. (a) Show that the route actually used will correspond to $c_{ij}^{(m+n-2)}$. Note that if the cheapest route from i to j is via $h_1, h_2, \ldots, h_r$, then each part of the route must be the cheapest route between its beginning and end points. This may be used to save calculation. (b) Once we know the minimum cost routes, the optimal shipping schedule becomes an ordinary transportation problem. Given the data below, draw up an optimal schedule.

i / j	1	2	3	4	5	6	7	8
1	—	8	8	3	4	5	4	8
2	6	—	4	4	2	8	3	12
3	10	9	—	7	7	1	6	11
4	15	12	16	—	6	3	10	14
5	20	8	14	11	—	4	12	13
6	18	9	18	9	5	—	9	6
7	14	11	12	14	19	8	—	10
8	8	14	11	12	11	10	12	—

Costs of direct shipment

1, 2, 3 are factories with outputs 20, 32, 28 and 4, 5, 6, 7, 8 are warehouses with requirements of 10, 12, 18, 24, and 16. Costs of transshipment are 1, 3, 2, 1, 1, 3, 2, 2 at cities 1, 2, ..., 8 respectively.

9. It is desired to purchase several trucks to move supplies from two plants to two distant warehouses. The periodic schedule of such movements in truck-load quantities for each consecutive 12-day period is given as follows:

Load at plant 1: one load each day on days 1, 3, 5, 7, 9, 11.
Load at plant 2: one load each day on days 2, 4, 6, 8, 10, 12.
Unload at warehouse 1: one load each day on days 1, 3, 4, 6, 7, 9, 10, 12.
Unload at warehouse 2: one load each day on days 2, 5, 8, 11.

The numbers of days required for the various trips, including loading and unloading times, are as follows:

From	P_1	P_2	W_1	W_2
P_1	—	—	2	3
P_2	—	—	3	4
W_1	2	3	—	—
W_2	3	4	—	—

(column header "To" spans P_1, P_2, W_1, W_2)

What is the minimum number of trucks required in continuous daily service?

10. A company market research team requires some household data from four different cities. The team has 2 days at its disposal and plans to spend half a day in each of the four cities.

Time Period	Probability of a household contact at each of four cities			
	1	2	3	4
First day, morning	0.73	0.03	0.95	0.86
First day, evening	0.21	0.11	0.57	0.37
Second day, morning	0.45	0.52	0.16	0.53
Second day, evening	0.76	0.62	0.11	0.90
Number of house-holds scheduled for interview	12	25	17	11

How should the team allocate the four half days to the four cities in order to maximize the expected number of successful interviews?

Part Five

The Mathematics of Finance

16

Interest, Annuities, and Investments

■ **16.1 Introduction**

The reader is already familiar with, and we have already drawn illustrations from, the theory of compound interest. The entire operation of our industrial civilization is based on the concept that money belonging to one individual may be used by others in *return* for periodic payments. Thus money can be *rented* in the same way as real estate, machine tools, vehicles, or other equipment. The only difference is that the *rent* or *interest* paid for the use of money is itself money, whereas, for example, the rent for a fleet of trucks is not usually additional trucks. Thus when money is loaned, and the lender receives periodic payments for its use, he can, if he chooses, lend the periodic payments, which, in turn, will yield him additional interest, and this interest may be loaned again and so on. In this chapter we discuss the mathematical theory of borrowing and lending money. The next chapter will utilize this chapter, together with the notion of probability, to give an introduction to life assurance, annuities, and related problems.

■ **16.2 Simple and Compound Interest**

Suppose that A lends B a sum P for n years and B agrees to pay *simple interest* at a rate i per year as long as the *principal*, P, is outstanding. Then B pays A the sum $(1 + ni)P$ at the end of n years. If, on the other hand, interest is paid each year, and payments are promptly reinvested at the same rate i—perhaps by lending them to B—then at the end of one year A is owed, or has invested, the sum $P(1 + i)$; at the end of the second year he has $P(1 + i)^2$, and at the end of n years he has $P(1 + i)^n$. From A's point of view it makes little difference whether B pays the annual interest and A reinvests it, or whether B pays nothing for n years and then *pays to A the sum* $P(1 + i)^n$. Such a loan is said to be at *compound interest*. From B's point of view the immediate use of P involves a payment of $P(1 + i)^n$ in n years time, and we say that P is the *present worth* of $P(1 + i)^n$, payable at the end of n years. To find the present worth of an amount Q, payable in n years time, we divide by $(1 + i)^n$, and we see that $(1 + i)^{-n}Q$ is the present worth of Q. It is convenient to write $v = (1 + i)^{-1}$ and obtain $v^n Q$ for the present worth of Q. It should be noted that we have assumed that interest is payable once a year; it may be payable semiannually, quarterly, or monthly. If it is at rate i, payable m times per year, then in n years P becomes $P(1 + i/m)^{nm}$, with a similar formula for the present worth.

Sometimes it is convenient to consider interest as being paid continuously instead of once every $(1/m)$ years. This is equivalent to letting m tend to infinity, and, so, in n years P becomes

$$\lim_{m \to \infty} P\left(1 + \frac{i}{m}\right)^{nm} = Pe^{in}$$

(see Section 5.7).

Let us compare the effects of

1. a rate i payable annually
2. a rate i payable quarterly
3. a rate i payable continuously.

Under (1) a dollar becomes $(1 + i)$ dollars at the end of a year. Under (2) a dollar becomes

$$\left(1 + \frac{i}{4}\right)^4 = 1 + i + \frac{3i^2}{8} + \frac{i^3}{16} + \frac{i^4}{256}$$

at the end of a year, whereas continuous interest yields

$$e^i = 1 + i + \frac{i^2}{2} + \frac{i^3}{3!} + \cdots$$

It is clear that three different rates of interest are involved; we talk of a *nominal* rate of interest, i, but unless the frequency of payment is specified, this has little meaning. In order to compare different investments we need to know the *effective* rate of interest, defined as the rate payable *once a year*, which would yield the same return. Thus (2) above has an effective rate of

$$\left(1 + \frac{i}{4}\right)^4 - 1 \simeq i + \frac{3i^2}{8}$$

while (3) has an effective rate of

$$e^i - 1 \simeq i + \frac{i^2}{2}$$

(Usually i is small, and we can ignore powers of i above the second.) We can also view continuous interest the other way around and ask: What rate payable continuously is equivalent to an effective rate i? Let the rate be δ; then

$$e^\delta = 1 + i \qquad \text{or} \qquad \delta = \log\,(1 + i)$$

We refer to δ as the *force of interest*. Sometimes it is convenient to write

$$d = 1 - v = 1 - \frac{1}{1 + i} = \frac{i}{1 + i}$$

This quantity is known as the discount rate. A very frequent practice is to quote a rate of interest and to deduct the interest from the sum to be loaned. For example, a bank agrees to make a loan of \$1000 for a year at 5% interest. Actually the borrower is given \$950 and signs a note for \$1000 due in a year's time. The so-called interest of 5% is actually a discount of 5%. The effective interest is 5%/0.95 = 5.263%.

As with interest rates, the frequency of discounting should be mentioned. However, in practice it is usual to take the quoted rate times the duration of the loan. If the thousand-dollar loan had been for 60 days, or $\frac{1}{6}$ year, the bank would have charged $\frac{50}{6}$ dollars and paid out \$1000 − \$8.33 = \$991.67 in return for a 60-day note, which is equivalent to an effective rate of

$$\left(1 + \frac{8.33}{991.67}\right)^6 - 1 \qquad \text{or} \qquad 5.147\%$$

■ 16.3 Annuities

A frequent contract is one that calls for fixed payments at agreed intervals for a specified term in return for a cash payment. Thus the proceeds of a life assurance policy might be invested so as to produce eight half-yearly payments, each sufficient to pay college fees as they became due. Alternatively, a man wishing to purchase a house, and not having sufficient cash to do so, might borrow a lump sum and in return agree to pay a fixed sum monthly for 20 years. Such contracts are known as *annuities*, or, more precisely, as *annuities certain*, to distinguish them from fixed payments, which continue only as long as some event does not occur (frequently as long as the death of one of the parties does not occur, as in a pension scheme).

Two questions are pertinent.

1. Given the fixed interval between payments, the amount of each payment, the rate of interest, and the number of payments, what is the cash payment required in return for the annuity contract?

2. Given the initial cash payment, the interval, the periodic payments, and the duration of the contract, what is the rate of return (i.e., what is the rate of interest)?

Of course both questions might be answered by direct calculation from first principles, but it is simpler, in practice, to use published tables of annuity functions. We have already seen that the sum Q payable in n years time has a present worth of $v^n Q$. Let us consider the present worth of an annuity contract that calls for a payment of one dollar each year, starting one year hence, and continuing for n years. Let i be the effective rate of interest per year. The present worth of a payment j years hence is v^j, $j = 1, 2, \ldots, n$. The total value of such a contract is denoted by $a_{\overline{n}|}$. Hence we see that

$$a_{\overline{n}|} = v + v^2 + v^3 + \cdots + v^n = \frac{v(1 - v^n)}{1 - v} = \frac{1 - v^n}{i}$$

since $v = 1/(1 + i)$.

Now suppose that, instead of annual payments, the money is to be paid in sums of $1/m$ at m equal intervals during a year, the first payment being due $1/m$ years hence and the last n years hence. The present value of such a contract is denoted by $a_{\overline{n}|}^{(m)}$:

$$a_{\overline{n}|}^{(m)} = \frac{1}{m}[v^{1/m} + v^{2/m} + v^{3/m} + \cdots + (v^{1/m})^{nm}]$$

$$= \frac{v^{1/m}}{m}\left[\frac{1 - v^n}{1 - v^{1/m}}\right] = \left[\frac{1 - v^n}{i}\right]\left[\frac{iv^{1/m}}{m(1 - v^{1/m})}\right]$$

$$= a_{\overline{n}|}\frac{i}{m[(1 + i)^{1/m} - 1]}$$

Now let $i^{(m)}$ be the nominal rate of interest payable m times per year, equivalent to an effective rate i. Then

$$\left(1 + \frac{i^{(m)}}{m}\right)^m = 1 + i$$

or
$$i^{(m)} = m[(1 + i)^{1/m} - 1]$$

and we see that

$$a_{\overline{n}|}^{(m)} = a_{\overline{n}|} \frac{i}{i^{(m)}}$$

Thus we only need tables of $a_{\overline{n}|}$ and $i/i^{(m)}$ for various m to obtain $a_{\overline{n}|}^{(m)}$. Note that if the first payment is due immediately, the values of the two annuities are denoted by $\ddot{a}_{\overline{n}|}$ and $\ddot{a}_{\overline{n}|}^{(m)}$. A little reflection will show that these may be obtained from the formulas

$$\ddot{a}_{\overline{n}|}^{(m)} = (1 + i)^{1/m} a_{\overline{n}|}^{(m)}$$

and in the special case, $m = 1$,

$$\ddot{a}_{\overline{n}|} = 1 + a_{\overline{n-1}|}$$

Sometimes a contract calls for the payment of a lump sum at the end of n years, in return for fixed annual payments of one dollar; the first payment being due one year from now and the last, n years hence. We use the symbol $s_{\overline{n}|}$ to denote the lump sum. If the annual payments are invested at a rate of interest i, we have

$$s_{\overline{n}|} = 1 + (1 + i) + (1 + i)^2 + \cdots + (1 + i)^{n-1} = \frac{(1 + i)^n - 1}{i}$$

If the payments are at the rate $1/m$, payable m times per year, then the reader should show that

$$s_{\overline{n}|}^{(m)} = \frac{i}{i^{(m)}} s_{\overline{n}|}$$

Extensive tables have been published of compound interest functions. These commonly give $(1 + i)^n$, v^n, $a_{\overline{n}|}$, $s_{\overline{n}|}$, $i^{(m)}$, $(1 + i)^{1/m}$, $i/i^{(m)}$, and $(a_{\overline{n}|})^{-1}$ for various rates of interest and values of n and m. An example of such tables, with $i = 0.02$, will be found in Tables 16.1 and 16.2. The reader should prove that $(s_{\overline{n}|})^{-1} = (a_{\overline{n}|})^{-1} - i$ so that, although the reciprocals of $a_{\overline{n}|}$ and $s_{\overline{n}|}$ are useful (see examples), we do not need to tabulate both.

TABLE 16.1 VALUES OF $(1+i)^n$, v^n, $a_{\overline{n}|}$, $s_{\overline{n}|}$, **AND** $a_{\overline{n}|}^{-1}$ **FOR**
$i = 0.02$

n	$(1+i)^n$	v^n	$a_{\overline{n}|}$	$s_{\overline{n}|}$	$a_{\overline{n}|}^{-1}$
1	1.020000	0.980392	0.980392	1.000000	1.020000
2	1.040400	0.961169	1.941561	2.020000	0.515050
3	1.061208	0.942322	2.883883	3.060400	0.346755
4	1.082432	0.923845	3.807729	4.121608	0.262624
5	1.104081	0.905731	4.713460	5.204040	0.212158
6	1.126162	0.887971	5.601431	6.308121	0.178526
7	1.148686	0.870560	6.471991	7.434283	0.154512
8	1.171659	0.853490	7.325481	8.582969	0.136510
9	1.195093	0.836755	8.162237	9.754628	0.122515
10	1.218994	0.820348	8.982585	10.949721	6.111327
11	1.243374	0.804263	9.786848	12.168715	0.102178
12	1.268242	0.788493	10.575341	13.412090	0.094560
13	1.293607	0.773033	11.348374	14.680332	0.088118
14	1.319479	0.757875	12.106249	15.973938	0.082602
15	1.345868	0.743015	12.849264	17.293417	0.077825
16	1.372786	0.728446	13.577709	18.639285	0.073650
17	1.400241	0.714163	14.291872	20.012071	0.069970
18	1.428246	0.700159	14.992031	21.412312	0.066702
19	1.456811	0.686431	15.678462	22.840559	0.063782
20	1.485947	0.672971	16.351433	24.297370	0.061157

TABLE 16.2 VALUES OF $i^{(m)}$, $(1+i)^{1/m}$,
$i/i^{(m)}$ **FOR** $i = 0.02$

m	$i^{(m)}$	$(1+i)^{1/m}$	$i/i^{(m)}$
2	0.019901	1.009950	1.004975
4	0.019852	1.004963	1.007469
6	0.019835	1.003306	1.008301
12	0.019819	1.001652	1.009134
52	0.019806	1.000381	1.009775
365	0.019803	1.000543	1.009940
∞	0.019803	1.000000	1.009967

Example 1. What is the present value of a monthly payment of $100, starting one month from now and continuing for 5 years? Assume interest is to be at 4%, convertible twice yearly.

It is simplest to work in time units of half years so that the effective interest rate for a time unit is 2%. The contract will continue for 10 time units, and payments are at intervals of $\frac{1}{6}$ time units. From Table 16.1 we find $a_{\overline{10}|}$ at 2% is 8.9826, and from Table 16.2 we have $i/i^{(m)} = 1.0083$. Hence the required value is $600\ a_{\overline{n}|}^{(m)} = \$600\ a_{\overline{n}|}(i/i^{(m)}) = \$600 \times 1.0083 \times 8.9826 = \$5434$.

Example 2. At 2% per annum, what is the present value of the following contract?

First payment of $100, 1 year from now.
Second payment of $150, 2 years from now.
Third payment of $200, 3 years from now.

.
.
.

Ninth payment of $500, 9 years from now.
The payments at the end of years 10, 11, ..., 20 to be $500.

Let P be the present value; then

$$P = 100[v + 1.5v^2 + 2v^3 + \cdots + 4.5v^8 + 5v^8(v + v^2 + \cdots + v^{12})]$$

$$= 100[v + 1.5v^2 + 2v^3 + \cdots + 4.5v^8 + 5v^8 a_{\overline{12}|}]$$

and, using Table 16.1, $P = \$6489$.

Example 3. A house purchase mortgage calls for a nominal rate of interest of 5%. Repayment is to be over 10 years by means of fixed monthly payments. Interest is charged on the outstanding loan at the *beginning* of each year. Compute the monthly payments. Draw up a schedule showing the amount owed at the start of each year, and find the effective interest charged.

Suppose a unit is borrowed initially. The bank will debit the borrower with 1.05 immediately. Let x be the annual repayment, paid at the rate of $x/12$ each month. At the end of the first year, the amount owing is $(1.05 - x)$, and, when the second lot of interest is charged, the debt becomes $1.05(1.05 - x)$ as of the start of the second year. At the end of the second year, the amount owed is $[1.05(1.05 - x) - x]$, which together with interest is $1.05[1.05(1.05 - x) - x]$ at the start of the third year.

In this way we see the amount owed as of the end of year n is

$$(1.05)^n - [(1.05)^{n-1} + (1.05)^{n-2} \cdots + 1.05 + 1]x$$

$$= (1.05)^n - x\left[\frac{(1.05)^n - 1}{1.05 - 1}\right]$$

$$= (1.05)^n - xs_{\overline{n|}}$$

Now at the end of 10 years, the loan is repaid. Hence

$$(1.05)^{10} - xs_{\overline{10|}} = 0$$

and from a table similar to Table 16.1, for $i = 0.05$,

$$x = \frac{1.62889}{12.5779} = 0.129504$$

Once we know x we can compute the amount owed at the end of each year from the formula above. We obtain Table 16.3.

TABLE 16.3

Year n	Sum Owed at End of Year	Sum Owed at Start of Following Year	Capital Repaid	Interest at End of Year
0	1.000000	1.050000	—	0.050000
1	0.920496	0.966521	0.079504	0.046025
2	0.837017	0.878868	0.083479	0.041851
3	0.749364	0.786832	0.087653	0.037468
4	0.657328	0.690194	0.092036	0.032866
5	0.560690	0.588725	0.096638	0.028035
6	0.459221	0.482182	0.101469	0.022961
7	0.352678	0.370312	0.106543	0.017634
8	0.240808	0.252848	0.111870	0.012040
9	0.123344	0.129511	0.117464	0.006167
10	0.000007	. . .	0.123337	. . .

Such a schedule of interest and capital repayments is often required because the interest is deductible for income tax purposes. To find the true interest paid, let v be the effective discount rate per month. Then, equating present values,

$$1 = \frac{x}{12}(v + v^2 + \cdots + v^{120})$$

$$= \frac{x}{12} v \frac{1 - v^{120}}{1 - v}$$

$$= \frac{x(1 - v^{120})}{12i}$$

where i is the true rate of interest per month. With the aid of logarithms, i is found by trial and error. Once i is known, the true annual rate of interest is $(1 + i)^{12} - 1$. We find that i is approximately 0.0045, and the annual rate of interest is 5.54%.

Exercises

1. Use the binomial theorem to expand $i^{(m)}/i$ in powers of i. Show that if we truncate the series with the term in i^n, the error is less than $i^{n+1}/(n + 2)!$. Use your formula to compute $i^{(m)}/i$ correct to 8 decimal places ($i = 0.05$, $m = 6$).

2. If interest is at 2% payable annually, compute the present worth of the following series of payments:

   (a) \$100 per year, starting one year hence, and continuing for 5 payments plus

   (b) \$150 per year, starting 6 years hence, and continuing for 5 payments plus

   (c) \$200 per year, starting 11 years hence, and continuing for 5 payments.

3. If, in exercise 2, the last payment is replaced by the return of the present worth of the entire contract, what would you be prepared to pay for the contract?

4. What difference would it make to exercise 2 if the annual payments were made quarterly (i.e., \$25.00 per quarter for 5 years, etc.)?

5. Rework exercise 3 if the annual payments are made in quarterly installments. (Assume 3 payments of \$50.00 in the last year and a final payment of the present worth.)

6. A man is offered the annuity described below:

   (a) at the end of each year for 10 years, a payment of \$5, plus

   (b) at the end of years 11 through 20, a payment of \$6, plus

   (c) at the end of year 20, a cash payment of \$100.

What should he pay if he wishes to obtain a return of 3% on his investment? [at 3%: $a_{\overline{10}|} = 8.5302$; $v^{10} = 0.74409$]?

■ 16.4   Stocks and Bonds

From an investment point of view, the price to be paid for an investment and the return required are very much dependent on the *risk* involved, that is, on the probable price at which the investment can later be sold and the probability of receiving periodic payments or dividends of various amounts. Unfortunately such probabilities are necessarily subjective, and their evaluation would take us too far afield. In this chapter we are only interested in investments where the contract calls for fixed periodic payments and a specified payment to terminate the contract. We will assume that the terms of the contract will be met, so that no question of risk arises. Examples of such investments may be found in federal, state, and municipal bonds, together with certain industrial bonds well secured by mortgages on real estate or other assets. We are not considering common stocks or even preferred stocks, for these always involve an element of risk.

Some Definitions

It is simplest to think of a bond in terms of a loan, which it really is. The company or government issuing the bond is borrowing money, on terms specified by the contract, and must either go on paying interest indefinitely or eventually repay the loan at a stated price. Generally the bonds are issued in units that carry *nominal values*, for example, $1000 or $5000. However, the nominal value need not be the same as the *issue price*. Bonds may be issued at a *discount*—below the nominal value—or at a *premium*—above the nominal value. Once issued they carry a fixed rate of interest, usually expressed as a percentage of the nominal value; it may be payable yearly, half yearly, or quarterly. Usually bonds carry a *redemption date*, that is, a date on which the borrower must repay the loan. Sometimes the borrower has the option to redeem at any time after a stated date or at any time between two specified dates. The bond also specifies the redemption price, which is stated as a percentage of the nominal value. If the price is merely the nominal value, the bond is said to be *redeemable at par*. If it is above the nominal value, it is redeemable at a premium. It is seldom redeemable at a discount.

During the *life* of a bond it may be bought and sold on the market and has a *market value*. This value depends entirely on the rates of interest presently offered for similar classes of securities. Frequently, in addition to redeeming bonds at the redemption date, the borrower is permitted to buy bonds on the open market and to cancel them. He would do so when prices make this to his advantage. An alternative method of repayment is to allot a fixed sum each year and to select bonds at random for redemption. For example, suppose the original issue is 10 million dollars in $5000 units, and it is to be redeemed at a 3% premium by annual drawings. Each year $412,000 is to be allotted for this purpose. This sum is just sufficient to repay 80 bonds per year, allowing for the 3% premium, and the entire issue of 2000 units will be repaid in 25 years. In such cases we cannot evaluate a single bond until we know its date of redemption. We can determine the value of the "average" bond, assuming that the investor holds a large amount of the issue.

When bonds are not repaid in this way, there are just two means by which the borrower can raise the necessary cash to repay the loan. He can either issue a new set of bonds in sufficient quantity or he can invest in a *sinking fund*. In the latter case he sets aside a sum each year to be invested at interest in such a way that the annual sum, together with the interest, will just repay the loan, including any premium. Often sinking funds are in the form of a policy with an insurance company, calling for fixed annual payments in return for a specified sum on maturity.

Example 1. A bond is issued at a 2% discount and will be redeemed in 20 years time at a premium of 5% or "redeemed at 105." In the meantime it carries interest at 4% per year, payable annually. Calculate the effective return.

In all problems of this type the method is to equate two expressions for the value of the bond at the same point in time. Any point will do, but usually the most convenient is the issue date or the maturity date.

If we use the issue date, the value of the issue price is 98. In return there will be 19 annual payments of 4 each and a final payment of 109 (5% premium, plus 4% interest, plus 100 for the nominal value). Thus

$$98 = 4(v + v^2 + \cdots + v^{19}) + 109v^{20}$$

$$= 4a_{\overline{19}|} + 109v^{20}$$

In order to find v, and hence the interest rate i, we use tables and interpolate. Thus at $4\frac{1}{2}\%$ the right-hand side is 95.5633 and at 4% it is 102.282, so that the rate of interest is approximately

$$4 + \frac{1}{2}\left(\frac{4.282}{6.719}\right) = 4.3\%$$

Alternatively, we can look at the maturity date. In this case the final payment of 109, together with the accumulated value of the interest payments, must just balance the accumulated value of the issue price, that is,

$$98(1 + i)^{20} = 4[(1 + i)^{19} + (1 + i)^{18} + \cdots + (1 + i)] + 109$$
$$= 4[(1 + i)^{19} + (1 + i)^{18} + \cdots + (1 + i) + 1] + 105$$
$$= 4s_{\overline{20}|} + 105$$

and again i may be found by interpolating on tabulated functions. (What is the mathematical relationship between the two methods?)

Example 2. In the previous example a sinking fund is to be set up with a rate of interest of 2%. What will be the annual payment to the fund?

The annual payment, which will normally be at the beginning of the year, must accumulate to 105 at the end of 20 years. Let the payment be x at the beginning of each year for 20 years. Then

$$105 = x[(1.02)^{20} + (1.02)^{19} + \cdots + (1.02)^2 + 1.02]$$
$$= x[s_{\overline{21}|} - 1]$$

or
$$x = \frac{105}{s_{\overline{21}|} - 1}$$

At 2%,
$$x = \frac{105}{24.7833} = 4.237$$

Note that the total annual cost of *servicing* the loan is 8.237, and we could compute the over-all interest rate that the borrower is paying. The student should do so as an exercise.

Hint: (98 − 4.237) has purchased a 19-year annuity of 8.237 plus a payment of 4 at the end of year 20.

Example 3. Suppose that, in Examples 1 and 2, the borrower has the option of spending part or all the sinking-fund payment to purchase bonds on the market. If the loan is at the end of its fifth year, what is the greatest price at which he would prefer to buy on the market instead of investing in the sinking fund?

Let p be the current price per cent of nominal value. The sum p could be invested at 2% for 15 years, in which case it must amount to 105 to redeem a bond, which can now be purchased and cancelled for p. Thus bonds will only be purchased if

$$p(1.02)^{15} < 105$$
$$p < 105(1.02)^{-15}$$
$$= 78.02 \quad \text{(from tables)}$$

■ 16.5 Makeham's Formula for Evaluating Securities

Consider an issue where the amount to be repaid at the end of n years is C and where the *dividend* is gC, payable m times per year. (Note that g is the rate per unit of the redemption price and has nothing to do with the nominal value.) Let A be the purchase price yielding an effective rate i per annum. Then

$$A = Cv^n + gCa_{\overline{n}|}^{(m)} \qquad \text{(at rate } i\text{)}$$

$$= Cv^n + gC \left[\frac{1 - v^n}{i^{(m)}} \right] \qquad \text{where } i^{(m)} = m[(1 + i)^{1/m} - 1]$$

Now let $K = Cv^n = $ value of the capital. Therefore

$$A = K + \frac{g}{i^{(m)}} (C - K)$$

This is Makeham's formula.

It should be noted that the formula remains true even when the issue is repaid by installments, provided K is the present value of the installments and C and g remain constant. The student should supply his own proof.

Example 1. We are offered the following investment. If we wish to realize a return of 4% convertible twice a year, what price should we pay? The investment will be repaid 40 years from now at 110. In the meantime it carries interest at 5% payable quarterly.

We will work in time units of a half year.

The value of the capital is

$$K = 110v^{80} \qquad \text{(at 2\%)}$$

$$= 110 \times 0.20511$$

$$= 22.562 \qquad \text{(from tables)}$$

$$g = \frac{2.5}{110} \qquad \text{(Note that the 5\% interest refers to the nominal value of the issue.)}$$

$$i^{(2)} = 2[1.02^{\frac{1}{2}} - 1]$$

$$= 0.019901$$

By Makeham's formula,

$$A = K + \frac{g}{i^{(m)}} (C - K)$$

$$= 22.562 + \frac{2.5}{110 \times 0.019901} (110 - 22.562)$$

$$= 122.418$$

Example 2. Suppose that an investor buying the stock in Example 1 wishes to replace his loss of capital by means of a sinking fund. He will purchase, by means of half yearly premiums, a policy that will mature at the end of 40 years and that will pay the difference between redemption price of 110 and the initial cost of the entire transaction. If the sinking-fund premiums are computed at 2%, payable half yearly, what must the investor pay for the stock in order to realize 4%, convertible half yearly, on the entire transaction?

Let x be the purchase price of the stock, so that the policy must secure $x - 110$. The half yearly premium will be $(x - 110)/\ddot{s}_{\overline{80}|}$, where $\ddot{s}_{\overline{80}|}$ is the accumulated value of 80 half yearly payments of $1.00 each, the first being due immediately, calculated at 1% per half year. Clearly $\ddot{s}_{\overline{80}|} = (1 + i)s_{\overline{80}|}$, where $s_{\overline{80}|}$ is the corresponding value when the first payment is due in 6 months time. From tables,

$$\ddot{s}_{\overline{80}|} = 122.8882$$

Thus the total initial outlay is

$$x + \frac{x - 110}{122.8882}$$

The half yearly dividend of 2.5 must provide interest at 2% on this sum, together with the half yearly premium. Thus

$$2.5 = 0.02 \left(x + \frac{x - 110}{122.8882} \right) + \frac{x - 110}{122.8882}$$

whence $x = 120.030$

The sinking fund will be set up to secure 10.03 at maturity and the half yearly premium will be 0.0816. Note that the sinking fund policy is only set up for $x - 110$ because the last dividend will be sufficient to pay interest and replace the capital spent on the initial premium.

Example 3. Suppose that tax on dividends is at a rate t and tax on capital gains is at a rate $t'(< t)$. Show how to modify Makeham's formula so that it may be used to compute a price to yield a net rate i after payment of tax.

Let A = the purchase price
C = the redemption price
gC = the yearly dividend, payable m times per year
n = the period until redemption (years)

The capital gains tax is $t'(C - A)$, and the net capital gain is $(1 - t') \times (C - A)$ if $C > A$. The net dividends are $g(1 - t)C$. Hence, at rate i,

$$A = [A + (1 - t')(C - A)]v^n + g(1 - t)Ca_{\overline{n}|}^{(m)}$$

$$= C(1 - t')v^n + At'v^n + g(1 - t)C\left[\frac{1 - v^n}{i^{(m)}}\right]$$

Therefore $\quad A(1 - t'v^n) = Cv^n(1 - t') + \dfrac{g(1 - t)}{i^{(m)}}C(1 - v^n)$

and if $Cv^n = K$, then

$$A = \frac{1}{1 - t'v^n}\left[K(1 - t') + \frac{g(1 - t)}{i^{(m)}}(C - K)\right]$$

If $C < A$, there is a capital loss rather than a gain. It is possible that this can be offset against other income, resulting in a reduction in tax that would otherwise be paid. The details would depend on the investor's financial position during the year in which the loss occurred. A conservative evaluation would be to ignore the tax rebate on the capital loss. The student should show that the value of A on this basis is given by letting $t' = 0$, and

$$A = K + \frac{g(1 - t)}{i^{(m)}}(C - K)$$

Exercises for Chapter 16

1. In order to compute $a_{\overline{n}|} = (1 - v^n)/i$, we could expand $v^n = (1 + i)^{-n}$ by the Binomial Theorem. Why is this not a practical method of calculation unless n is small (say $n = 1, 2,$ or 3)?

2. Prove that $(s_{\overline{n}|})^{-1} = (a_{\overline{n}|})^{-1} - i$:

    (a) by demonstrating an algebraic identity.
    (b) by considering (i) $(s_{\overline{n}|})^{-1}$ is the annual payment that will produce a unit at the end of n years; (ii) $(a_{\overline{n}|})^{-1}$ is the annual payment to be received in return for an immediate cash payment of a unit; and (iii) comparing their difference by general reasoning.

3. A house purchase loan of $10,000 has been arranged on the following terms:

(a) Interest will be computed semiannually in advance at a nominal rate of 4% per year, payable twice yearly.

(b) Repayment will be by monthly payments over 8 years. During the last 4 years, the payments will be twice as large as during the first 4.

Compute the monthly payments during the first 4 years, and draw up a table showing the division of each payment into capital and interest.

4. At the end of 4 years the borrower in exercise 3 finds he has the possibility of refinancing his outstanding debt with a new loan. Repayment would be by monthly installments, with interest at 4%, effective per annum. He approaches the original lender, who agrees to cancel the contract in return for the immediate payment of the outstanding capital, plus a penalty of 1%. How much would the monthly payments be if the borrower refinances? Would it pay him to do so?

5. A bank finances the purchases of automobiles at "5% interest," by which it means that a loan of 100 repayable over n years is repaid by $12n$ installments of $(100 + 5n)/12n$ each. What is the effective rate of interest?

(a) if the loan is repaid over 1 year?

(b) if the loan is repaid over 2 years?

[at $\frac{1}{2}\%$: $a_{\overline{12}|} = 11.6189$; $a_{\overline{24}|} = 22.5629$; $(1 + i)^{12} = 1.06168$

at $\frac{3}{4}\%$: $a_{\overline{12}|} = 11.4349$; $a_{\overline{24}|} = 21.8891$; $(1 + i)^{12} = 1.09381$

at 1%: $a_{\overline{12}|} = 11.2551$; $a_{\overline{24}|} = 21.2434$; $(1 + i)^{12} = 1.12683$]

6. Suppose that the investor in exercise 6, following Section 16.3, wishes to replace his loss of capital by means of a sinking fund. He is offered a policy with annual premiums payable in advance and with interest at 2% per year. What price should he pay for the annuity so as to realize 3% annually on the entire transaction?

7. An increasing annuity is one in which a payment of one dollar is made at the end of the first year, two dollars at the end of the second year, three at the end of the third, and so on, with a final payment of n dollars after n years. Find a formula for the present worth of such an annuity in terms of $a_{\overline{1}|}, a_{\overline{2}|}, \ldots, a_{\overline{n}|}$ and $v, v^2, v^3, \ldots, v^{n-1}$. Show that the result reduces to $(a_{\overline{n}|} - nv^n)/i$.

8. Some individuals find that paying installments on a variety of debts each month is inconvenient. A finance company offers the following consolidation loan service to help such people. In return for agreed payments $u_1, u_2, \ldots, u_n$ to the finance company each month for n months, the company will pay bills of $v_1, v_2, \ldots, v_n$ at the end of each month provided (i) the present values of the two sets of payments (at 1% per month) are equal; (ii) at no time during the contract shall the company's outgoings, accumulated at 1% per month, exceed the customer's payments to the company, also accumulated at 1% per month, by more than $100. Would the company accept the following contracts?

(First find x; then check whether or not condition (ii) is met.)

(a) Proposed Contract

n	1	2	3	4	5	6	7	8	9	10	11	12
v_n	25	25	25	20	20	15	15	15	0	0	0	0
u_n	0	0	0	0	x	x	x	x	x	x	x	x

(b) *Proposed Contract*

$$v_n = 25, \qquad\qquad n = 1, 2, 3, \ldots, 12$$
$$u_n = 10 + (n-1)x, \qquad n = 1, 2, 3, \ldots, 12$$

9. A schoolboard floats a bond issue of one million dollars in $500 units. The loan is to be repaid at 105, and 400 units are to be redeemed at the end of years 10, 11, 12, 13, and 14. Outstanding bonds are to carry interest at 4%, payable quarterly.

(a) Calculate the issue price to give an average yield of 4%, payable quarterly.
(b) If tax is at the rate of 52¢ in the dollar on income and 26¢ in the dollar on capital gain, calculate the price that would yield 3% net after payment of tax [at 3%: $a_{\overline{5}|} = 4.5797$; $v^9 = 0.76642$; $i^{(4)} = 0.020668$; $v^{14} = 0.66112$].

10. A company issues a loan of one million dollars, redeemable at par at the end of 15, 20, 25, and 30 years in four equal amounts. The issue carries interest at 6% per annum. Each year the company pays a fixed sum into a service fund. Interest on the loan is paid out of the service fund, and any balance is invested at 4%, convertible twice yearly. The accumulated fund is also used to make the capital payments as they fall due. How much should be paid into the service fund each year?

Hint: The present value, at 4% convertible twice yearly, of all sums paid out of the service fund must equal the present value of all sums paid into the fund at the same rate of interest. Let this value be A, and use Makeham's formula.

11. Fifteen years ago an investment trust borrowed $500,000, at 4%, from an insurance company, to be repaid in 25 equal annual installments of capital and interest. The trust is about to issue a stock at a price of 95% of nominal value, repayable at par in 20 years time and carrying interest at the annual rate of $3\frac{1}{2}\%$ of the nominal value.

(a) What is the level annual payment on the original loan?
(b) How much does the trust now owe the insurance company?
(c) The trust offers to repay its outstanding debt by allotting the insurance company part of the stock. How much (nominal value) should be offered? [Assume the insurance company will insist that its funds continue to earn 4% (at 4%: $a_{\overline{25}|} = 15.6221$; $a_{\overline{10}|} = 8.1109$; $v^{20} = 0.45639$).]

12. On June 2 of a certain year, an investor purchased the stock described below at a price to yield 4%, convertible twice yearly, after paying income tax at 52% and capital gains tax at 26%. It is now June 2—7 years later—and the stock is quoted at $92\frac{1}{2}\%$. What will the investor's net capital be after paying the capital gains tax if he sells at the current price? The investor finds he can buy municipal stock, which is free of tax, carries annual interest at 3%, payable half yearly, and is redeemable at par in 20 years time. What is the highest price of the municipal stock which would make it worthwhile to sell his current holdings and purchase the municipal stock? Assume he will only change if he can obtain a better return than from his present holdings. Stock currently held: interest at 5% payable quarterly on January 1, March 1, June 1, and September 1, redeemable at 105 on June 1, 20 years later.

17

Actuarial Tables: Personnel, Financial and Equipment Problems Involving Probability

■ 17.1 The Life Table

In this chapter we will use (x) to denote a life aged x exactly—that is, a human being who is alive and aged x. Suppose that we are given the probability p_x that (x) will be alive one year from now and that, starting with some convenient age k (sometimes age 0, perhaps age 21), we form a table l_x showing the number of survivors from a group of, say 1000 aged k, all subject to the same mortality. Thus

$$l_k = 1000$$

$$l_{k+1} = 1000p_k$$

$$l_{k+2} = 1000p_kp_{k+1}$$

In general $$l_{k+t+1} = l_{k+t}p_{k+t}$$

The last entry is usually written l_ω, ω being the age at which it is assumed there is no probability of surviving another year. Such a table is called a *life table*, and the initial entry l_k is called the *radix*. The life table is the basic data from which all life insurance premiums are computed—usually with the aid of auxiliary tables, which we will discuss later. Before doing so, let us briefly examine how we would collect and analyze data from which l_x could be computed. It is clearly not practicable to take one large group of lives at an early age and observe them until they are all dead. For one thing, it would take far too long; for another, mortality rates would change over a lifetime. Instead we take a large group of known ages and count the survivors one year later in each age group. Ideally the age groups would be one year each, but, in practice, sparcity of data may sometimes require coarser grouping. Suppose we start by grouping in 5-year intervals; initially we have l'_{20}, l'_{25}, l'_{30} ... lives in the age intervals over 20 and under 25, over 25 and under 30, etc. One year later we find l''_{21} over 21 and under 26, l''_{26} over 26 and under 31, etc. Then, as a first approximation, we may take the probability of surviving one year at age $22\frac{1}{2}$ as $l''_{21}/l'_{20} = p'_{22.5}$, and at $27\frac{1}{2}$ we have $p'_{27.5} = l''_{26}/l'_{25}$.

If we plot $p'_{22.5}$, $p'_{27.5}$, $p'_{32.5}$, ... on graph paper, we may assume that there is an underlying smooth curve p_x from which these values have been derived. By sketching such a curve we can determine p_{20}, p_{21}, ... by interpolating on it. Such a system is admittedly crude. In the first place, it assumes a uniform age distribution within quinquennial groups. Next, we have not considered the fact that some of the l'_{20} may leave the group for reasons other than death, while some of the l''_{26} may have entered the group during the year. This problem of entry and exit can be handled by assuming that, on the average, entries and exits took place halfway through the year and correcting l' and l'' accordingly. The problem of nonuniform age grouping can be handled to some extent by computing the average age in each group at the start of the year and using this as a subscript instead of the mid-age.

Of course, if data are sufficient, a much better plan is to divide the lives observed into groups of one year each. This will permit more or less direct calculation of p_x (after allowing for entries and exits other than by death). From p_x we compute l_x and plot the results. It is intuitively clear that l_x should have a "smooth" curve, and, if it does not, we may assume the derivations are due to statistical errors. Usually we correct the l_x graph, in principle by sketching in a smooth curve, but often more sophisticated mathematical formulas are used. Once a satisfactory l_x function is available, we recompute p_x. From now on we will assume we have an acceptable function for l_x.

■ 17.2   Insurance Problems

Now consider the problem of an insurance company that, in return for an annual premium P_x, undertakes to pay one unit on the death of a life aged x. The company will wish to charge that sum which, together with interest, will, on the average, equal the amount it has to pay out. For simplicity we will assume that (x) dies just before the anniversary of the insurance. Suppose he dies after paying t premiums, just before the $(t + 1)$st is due at age $x + t$. The present worth of his premiums is $P_x[1 + v + v^2 + \cdots + v^{t-1}]$, and the present worth of his benefit of one unit is v^t. However, this is only one of many cases, and we must take into account the probability that each occurs. Let us define d_x by the equation

$$d_x = l_x - l_{x+1} = -\Delta l_x$$

Then, according to our life table, the probability of death just before age $x + t$ for a life now aged x is

$$_t|q_x = \frac{d_{x+t-1}}{l_x}$$

Hence the expected benefit is *

$$\sum_{t=1}^{\omega} v^t \frac{d_{x+t-1}}{l_x} = \sum_{t=0}^{\omega} v^{t+1} \frac{d_{x+t}}{l_x}$$

and the expected value of the premiums is

$$P_x \sum_{t=1}^{\omega} \frac{d_{x+t-1}}{l_x} [1 + v + v^2 + \cdots + v^{t-1}] = P_x \sum_{t=0}^{\omega} \frac{d_{x+t}}{l_x} [1 + v + \cdots + v^t]$$

$$= \frac{P_x}{l_x} \left[\sum_{t=0}^{\omega} d_x + \sum_{t=1}^{\omega} v\, d_{x+1} + \sum_{t=2}^{\omega} v^2\, d_{x+2} + \cdots \right]$$

From the definition of d_x we see

$$\sum_{t=0}^{\omega} d_{x+t} = l_x$$

Hence the expected benefit is

$$\frac{P_x}{l_x} [l_x + vl_{x+1} + v^2 l_{x+2} + \cdots] = \frac{P_x}{l_x} \sum_{t=0}^{\omega} l_{x+t} v^t$$

It is convenient to introduce the functions

$$D_x = v^x l_x, \quad N_x = \sum_{t=0}^{\omega} D_{x+t}$$

and

$$C_x = v^{x+1} d_x, \quad M_x = \sum_{t=0}^{\omega} C_{x+t}$$

They are called *commutation* functions. We may then write the expected worth of the premiums as

$$P_x \frac{N_x}{D_x}$$

---

* When ω appears in the limit of a sum, we mean that the sum is continued until all further terms are zero.

and the worth of the benefit as

$$\frac{M_x}{D_x}$$

Since these two quantities must be the same, we have

$$P_x \frac{N_x}{D_x} = \frac{M_x}{D_x}$$

or

$$P_x = \frac{M_x}{N_x}$$

Of course, in practice some amount will be added to the theoretical value of P_x to cover expenses and to allow the company to make a profit. The quantities N_x/D_x and M_x/D_x are capable of verbal interpretation. The annual premium constitutes an *immediate* annuity, payable during the lifetime of (x). The word *immediate* is used to indicate that the first payment is due at the present time and not one year hence. (Compare the annuities discussed earlier.) The symbol $\ddot{a}_x$ is used to denote the expected value of such an annuity on a life aged x. We have

$$\ddot{a}_x = \frac{N_x}{D_x}$$

We also use the symbol A_x to denote the value of the insurance and write

$$A_x = \frac{M_x}{D_x}$$

Mortality tables usually show the following functions: l_x, d_x, p_x, q_x, D_x, C_x, N_x, M_x, $a_x = \ddot{a}_x - 1$, A_x, and P_x. (a_x is the value of an annuity where the first payment is due one year hence; it is the exact analogy of $a_{\overline{n}|}$.)

Problems in life insurance can always be solved by equating two expressions for present worth. However, some skill is required to express the results in terms of tabulated functions.

Example 1.   A pension scheme provides that \$1000 be paid at the start of each year following age r and that payments continue for 5 years and as long thereafter as the pensioner is alive. What is the single premium required to pay for such a pension?

The expected value of the benefits is

$$1000(1 + v + v^2 + v^3 + v^4)$$

$$+ 1000 \left(v^5 \frac{l_{r+5}}{l_r} + v^6 \frac{l_{r+6}}{l_r} + v^7 \frac{l_{r+7}}{l_r} + \cdots \right)$$

$$= 1000[1 + a_{\overline{4}|}] + 1000 \frac{N_{r+5}}{D_r}$$

It is usual to write $\ddot{a}_{\overline{5}|} = 1 + a_{\overline{4}|}$.

Example 2. Instead of paying for the pension in Example 1 by a single premium at age r, the pensioner can couple his retirement benefit with insurance during his lifetime by paying an annual premium π_x, starting at age x. The terms are as follows:

(a) At the end of the year of death prior to age r, the estate of the assured will receive a lump sum of

$$1000 \left[\ddot{a}_{\overline{5}|} + \frac{N_{r+5}}{D_r} \right]$$

(b) If the assured survives to age r, he will receive the pension above, and premiums will cease. Calculate π_x.

The present worth of the premiums is the same as that of an immediate annuity, less the payments due from age r onwards. Thus their expected worth is

$$\pi_x \left(\ddot{a}_x - \frac{N_r}{D_x} \right)$$

The benefits consist of an assurance of amount

$$1000 \left[\ddot{a}_{\overline{5}|} + \frac{N_{r+5}}{D_r} \right]$$

up to age r and, in effect, payment of the sum assured at age r if (x) is still alive. The value of such an assurance of amount one dollar is

$$\frac{1}{l_x} \sum_{t=0}^{r-x-1} v^{t+1} d_{x+t} + v^{r-x} \frac{l_r}{l_x} = \frac{1}{D_x}[M_x - M_r] + \frac{D_r}{D_x}$$

Equating the benefits to the premiums yields

$$1000 \left(\ddot{a}_{\overline{5}|} + \frac{N_{r+5}}{D_r} \right) \left(\frac{M_x - M_r + D_r}{D_x} \right) = \pi_x \left(\ddot{a}_x - \frac{N_r}{D_x} \right)$$

or

$$\pi_x = \frac{1000 \left(\ddot{a}_{\overline{5}|} + \frac{N_{r+5}}{D_r} \right) (M_x - M_r + D_r)}{\ddot{a}_x D_x - N_r}$$

Many practical problems arise, and we mention the following. Premiums and/or benefits may not be payable on the policy anniversaries. Death benefits are usually payable immediately on proof of death. Premiums may be payable quarterly or even monthly, and pensions are payable monthly. As already mentioned, premiums are increased above their theoretical values to allow for expenses and profits. If the pensioner has any option about accepting the pension or cash in lieu at age r, it is fairly certain that the healthier pensioners will tend *not* to take cash. Thus there will be *selection*, and the pension should be evaluated by using a special table with light mortality and perhaps a low interest rate. A fuller discussion of these details can be found in *Life and Other Contingencies* by P. F. Hooper and L. H. Longley.

Exercises

1. A temporary insurance (or term insurance) provides death benefits for a fixed period of years in return for a level annual premium. Find an expression for the annual premium for a temporary insurance of one dollar for n years on a life (x), in terms of the commutation functions M and D.

2. A frequent arrangement for whole life insurance is that the annual premium ceases when the life assured reaches a given age r. Express the annual premium for a life aged $x(< r)$, in terms of commutation functions.

3. A special family protection policy offers the following benefits. If death occurs within 20 years, the company will pay a lump sum of \$4000 and \$500 per year for the balance of the 20 years. At the end of 20 years the policy pays \$5000 if the life assured is still alive or \$1000 if he is already dead. Premiums are payable annually for 20 years or until the life assured dies, whichever occurs first. Find expressions for the annual premium. (Ignore interest in finding the sum payable at death, i.e., in the first year, the total benefit is \$15,000; in the second year, \$14,500, etc.)

4. Sometimes, instead of paying an annual premium, the life assured prefers to pay a single premium at the start of the insurance. For a whole life policy on (x) we use A_x to denote such a single premium. Find an expression for A_x. How is the expression modified if (i) Benefits are payable at age 65 or on previous death, (ii) insurance ceases at age 65?

5. Since the probability of death increases with age, the level annual premium for an insurance on (x) increases with x. Suppose that a life now aged $x + t$ took out a policy at age x. His premiums P_x are less than if he now took out a new policy with premiums P_{x+t}. The difference is paid by the reserve value of the policy, that is, the premiums paid over the last t years are greater than those required for the life insurance

already received. Find expressions for:

(a) The expected value of the premiums P_x paid by a life aged x in the t years following x.

(b) The expected value of the death benefits between age x and $x + t$.

(c) The surrender value of the policy (the difference between (a) and (b)). If the policy is cancelled, the insurance company would be prepared to return the surrender value, less expenses.

6. (contd.) Find expressions for the following:

(a) The expected value of the premiums P_x paid from age $x + t$ onward.

(b) The expected value of the death benefit from age $x + t$ on.

Show that the difference between (a) and (b) is exactly accounted for by the surrender value of the policy at age $x + t$ as defined in exercise 5.

7. When purchasing a house by means of a mortgage, it is quite common to take out a decreasing term assurance so that if the life assured dies, the benefits are just sufficient to repay the amount of the loan outstanding. For example, if a mortgage for $20,000 is obtained under the terms of Example 3, Section 16.3, the policy would pay $20,000 in the first year, $18,410 the second year, $16,740 the third year, and so on. (Multiply the second column on Table 16.3 by 20,000.)   Given the data below, what would the single premium be for such a policy?

[Insured aged 30, interest at 3%:

x	30	31	32	33	34	35	
l_x	84,416	84,129	83,835	83,532	83,216	82,885	
n	1	2	3	4	5	6	7
v^n	.97087	.94260	.91514	.88849	.86261	.83748	

x	36	37	38	39	40
l_x	82,536	82,167	81,778	81,367	80,935
n	8	9	10		
v^n	.81309	.78941	.76642	.74409	

Assume death occurs only at the start of the policy year.]

8. If the policy described in exercise 7 is effected by level annual premiums, how much would they be? Calculate the difference between the expected value of the premiums paid and of the benefits received in each year of the policy.

(It will be found that this difference becomes negative. No insurance company will issue such a policy because, if the life assured cancels during the term of the policy, it will lose money. Instead, decreasing term policies are sometimes issued with premiums payable only during the first half or two thirds of the term.)

9. A frequent form of insurance for pension purposes is the *double endowment*. Under such policies the benefit at death before age r is one unit, and on survival to age r the policy pays two units. Find an expression for the level annual premium for such a policy on a life aged x.

10. Sometimes policies are issued on two lives. In such cases the benefits may be payable either on the first death or on the death of the survivor. Calculate the level annual premiums for the 5-year term assurances described below (use the data of exercise 7).

   (a) Two lives now aged 32 and 34. A unit sum to be paid on the first death. Premiums payable as long as both lives survive.
   (b) Two lives now aged 32 and 34. A unit sum to be paid on the death of the survivor. Premiums payable as long as either life survives.
   (c) Same as (b) except that premiums cease on first death.

(In all cases the contract is terminated after 5 years.)

■ **17.3   Problems Not Involving Interest**

Many practical problems in replacement and maintenance of capital equipment, as well as some problems in staff planning, can be phrased in the language of the life table. Generally such problems do not involve rates of interest. We start our discussion of such problems with the concept of *force of mortality*.*

We have seen that the probability (x) dies before age $x + 1$ is

$$\frac{d_x}{l_x} = \frac{-(l_{x+1} - l_x)}{l_x}$$

Suppose we take some other time interval h and consider the probability (x) dies before $x + h$. This is

$$\frac{-(l_{x+h} - l_x)}{l_x} = -\left(\frac{(l_{x+h} - l_x)}{h} \cdot \frac{1}{l_x}\right) \cdot h$$

---

* In this context mortality may mean failure of equipment or staff who leave for any reason, including death.

If we let h tend to zero, we have approximately, for the expression in parentheses

$$- \frac{1}{l_x} \times \frac{dl_x}{dx}$$

Thus the number of deaths prior to $x + h$ among l_x lives aged x is approximately $(l_x \mu_x)h$, where we define the *force of mortality*

$$\mu_x = - \frac{1}{l_x} \frac{dl_x}{dx}$$

From the definition of μ_x we see

$$\int \mu_x \, dx = - \int \frac{dl_x}{l_x}$$

$$= - \log l_x + \text{constant}$$

or

$$l_x = l_0 \exp \left(- \int_0^x \mu_t \, dt \right)$$

A case of particular importance is in replacement theory when failures occur at random. In this case μ_x is independent of x, and the number of survivors aged x is $l_0 e^{-\mu x}$, where μ is the fixed rate at which failures occur.

Example. The distribution of failures on a certain piece of equipment is given by $p(t) = kt^n e^{-\mu t}$ (n is an integer), where, for small h, $hp(t)$ is the probability of failure between ages t and $t + h$, and k is a constant such that $\int_0^\infty p(t) \, dt = 1$ (i.e., the equipment fails at some age). Find l_t and μ_t.

We have approximately

$$\frac{1}{l_0} (l_t - l_{t+h}) = kt^n e^{-\mu t} h$$

or

$$- \frac{1}{l_0} \times \frac{l_{t+h} - l_t}{h} = kt^n e^{-\mu t}$$

or

$$- \frac{1}{l_0} \times \frac{dl_t}{dt} = kt^n e^{-\mu t}$$

By integration,

$$-\frac{1}{l_0}[l_t]_0^t = \int_0^t kt^n e^{-\mu t}\, dt$$

$$\frac{l_0 - l_t}{l_0} = -\frac{ke^{-\mu t}}{\mu}\left[t^n + \frac{nt^{n-1}}{\mu} + \frac{n(n-1)t^{n-2}}{\mu^2} + \cdots + \frac{n!}{\mu^n}\right]_0^t$$

Therefore

$$\frac{l_t}{l_0} = 1 - \frac{kn!}{\mu^{n+1}} + \frac{ke^{-\mu t}}{\mu^{n+1}}\, n!\left(1 + \mu t + \frac{(\mu t)^2}{2!} + \frac{(\mu t)^3}{3!} + \cdots + \frac{(\mu t)^n}{n!}\right)$$

Now, when $t = \infty$, $l_t = 0$, so

$$k = \frac{\mu^{n+1}}{n!} \quad \text{and} \quad p(t) = \frac{\mu^{n+1}t^n e^{-\mu t}}{n!}$$

It is usual to take $l_0 = 1$ so that l_t is the proportion of survivors to age t, that is,

$$l_t = e^{-\mu t}\left[1 + \mu t + \frac{(\mu t)^2}{2!} + \frac{(\mu t)^3}{3!} + \cdots + \frac{(\mu t)^n}{n!}\right]$$

and

$$\mu_t = \lim_{h \to 0} \frac{l_t - l_{t+h}}{l_t} = \frac{l_0 p(t)}{l_t}$$

$$= \frac{\mu^{n+1}}{n!\left[1 + \mu t + \cdots + \frac{(\mu t)^n}{n!}\right]}$$

(*Check:* When $n = 0$, $\mu_t = \mu$, and $l_t = e^{-\mu t}$ as before.)

■ 17.4 Expectation of Life

By *expectation of life* we merely mean the average time lived by persons now aged x. The number out of l_x, now aged x, who will die between $x + t$ and $x + t + h$ is $hl_{x+t}\mu_{x+t}$, and each lives t more years. Hence the total number of years lived by the l_x lives is

$$\int_{t=0}^{\infty} tl_{x+t}\mu_{x+t}\, dt$$

and the average number of years, denoted by $e_x{}^0$, is

$$e_x{}^0 = \frac{1}{l_x}\int_0^{\infty} tl_{x+t}\mu_{x+t}\, dt$$

Now integrate by parts, recalling that

$$l_{x+t}\mu_{x+t} = -\frac{dl_{x+t}}{dt}$$

Therefore $$e_x^{\,0} = \frac{1}{l_x}\{[-\,tl_{x+t}]_{t=0}^{\infty} + \int_0^{\infty} l_{x+t}\,dt\}$$

$$= \frac{1}{l_x}\int_0^{\infty} l_{x+t}\,dt$$

Thus the average age at death for (x) is $x + e_x^{\,0}$. Examination of mortality tables, as well as intuition, shows that, in general, if $x > y$, then

$$x + e_x^{\,0} > y + e_y^{\,0}$$

On the other hand, when $x > y$, we usually find

$$e_x^{\,0} < e_y^{\,0}$$

There are some exceptions—at very young ages. Due to the high incidence of infant mortality, we find that the life expectation of new-born babies is less than that of children aged one month. However, this effect disappears by the age of one year, and from then on life expectation declines. These facts have their parallel in certain industrial equipment. It is well known that some vacuum tubes have a high probability of failure in the first few hours of use. Once the initial period is over, their life expectation is quite high. Two conclusions emerge:

1. If failure in service is expensive (e.g., an aircraft navigational radio goes out), the tubes can be artificially aged to eliminate the early failures before they are placed in service.

2. If life expectation does not decrease with age, there is no point in preventative maintenance or replacement before failure.

In practice, some form of numerical integration will be required to find $e_x^{\,0}$. The trapezoidal rule (Chapter 10) is sufficient for most purposes. That is,

$$e_x^{\,0} = \frac{1}{l_x}\int_0^{\infty} l_{x+t}\,dt = \frac{1}{l_x}\left\{\frac{1}{2}l_x + \sum_{t=1}^{\infty} l_{x+t}\right\}$$

$$= \frac{1}{2} + \frac{1}{l_x}\sum_{t=1}^{\infty} l_{x+t}$$

$$= \tfrac{1}{2} + l_x$$

The average number of *complete* years lived by a life aged x (i.e., not counting the fraction of a year for the year of death) is

$$e_x = \sum_{t=1}^{\infty} l_{x+t}$$

and is called the *curtate expectation*.

■ 17.5 Stationary Populations

By a *stationary population* we mean one free from emigration and immigration, in which deaths are immediately replaced by births, and in which the age distribution remains constant. No human population is of this type, but many industrial replacement situations where parts are replaced immediately on failure conform to the definitions.

Suppose that we have a population which at time zero has an age distribution $f(x)$. That is, the number in the population between ages x and $x + h$ is $f(x)h$. Let $f(t, x)$ be the age distribution at time t. Then the number of deaths at time t to $t + h$ is

$$h \int_0^{\infty} f(t, x)\mu_x \, dx$$

and the rate of dying, which equals the rate of being born, is

$$g(t) = \int_0^{\infty} f(t, x)\mu_x \, dx$$

Let us set $l_0 = 1$ so that $l_u/l_0 = l_u$ is the probability of surviving to age u. Then, of the $g(t)$ births at time t, there will be $g(t)l_u$ survivors at time $t + u$, and among these the rate of dying is $g(t)l_u\mu_u$. Now, let $t + u = v$ so that at time v the number of deaths will consist of two parts:

1. deaths among survivors of the original population.
2. deaths among those born at time $t < v$.

Therefore $g(v) = \int_0^{\infty} f(x) \dfrac{l_{x+v}}{l_x} \mu_{x+v} \, dx + \int_0^v g(v - t)l_t\mu_t \, dt$

The first integral is a known function of v, and we may write it as $h(v)$ so that

$$g(v) = h(v) + \int_0^v g(v - t)l_t\mu_t \, dt$$

This is an integral equation for $g(t)$, and its solution would take us too far afield. However, we may suppose that the number of survivors of the original population will tend to zero, and for large v,

$$g(v) = \int_0^v g(v - t) l_t \mu_t \, dt$$

One solution of this equation is $g(v) = $ constant, say $g(v) = k$. Then

$$k = \int_0^v k l_t \mu_t \, dt$$

The left-hand side does not depend on v, whereas the right-hand side does. However, v is to be large so that we may write

$$k = \int_0^\infty k l_t \mu_t \, dt$$

$$= -k \int_0^\infty \frac{dl_t}{dt} \, dt$$

$$= k l_0$$

$$= k \quad \text{(since we set } l_0 = 1)$$

It can be shown that, no matter what the original age distribution was, the deaths (and births) will settle down to a constant rate k. Once this happens, the survivors aged x will be $k l_x$, and so, for large t, we see the age distribution is given by

$$f(\infty, x) = k l_x$$

The total population is thus

$$\int_0^\infty k l_x \, dx = k e_0{}^0$$

If the original population comprised N people (i.e., $\int_0^\infty f(x) \, dx = N$), then, since the population has been kept constant,

$$k e_0{}^0 = N \quad \text{or} \quad k = \frac{N}{e_0{}^0}$$

Stated in words, we see that if births exactly balance deaths, and if there is no immigration or emigration, the population eventually becomes stationary, the age distribution remains constant, and the birth (and death) rate can be found by dividing the total population by the average life.   In practice, about three generations are sufficient to reduce a population to a stationary condition.

Exercises for Chapter 17

1. A company employing a large clerical staff has kept records of how staff leave their service for several years past.   The table below shows the "survivors," computed for 1000 entrants at age 20.   Calculate a table of p_x.   (Retirement is at age 65.)

Given the age distribution shown for the present staff, how many must be recruited so that the total number of staff is the same next year as this?

Age x	20	21	22	23	24	25	26	27	28	29	30	31
l_x	1000	995	983	969	940	903	867	840	815	793	777	762
Number of Staff	50	47	45	40	35	30	28	—	27	—	—	25

Age x	32	33	34	35	36	37	38	39	40	41	42	43
l_x	749	736	724	714	705	696	687	679	672	665	658	652
Number of Staff	—	—	—	15	—	12	16	15	—	—	—	—

Age x	44	45	46	47	48	49	50	51	52	53	54	55
l_x	647	643	640	637	635	632	629	627	626	625	623	620
Number of Staff	10	8	6	—	—	5	—	4	—	—	—	2

Age x	56	57	58	59	60	61	62	63	64	65
l_x	619	618	616	614	613	612	611	610	609	0
Number of Staff	—	—	1	2	1	3	—	—	—	—

2. If in exercise 1 it is desired to promote staff reaching a fixed age to a supervising grade, what will this age be next year?   (Assume 30 promotions will take place.)

3. If exits from the staff described in exercise 1 have been replaced by recruitment for a very long time, so that the "population" has become stationary, find the number of recruits required each year.

4. A piece of industrial equipment has a failure rate p_x at age x.   A preventive maintenance scheme is to be introduced under which all parts not failing previously are to be replaced at age t.   Show that the average age at which parts are replaced for any reason is given by $\bar{x}(t)$, where

$$\bar{x}(t) = \frac{1}{l_0} \{ \tfrac{1}{2}(l_0 + l_t) + \sum_{x=1}^{t-1} l_x \}$$

(Assume failures between age x and $x + 1$ take place age $x + \frac{1}{2}$.)

5. (contd.) Show that if we set $l_0 = 1$, then the rate of replacement due to failures will eventually be $(1 - l_t)/\bar{x}(t)$ and that the rate of replacement due to

reaching age t will become $l_t/\bar{x}(t)$. If the cost of a failure, including replacement, is C_1 and the cost of replacement at age t is $C_2 < C_1$, find an expression for the average cost per unit time of the preventative replacement scheme. How could this cost be minimized?

6. Consider a large number of populations where the number of populations containing x individuals at time t is $f(x, t)$. Suppose that a population of x individuals is subject to a force of mortality μ_x, and let h be a small interval of time such that, at most, one death can take place in time t to $t + h$. Show that we have the approximate equation

$$f(x, t + h) = (1 - \mu_x h)f(x, t) + \mu_{x+1}hf(x + 1, t), \qquad x \geq 0$$

By subtracting $f(x, t)$ from each side, dividing through by h, and allowing h to tend to zero, show that

$$\frac{df}{dt}(x, t) = -\mu_x f(x, t) + \mu_{x+1}f(x + 1, t)$$

Show, also, that if at time $t = 0$ we have $f(x, 0) = N_x$ ($x = 0, 1, 2, \ldots, k$) and $f(x, 0) = 0$, $x > k$, then

$$\frac{df}{dt}(k, t) = -\mu_k f(k, t)$$

whence
$$f(k, t) = N_k e^{-\mu_k t}$$

7. (contd.) Show that if $f(x + 1, t) = A_{x+1,x+1}e^{-\mu_{x+1}t} + A_{x+1,x+2}e^{-\mu_{x+2}t} + \cdots + A_{x+1,k}e^{-\mu_k t}$

then
$$f(x, t) = A_{xx}e^{-\mu_x t} + \sum_{r=x+1}^{k} \frac{\mu_{x+1}A_{x+1,r}}{\mu_x - \mu_r} e^{-\mu_r t}$$

where the A's are determined from the conditions

$$f(x, 0) = N_x$$

8. (contd.) Solve also for the case where $\mu_x = \mu$ for all x.

9. We can extend the situation of exercise 6 to one in which, in addition to deaths, the populations are subject to a birth rate. Suppose that at time t there are $f(x, t)$ populations containing x individuals, and that a population with x individuals is subject to a birth rate λ_x. That is, the probability of a birth in the small interval t to $t + h$ is $\lambda_x h$ and the probability of no birth is $1 - \lambda_x h$. Show that we have the approximate equations

$$f(0, t + h) = (1 - \lambda_0 h)f(0, t) + \mu_1 hf(1, t)$$

$$f(x, t + h) = \lambda_{x-1}hf(x - 1, t) + (1 - \lambda_x h)(1 - \mu_x h)f(x, t)$$
$$+ \mu_{x+1}hf(x + 1, t), \qquad x > 0$$

and hence

$$\frac{df}{dt}(0, t) = -\lambda_0 f(0, t) + \mu_1 f(1, t)$$

$$\frac{df}{dt}(x, t) = \lambda_{x-1}f(x - 1, t) - (\lambda_x + \mu_x)f(x, t) + \mu_{x+1}f(x + 1, t), \qquad x > 0$$

10. The general equations of exercise 9 are difficult to solve, but some special cases are relatively easy. Consider a large number of mechanical systems, each of which is either in working order or under repair. When a system is working, the "force of failure" is μ, and when it is under repair, the "force of repair" is λ. Let $f(t)$ be the number of systems that are working at time t and $g(t)$, the number under repair. Show that the systems are governed by the equations

$$f'(t) = -\mu f(t) + \lambda g(t)$$

$$g'(t) = \mu f(t) - \lambda g(t)$$

If at time $t = 0$, $f(0) = N_1$ and $g(0) = N_2$, find expressions for $f(t)$ and $g(t)$. What happens when t is large?

11. In certain marketing situations, the force of gaining customers can be represented by $k_1 a_1$, where k_1 is a constant and a_1 is our rate of expenditure on advertising. The force of losing customers is $k_2 a_2$, where k_2 is another constant and a_2 is our competitor's rate of advertising expenditure. Let $f(t)$ be the number of our customers at time t and $g(t)$, our competitor's customers. Assuming that the total number of customers remains constant, show that f and g satisfy the equations of exercise 10, with $\mu = k_2 q_2$ and $\lambda = k_1 a_1$.

If our gross profit is at the rate $pf(t)$ at time t, find the total profit between times $t = 0$ and $t = T$. [Assume $f(0) = N_1$, $g(0) = N_2$.] Show that the average profit per unit time tends to a constant as T increases, and assuming a_2 remains constant, find the value of a_1 that maximizes our long-run *net* profit per unit time.

Appendix

The General Linear Differential Equation
with Constant Coefficients

■ 1 Introduction

The general linear differential equation with constant coefficients (Section 11.5) is given by

$$(1) \qquad\qquad L(D)x = g(t)$$

where $\quad L \equiv L(D) \equiv A_n D^n + A_{n-1} D^{n-1} + \cdots + A_1 D + A_0$

and $D \equiv \dfrac{d}{dt}$ is the linear differential operator. This appendix develops methods for solving equation (1).

■ 2 The Complimentary Equation

$$(2) \qquad\qquad Lx = 0$$

is called the *complimentary equation* of (1) and its general solution is called the *complimentary function*. As we saw in Section 11.5 the solution of (1) is made up of the complimentary solution plus any particular solution   Some equations of this type were solved earlier, but we will give some additional examples here.

Example 1. Solve

$$\frac{d^2x}{dt^2} - 5\frac{dx}{dt} + 6x = 0$$

or $\qquad\qquad\qquad (D^2 - 5D + 6)x = 0$

The secular equation, obtained by substituting, $x = e^{mt}$, is

$$m^2 - 5m + 6 = 0$$

whence $m = 3$ or 2. The general solution is

$$x = Ae^{3t} + Be^{2t}$$

It may be checked by direct substitution.

Example 2.   Solve

$$\frac{d^2x}{dt^2} + 9x = 0$$

or

$$(D^2 + 9)x = 0$$

The secular equation is

$$m^2 + 9 = 0$$

and the roots are $m = 3i$ or $m = -3i$ where $i^2 = -1$. The general solution is thus

$$x = Ae^{3it} + Be^{-3it} = A(\cos 3t + i \sin 3t) + B(\cos 3t - i \sin 3t)$$

$$= (A + B) \cos 3t + i(A - B) \sin 3t$$

Apparently x must be a complex quantity.   However we may suppose that A and B are also complex, say

$$A = A_1 + iA_2 \qquad \text{and} \qquad B = B_1 + iB_2; \text{ then}$$

$$x = [(A_1 + B_1) \cos 3t + (B_2 - A_2) \sin 3t]$$

$$+ i[(A_2 + B_2) \cos 3t + (A_1 - B_1) \sin 3t]$$

Now the general solution for x involves two arbitrary constants and we have four (A_1, A_2, B_1, B_2).   We may choose two of them so as to make the imaginary part of x disappear.

Thus $\qquad\qquad\qquad\qquad A_2 = -B_2$

and $\qquad\qquad\qquad\qquad A_1 = B_1$

We then have

$$x = 2B_1 \cos 3t + 2B_2 \sin 3t$$

or $\qquad x = P \cos 3t + Q \sin 3t, \qquad$ where $P = 2B_1$, $Q = 2B_2$

We now have a general solution (it has two arbitrary constants P and Q) and it is completely real.

Example 3.   Solve

$$\frac{d^2x}{dt^2} + 4\frac{dy}{dx} + 20x = 0$$

The secular equation is

$$m^2 + 4m + 20 = 0$$

and the roots are $m = -2 + 4i$ and $-2 - 4i$ where $i^2 = -1$. The general solution is

$$x = Ae^{-(2+4i)t} + Be^{-(2-4i)t}$$
$$= e^{-2t}(Ae^{-4it} + Be^{4it})$$

Just as in the previous example we can show that suitable choice of the real and imaginary parts of A and B leads to

$$x = e^{-2t}[P\cos 4t + Q\sin 4t]$$

Notice that as $t \to \infty$ the exponential part tends to zero and thus $x \to 0$. Since $\cos 4t$ and $\sin 4t$ are periodic functions, x is said to have a *damped oscillation*. Such equations are common in electric circuit theory, but somewhat rare in business. They do occur indirectly in the analysis of systems where waiting lines are present.

Example 4.   Solve

$$\frac{d^3x}{dt^3} + 5\frac{d^2x}{dt^2} + 8\frac{dx}{dt} + 4x = 0$$

The secular equation is

$$m^3 + 5m^2 + 8m + 4 = 0$$

or $$(m + 2)^2(m + 1) = 0$$

There are only two roots $m = -2$ (which is repeated) and $m = -1$. In order to have a general solution, with three independent parts and three constants, we need three distinct roots. We will try to find a third independent solution of the form

$$x = u(t)e^{-2t}$$

Now $$\frac{dx}{dt} = e^{-2t}[u'(t) - 2u(t)]$$

$$\frac{d^2x}{dt^2} = e^{-2t}[u''(t) - 4u'(t) + 4u(t)]$$

$$\frac{d^3x}{dt^3} = e^{-2t}[u'''(t) - 6u''(t) + 12u'(t) - 8u(t)]$$

Substitution in the original equation yields $e^{-2t}[u''' - u''] = 0$. (Why do we discard the other solution $u = e^{-t}$?) A simple form for u satisfying this equation is $u = A + Bt$ and we conclude that the required general solution is

$$x = e^{-2t}[A + Bt] + Ce^{-t}$$

The argument always works for repeated roots. If a root, say m, is repeated k times the general solution has terms

$$e^{mt}(A_0 + A_1t + A_2t^2 + \cdots + A_{k-1}t^{k-1})$$

■ 3 Particular Solutions

In this section we wish to find any *particular solution* of the equation

$$(3) \qquad\qquad Lx = g(t)$$

When we have such a solution we merely add the *complimentary function* (solution of the complimentary equation) to find a *general solution*. There are three approaches possible. The most powerful, which works for any function $g(t)$ is the *Laplace Transformation*. Unfortunately a full understanding of this requires a knowledge of the theory of complex variables and is beyond our scope. The second method is to "guess" the form of the solution and fit the unknown parameter, such as in the way that we used e^{mt} in the complimentary equation. The last method is to manipulate the operator $L(D)$ as if D were an algebraic quantity. Properly interpreted such manipulation can lead to many useful results. We will illustrate the second and third techniques by examples.

Example 5. Solve

$$\frac{d^2x}{dt^2} + \frac{dx}{dt} - 6x = \sin 2t$$

By the usual reasoning the complimentary function is

$$Ae^{-3t} + Be^{2t}$$

We "guess" that a particular solution has the form $x = \alpha \sin 2t + \beta \cos 2t$ and attempt to find α and β. The reason for this guess is that the right side of the original differential equation is a trigonometric function, $\sin 2t$.

$$\frac{dx}{dt} = 2\alpha \cos 2t - 2\beta \sin 2t$$

$$\frac{d^2x}{dt^2} = -4\alpha \sin 2t - 4\beta \cos 2t$$

Substituting the above equations in the original equation, we obtain

$$\sin 2t[-4\alpha - 2\beta - 6\alpha] + \cos 2t[-4\beta + 2\alpha - 6\beta] = \sin 2t$$

Therefore $$-10\alpha - 2\beta = 1$$

$$2\alpha - 10\beta = 0$$

Hence $\beta = -\frac{1}{52}$ and $\alpha = -\frac{5}{52}$. The general solution is thus

$$x = Ae^{-3t} + Be^{2t} - \frac{1}{52}[5 \sin 2t + \cos 2t]$$

Note that because $g(t) = \sin 2t$ we assumed a solution involving $\sin 2t$ and $\cos 2t$. If $g(t) = P \sin kt + Q \cos kt$ we can always find a solution by assuming $x = \alpha \sin kt + \beta \cos kt$.

Example 6. Solve

$$\frac{d^2x}{dt^2} - \frac{7 \, dx}{dt} + 12x = 2t^2 - 3t + 5$$

As usual the complimentary function is $Ae^{4t} + Be^{3t}$. To find a particular solution we write the equation as

$$L(D)x = 2t^2 - 3t + 5$$

and then treat $L(D)$ as if it were an ordinary algebraic quantity.

Therefore $$x = \frac{1}{L(D)}(2t^2 - 3t + 5)$$

$$= \frac{1}{D^2 - 7D + 12} \cdot (2t^2 - 3t + 5)$$

$$= \frac{1}{12}\left(1 - \frac{7}{12}D + \frac{D^2}{12}\right)^{-1}(2t^2 - 3t + 5)$$

We now expand the reciprocal by long division or by the Binomial Theorem.

$$x = \frac{1}{12}\left(1 + \frac{7D}{12} - \frac{D^2}{12} + \frac{49}{144}D^2 + \cdots\right)(2t^2 - 3t + 5)$$

$$= \frac{1}{12}\left(1 + \frac{7D}{12} + \frac{37}{144}D^2 + \cdots\right)(2t^2 - 3t + 5)$$

Now D is differential operator and D^2 is the differential operator D applied twice.

Therefore $\quad x = \dfrac{1}{12}(2t^2 - 3t + 5) + \dfrac{7}{144}(4t - 3) + \dfrac{37}{1728}$ (4)

$$= \dfrac{t^2}{6} - \dfrac{t}{18} + \dfrac{77}{216}$$

and the general solution is

$$x = Ae^{4t} + Be^{3t} + \dfrac{t^2}{6} - \dfrac{t}{18} + \dfrac{77}{216}$$

This solution should be checked by substituting in the original equation. The above procedure always works; it can be formally justified by showing that D obeys all the normal laws of algebra and may thus be manipulated as if it were an ordinary quantity. It will be noted that we only expanded the reciprocal as far as square terms. This was because D^3 and higher powers operating on a second degree polynomial produce zero. If the polynomial contained the nth power of t we would need the expansion as far as the nth power of D.

Example 7. Solve

$$\dfrac{d^2x}{dt^2} - 7\dfrac{dx}{dt} + 12x = e^{-2t}(2t^2 - 3t + 5)$$

To find a particular solution write the equation as

$$L(D)x = e^{-2t}(2t^2 - 3t + 5)$$

$$x = \dfrac{1}{L(D)}e^{-2t}(2t^2 - 3t + 5)$$

Now, by the rule for differentiating products,

$$De^{mt}f(t) = me^{mt}f(t) + e^{mt}f'(t)$$

$$= e^{mt}(D + m)f(t)$$

We can show inductively that

$$L(D)e^{mt}f(t) = e^{mt}L(D + m)f(t)$$

By analogy we write

$$x = \dfrac{1}{L(D)}e^{mt}f(t) = e^{mt}\dfrac{1}{L(D + m)}f(t)$$

But $\dfrac{1}{L(D + m)} f(t)$ is simply a solution of the equation $L(D + m)x = f(t)$, so the problem has been reduced to a simpler problem, without any exponential term. In our example $f(t)$ is a polynominal which can be handled as in the previous case.

$$x = e^{-2t} \frac{1}{(D - 2)^2 - 7(D - 2) + 12} (2t^2 - 3t + 5)$$

$$= e^{-2t} \frac{1}{D^2 - 11D + 30} (2t^2 - 3t + 5)$$

$$= \frac{e^{-2t}}{30} \left(1 - \frac{11D}{30} + \frac{D^2}{30} \right)^{-1} (2t^2 - 3t + 5)$$

$$= \frac{e^{-2t}}{30} \left(1 + \frac{11D}{30} + \frac{91D^2}{900} \cdots \right) (2t^2 - 3t + 5)$$

$$= \frac{e^{-2t}}{30} \left(2t^2 - \frac{46}{30} t + \frac{3874}{900} \right)$$

The general solution is found by adding the complimentary function.

Example 8. Solve

$$\frac{d^2x}{dt^2} - 7 \frac{dx}{dt} + 12x = e^{-6t}$$

To find a particular solution write the equation as

$$L(D)x = e^{-6t}$$

where $\qquad L(D) = D^2 - 7D + 12$

We have seen that $L(D)e^{mt} = L(m)e^{mt}$. We write

$$x = \frac{1}{L(D)} e^{-6t}$$

and then replace D by -6.

Thus $\qquad x = \dfrac{1}{(-6)^2 - 7(-6) + 12} e^{-6t}$

$$= \frac{e^{-6t}}{90}$$

It is easy enough to verify that $x = \dfrac{e^{-6t}}{90}$ does in fact satisfy the orig-

inal equation. The general solution is $x = Ae^{4t} + Be^{3t} + \dfrac{1}{90}e^{-6t}$.

The procedure may be justified formally as follows. Suppose $L(D)$ is a linear function of D and $L(D)x = e^{mt}$. Now $L(D)e^{mt} = L(m)e^{mt}$.

Therefore $L(D) \dfrac{e^{mt}}{L(m)} = e^{mt}$.

Example 9. Solve

$$\frac{d^2x}{dt^2} - 7\frac{dx}{dt} + 12x = e^{4t}$$

This example has the same operator $L(D)$ as the previous one, but the exponent on the right has been changed. When we write

$$x = \frac{e^{4t}}{L(4)}$$

we obtain $\dfrac{e^{4t}}{0} = \infty$.

It appears that the above method fails, when the exponent on the right is also a root of $L(m) = 0$. Now $e^{4t} = e^{4t} \cdot 1$, and we can use the method of Example 6. Thus

$$x = e^{4t} \frac{1}{(D+4)^2 - 7(D+4) + 12} \cdot 1$$

$$= e^{4t} \frac{1}{D^2 + D} \cdot 1$$

$$= e^{4t} \times \frac{1}{D} \times \frac{1}{1+D} \cdot 1$$

$$= e^{4t} \frac{1}{D}(1+D)^{-1} \cdot 1$$

$$= e^{4t} \frac{1}{D}(1 - D + D^2 \ldots) \cdot 1$$

$$= e^{4t} \left(\frac{1}{D} - 1 + D \ldots\right) \cdot 1$$

Now D means *differentiate* so $\dfrac{1}{D}$ must be interpreted as *integrate*. We have

$$x = e^{4t}(t - 1)$$

since D, D^2, ..., operating on 1 all yield zero. The general solution is

$$x = Ae^{4t} + Be^{3t} + e^{4t}(t - 1)$$

$$= A'e^{4t} + Be^{3t} + te^{4t}$$

Note that since A is an arbitrary constant $A' = A - 1$ is also an arbitrary constant.

■ 4 Summary of Methods for Finding Particular Solutions

The methods for the general linear equation $L(D)x = g(t)$ are summarized in the table below.

$g(t)$	Method
$a_n t^n + a_{n-1}t^{n-1} + \cdots + a_1 t + a_0$	$x = \dfrac{1}{L(D)} g(t)$; expand $\dfrac{1}{L(D)}$ as a power series in D.
$e^{mt}f(t)$	$x = e^{mt} \dfrac{1}{L(D + m)} f(t)$.
e^{mt}	$x = \dfrac{1}{L(m)} e^{mt}$ provided $L(m) \neq 0$ If $L(m) = 0$, $x = e^{mt} \dfrac{1}{L(D + m)} \cdot 1$
$a \sin kt + b \cos k$	Assume $x = \alpha \sin kt + \beta \cos kt$; equate coefficients of $\sin kt$ and $\cos kt$ to find α and β.

Exercises on the Appendix

Find the general solution of each of the following differential equations:

1. $\dfrac{d^2x}{dt^2} + \dfrac{dx}{dt} = 2$

2. $\dfrac{d^2x}{dt^2} + 3\dfrac{dx}{dt} = 6t$

3. $\dfrac{d^2x}{dt^2} + \dfrac{dx}{dt} - 2x = 3e^t$

4. $\dfrac{d^2x}{dt^2} + 4\dfrac{dx}{dt} + 5x = 4\sin 2t + 32\cos 2t$

5. $\dfrac{d^2x}{dt^2} + 2\dfrac{dx}{dt} + x = e^t\cos t$

6. $\dfrac{d^2x}{dt^2} + \dfrac{dx}{dt} = e^t + e^{2t}$

Index